GARGOYLE

EDITOR/PUBLISHER: Richard Peabody

DESIGN/COPYEDIT: Nita Congress

LAYOUT: Stephen Caporaletti

WEBMASTER/EMT: John Barclay-Morton

READERS: Jenn Bennett
Rebecca Conway
Theresa Senato Edwards
Kristy Feltenberger
Victoria Gaffney
Jess Stork Glicoes
Ivy Grimes
Lia Milgram
Elisha Wagman
Bonnie ZoBell

Gargoyle is on the web at www.gargoylemagazine.com.

Founded 1976
Gargoyle is published annually in the USA by Paycock Press.

Contact us:
GARGOYLE
3819 13th Street North
Arlington, VA 22201
Phone: 703-380-4893
Email: rchrdpeabody9@gmail.com

Our next reading period will begin June 1, 2018, and we accept/reject until we're full. Please use the Submittable tool on our website.

Price per single issue varies.

Subscriptions: $30/two issues to individuals; $40/two issues for institutions

ISBN-10: 0-931181-68-2
ISBN-13: 978-0-931181-68-9
ISSN 0162-1149

Charles Ciccoretti's "Hey" reprinted from *Penman Literary-Art Magazine 2017*, Washington-Lee High School. George Kalamaras's "So Many Roads" appeared on the Chicago Blues Guide website, July 2016.

Cover art: *House* (collage, 2004—front cover) and *Reduction* (collage, 2005—back cover) by Star Black.

Gargoyle is distributed by:

- Direct from us through our website
- Amazon.com
- Sundial Books, 4065 Main Street, Chincoteague, VA 23336
- NewPages Magazine Webstore, www.newpageswebstore.com

Copies are also available from Bell and Howell Information and Learning.

Printed by Main Street Rag Publishing, Charlotte, NC.

66 The first thing a writer has to do is find another source of income. Then, after you have begged, borrowed, stolen or saved up the money to give you time to write and you spend all of it staying alive while you write, and you write your heart out, after all that, maybe no one will publish it, and if they publish it, maybe no one will read it. That is the hard truth, that is what it means to be a writer. **99**

—*Ellen Gilchrist*

ALLEN FORREST

CLANDESTINE SERVICE

Special thanks to Cynthia Atkins, Rae Bryant, Ron Burch, Cleopatra Cadillac, Joyce Maust Enzor, Eric D. Goodman, Nathan Leslie, Anna March, Adrian Matejka, Devon Miller-Duggan, Marci Nadler, Julie Wakeman-Linn, for gigs, support, and some of this issue's last words. Much love to Star Black for gifting us with her divine artwork for both front and back covers.

Several attendees at AWP 2017 in D.C. told me afterwards that our "Grace and Gravity" panel was their favorite of the entire conference. Thanks again to Michelle Brafman for moderating and to Melanie Hatter, Yejide Morowa, and Hananah Zaheer for delivering laughs and wisdom.

To celebrate our two-volume fortieth anniversary publication, we held two events. A shout out to the readers at our Teaism AWP 2017 party—JoAnn Balingit, Doritt Carroll, WF Lantry, Mary Ann Larkin, Susan Lewis, Jeff Richards, Devin Taylor, Pamela Murray Winters, and singer Kate Lantry. We owe Doritt Carroll big time for lending us her compact sound system. And hats off to the folks at Teaism who graced us with a great space, a good time, and memorable eats.

A second, larger, celebration was held at the Batelle-Atrium at American University in September 2017. Melissa Scholes Young and the Literature Department allowed us to pack the space with a plethora of readers from issues 65, 66, and 67—E.A. Aymar, Tara Campbell, Suzanne Feldman, Andrew Gifford, Holly Karapetkova, Kateema Lee, Leeya Mehta, Meg Opperman, Frances Park, Marija Stajic, Gregg Wilhelm, and Sarah Louise Williams.

Kudos to you all.

IN MEMORIAM

Magdalena Abakanowicz
John Abercrombie
Peter Abrahams
Richard Adams
Ilse Aichinger
Edward Albee
Brian Aldiss
Geri Allen
Mose Allison
Gregg Allman
Bill Anderson
David Antin
John Ashbery
Dore Ashton
Svend Asmussen
David Axelrod
Natalie Babbitt
Luis Bacalov
Victor Bailey
Donald Bain
Michael Ballhouse
Dennis Banks
Bill Barlow
Wayne Barrett
Don Baylor
Walter Becker
Melissa Bell
Trevor Bell
John Berger
Shelley Berman
Chuck Berry
Howard Bingham
Ann Birstein
William Peter Blatty
Chana Bloch
Arthur Blythe
Michelle Boisseau
Michael Bond
Powers Boothe
Daisy Boyd
E. R. Braithwaite
Oscar Brand
George Braziller
Jimmy Breslin
Lonnie Brooks
Frank Broyles
Don Buchla
Paul Buckmaster
David Burwell
John Byrne Cooke

Al Caiola
Eamonn Campbell
Glen Campbell
Tom Cannon
Charmian Carr
Valerie Carter
Paul Casanova
Bernie Casey
Fay Chiang
William Christenberry
William Christopher
Leonard Cohen
Miriam Colon
Mike Connors
Barbara Cook
Irwin Corey
Chris Cornell
Larry Coryell
James Cotton
Raoul Coutard
Caroline Crawley
Anthony Cronin
Jay Cronley
Terry Cryer
Jose Luis Cuevas
Holger Czukay
Cool "Disco" Dan
Mireille Darc
Danielle Darrieux
Robert de Cormier
Frank Deford
Paula Dell
Jonathan Demme
Michel Deon
Anna Dewdney
Colin Dexter
Digby Diehl
Ray DiPalma
Fats Domino
J. P. Donleavy
Claire Dratch
Randy Duncan
Helen Dunmore
Stanley "Buckwheat"
  Dural Jr.
Lucinda Ebersole
Susan Elbe
Okla Elliott
Buchi Emecheta
Mari Evans

Larry Fagin
Miguel Ferrer
Carrie Fisher
Roy Fisher
June Foray
Bernard Fox
Paula Fox
Shirley Bunnie Foy
Bobby Freeman
Warren Frost
Nancy Friday
Nan Fry
Sonny Geraci
John Glenn
Terry Glenn
Robert Goldstein
Anne Golon
Cuba Gooding Sr.
Arlene Gottfried
Juan Goytisolo
Jim Graham
Stanley Greene
Sam Greenlee
Hal Greer
Dick Gregory
Roger Grenier
Tammy Grimes
Ralph Guglielmi
Ralph Guillaume
A.R. Gurney
Barbara Hale
Richard Hambleton
David Hamilton
Monica Hand
Curtis Hanson
Ty Hardin
Grant Hart
Connie Hawkins
Tom Hayden
Skip Haynes
Shirley Hazzard
Glenne Headly
John Heard
Pierre Henry
Nate Hentoff
William "Gatz" Hjortsberg
William M. Hoffman
Allan Holdsworth
Clare Hollingworth
Tobe Hooper

Klaus Huber
John Hurt
Gwen Ifill
Shirley Jaffe
Al Jarreau
Anne Jeffreys
Elfriede Jelinek
Evan Johns
Dennis Johnson
Judith Jones
Sharon Jones
Thom Jones
Scott Eric Kaufman
Mike Kellie
Dolores Kendrick
W. P. Kinsella
Joanne Kyger
Greg Lake
Martin Landau
Eugene Lang
Bruce Langhorne
Yale Lary
Walter Lassally
Martha Lavey
Dahlia Lavi
Katie Lee
Deke Leonard
Philip Levy
Jerry Lewis
Jaki Liebezeit
Don Lock
John D. Loudermilk
Tom Lux
Nancy Mairs
D. Keith Mano
Elsa Martinelli
Harry Mathews
Don Matthews
Alec McCowen
Jill McElmurry
Goldy McJohn
William McPherson
Thomas Meehan
David Meltzer
Mark Merlis
Dina Merrill
Gustav Metzger
George Michael
Tomas Milian
Phil Miller
Jean Millican
Robert Ellis Miller
Kate Millett
Mary Tyler Moore
Roger Moore

Erin Moran
Howard Frank Mosher
Nicholas Mosley
Alphonse Mouzon
Jeanne Moreau
Bharati Mukherjee
Bryan Murray
Jimmy Nalls
Gloria Naylor
Richard Neville
Linda Nochlin
Bill Nunn
Michael Nyqvist
Glenn O'Brien
Hugh O'Brian
Pauline Oliverios
Paul O'Neill
Robert Osborne
Tom Paley
Anita Pallenberg
Arnold Palmer
Babe Parilli
Michael Parks
Angel Parra
Ara Parseghian
Bill Paxton
David Peel
Lucia Perillo
Roberta Peters
Tom Petty
Jimmy Piersall
Robert M. Pirsig
Tim Pigott-Smith
Bernard Pomerance
E. Barrett Prettyman
Tom Raworth
Kit Reed
Della Reese
Janet Reno
Debbie Reynolds
Don Rickles
Emmanuelle Riva
Maggie Roche
Jean Rochefort
George A. Romero
Mel Rosenthal
Lillian Ross
Vera Rubin
Leon Russell
Andrew Sachs
Trevor Sandford
Peter Sarstedt
Richard Schickel
Susan Selby
John Severson

Stanley Sheinbaum
Sam Shepard
Roy Sievers
Clancy Sigal
Bunny Sigler
Charles Simmons
Barry "Frosty" Smith
Roger Smith
Mick Softley
Rosalie Sorrels
Harry Dean Stanton
Jean Stein
Judy Stone
Martin Stone
David Storey
Clyde Stubblefield
John Surtees
Martha Swope
Grady Tate
James Tate
Sheri S. Tepper
Jay Thomas
Lowell Thomas, Jr.
Jim Tolan
William Trevor
Butch Trucks
Dave Valentin
Jim Vance
Peter Vaughan
Robert Vaughn
Andrzej Wajda
Derek Walcott
Wayne Walker
Bill Walsh
Pete Overend Watts
Fritz Weaver
Ann Wedgeworth
Fred Weintraub
Adam West
John Wetton
Margaret Whitton
Anne Wiazemsky
Richard Wilbur
Roger Wilkins
Nancy Willard
Gordon Williams
Heathcote Williams
Bob Wolff
Bernie Wrightson
Brock Yates
Yevgeny Yevtushenko
Ritchie Yorke
George Young
Malcolm Young
John Zacherle "Zacherley"

CONTENTS

NONFICTION

POETRY

SCREENPLAY

FICTION

ART

MARILYN STABLEIN

CLOUD BOAT IN RISING SEAS

NANCY NAOMI CARLSON
UNTIL I DIE OF SOMETHING ELSE

Until this past year and a half, I have avoided uttering the C-word, as if saying "cancer" would be akin to inviting it into my body, like asking a vampire to enter a home. Even before I knew the true power of words, before I learned a foreign language or two, before I became a writer, I learned to be wary of my wayward mouth that might pick up just about anything. "Hepatitis." Sixth grade. Billie Jean King coming down with the disease. Oh where, oh where was my liver? Right or left lower quadrant? Did I suddenly feel an acute pain in my side? I was so sure I had fallen victim to hepatitis A, or was it B, or maybe C, that I didn't put much effort into the next day's IQ test which would determine whether I could be labeled "gifted." What did it matter, now that I was never going to make it out of elementary school? In the end, Billie Jean recovered, I was identified as "borderline gifted," and I learned the location of my liver.

My parents did their best to assuage my growing health concerns by reminding me I came from a hardy blood line. My paternal grandfather lived to a hundred, and would probably have survived longer had he not been mugged on a walk to the Brooklyn museum at age ninety-five. My maternal grandmother died at eighty-eight. One morning she woke up, collapsed, clutching her heart, and, after CPR from my ninety-year-old grandfather, shook her head "no" to an ambulance drive, and died.

My first "heart attack" occurred during my first year of graduate school in Maryland. First year living away from home, as I had commuted to Queens College for four years. My first-serious-boyfriend-to-later-become-my-husband arranged for me to meet his brother. Bob and I arrived early one evening at a small apartment in Hyattsville, not far from the University of Maryland, where I was studying five centuries' worth of French literature. After classes at the Sorbonne in Paris the previous summer, I was eager to learn more lessons from the eighteenth-century *philosophes*. From Voltaire, I was inspired to cultivate my garden. I got depressed from Pascal's stark description of my worldly existence. I was Sisyphus rolling my boulder up a mountain, doomed each time to almost reach the summit before being overcome by the weight of the boulder and propelled back down the slope, only to have to start the futile climb again. I was waiting for Godot, who would never come. I became a card-carrying existentialist and spoke in erudite tones of the human condition where we seek answers that the world cannot supply. And then we all die.

And so, after I nervously shook the hand of my ex-brother-in-law-to-be and his wife, after several sips of beer from a can of an unknown brand, after I realized that I had not eaten anything since breakfast, I felt a strange numbness creep up my left arm, like a larger-than-life caterpillar. I knew the signs of a heart attack. Soon would come the crushing pain to my chest, the tightening of my jaw, and the sweats. With a hasty excuse to my confused boyfriend and equally confused hosts, I bolted for the door, the light, the air. Bob followed, and drove me back to my small rented room on Knox Road, stopping only at Baskin-Robbins for a cup of chocolate chip ice cream we hoped would counteract the small quantity of alcohol I had consumed. Almost home, I unsnapped the wide leather watchband, hand-tooled by Bob at his job at the Joint Possession, which seemed to be obstructing my blood from traveling past my left wrist—the explanation for what would become my lifelong habit of only wearing a watch on my right wrist. A loose watch. These days, a bangle bracelet watch. No one suspects a backstory.

I did not die. Panic attacks make you feel like you're dying, but you don't. You make your way back up the mountain, back into your life, inch by inch. Until the next panic attack throws you down again.

As it was not always possible for me to rush out of a room every time an attack occurred, I learned to open a window for air. I learned to breathe deeply, tensing and releasing each muscle group in my body. I learned to drop my head lower than my heart each time I felt panic's rise, though sometimes this maneuver was difficult to pull off, depending on the context in which the attack threatened to occur. Usually I found myself in the worst possible situations—in front of the seventh-grade Spanish class I was teaching, during job interviews, or at my dissertation defense. I learned I could let something—a pen or tissue—drop to the ground, which necessitated my leaning over to retrieve it. To make myself more immune to panic, I practiced transcendental meditation. I jogged. I ate probiotic-rich foods. While everyone else was taking quaaludes, I was stuffing vitamins down my throat by the handfuls. I even had a baby, which, in the end, was perhaps what had the biggest impact on helping me manage my panic attacks, as someone else's life depended on my being fully and rationally present at all times.

I would like to say I was rational a year ago, in the midst of drinking a soy chai latte at a Starbucks just past the traffic circle that separates Maryland from Washington, D.C. An arbitrary divide, not unlike the one between life and death. I had just been to my osteopath, where I had completed close to a hundred "back-forths" on a nine-foot slide board, struggled through twenty chin-ups wrapped in a giant rubber band, and been bent and stretched to the floor on a Roman chair. Three days earlier, I had rushed to a breast surgeon for a biopsy of a "suspicious mass," one that I couldn't even feel, that had been spotted during a routine mammogram, squeezed into my schedule before seeing *Sideshow* at the Kennedy Center. In hindsight, that particular musical's theme of cutting away a part of you that blocked your way to living a complete life was prophetic, though the show had to do with conjoined sisters and not disease. When the breast surgeon announced my invasive ductal carcinoma, he had to repeat it several times, as the cell phone reception was spotty and the café noisy. Could he mean "ductal carcinoma in situ" the pre-cancerous condition I had come across as part of my Internet search? Wasn't I a poster child for healthy living? Hadn't I said "no" to skydiving, hot air balloons, roller-coaster rides, and a trip to Calcutta, all expenses to be paid by my publisher? I could not deny my vices, the worst of which was my propensity for staying up until two or three or even four in the morning, ever since I had retired as a school counselor, three years earlier. I justified this practice by the poetry and translation work I accomplished in a quiet house, while everyone slept, including the dog. But hadn't there been research that reported a connection between working night-shift hours and breast cancer?

In the weeks that followed, I learned the lexicon of cancer. The higher the rate of proliferation of cancer cells, the more aggressive they are. The more undifferentiated they look under a microscope, the more aggressive. The higher the Ki-67 score, the more aggressive. I learned about "oncotype scores," a tool to calculate risk of recurrence for those with early stage breast cancer, based on the exact genetic makeup of a particular tumor. Hormone positive is good. HER positive, not so good. Triple negative, worse, but all more likely than not to have good outcomes if caught before spreading to lymph nodes. The bad news? No one really knows why some cancer cells escape the original tumor—perhaps joy-riding on some nearby blood vessel—and hide beyond treatment's reach, maybe dormant for years and years, before suddenly reawakening. All it takes is one. Despite campaigns with pink ribbons and marathon runs, I will not be considered "cured" until I die of something else.

After two lumpectomies, four rounds of chemotherapy that left me each time with blood counts close to zero, necessitating me to quarantine myself for four to five days each cycle, not to mention losing my hair, including my eyelashes, as well as nineteen days straight (except for two weekends) of radiation, ending on Christmas eve, my medical oncologist told me my body shows "no evidence of disease." This is doctor speak for "we can't make any guarantees, but for now there's nothing we see that needs to be treated." I know this experience is a wakeup call. Besides the obvious meaning that my days of boulder rolling are numbered, I keep obsessing about what I should be doing with this knowledge. I still startle at my face in the mirror. My shoulder-length and wavy brown hair with blonde highlights is now a thick mass of tightly wound dark curls. My eyebrows are missing in key places that I pencil in with chocolate brown eyeliner bought at the health food store. My eyelashes are intact again. I read the latest research studies and hope I will not regret the treatment decisions I made. Medicine is an inexact science, a fact illustrated by the soy debate. Some researchers, citing a study involving mice, argue that soy increases the likelihood of recurrence of estrogen-positive tumors, as it weakly binds with cancer cells before they can get the benefit of the stronger blocking activity of tamoxifen. Others praise the tumor-inhibiting qualities of soy. The key seems to be the kind of soy studied, which includes soy protein, soybeans, soy flour, soy lecithin, and soy sauce. My breast surgeon observed, "A little edamame every now and then won't kill you." I have chosen this approach. My medical oncologist said I should expect to see micro improvements in my physical functioning every day. That seems to be the case. The last therapist I consulted (number six) asked me how many times a day I think about my breast cancer experience, and if the number has changed with time. When I told her there has been little change, she reassured me that it takes at least two years to adjust. After two years, I wonder if I will relive my experience each time I hear about someone newly diagnosed, or a friend who has died, or at the anniversary of my diagnosis. I still won't try sky diving, hot air balloons, or roller coasters, but yesterday I said yes to Calcutta.

IRENE FICK

THE WISHFUL ENTREPRENEUR

This year, I became an entrepreneurial consultant, a venture that requires a fertile imagination and some business cards. In this role, I generate new-business ideas for others. Here is just a sampling:

Undie-Takers—Remember Mom's warning to keep your underwear in good shape in case, God forbid, you were in a car accident? Undie-Takers provides emergency road service, much like Triple A. For an annual fee and a membership card with a toll-free number, this business supplies clean, fresh, hole-less underwear, even socks—delivered directly to the scene of the accident.

Mother Tuckers—This business serves the old, the sick, and the lonely who yearn for the security and comfort of being tucked into bed as a child. Mother Tuckers provides a nightly visit from a maternal type who will tuck clients into bed, serve warm milk, read a bedtime story, or hum a lullaby. For those traveling alone at night, Mother Tuckers offers a roadside version: The Tuck Stop, which provides lodging, comfort food, and a tucking service.

Arrivederci Rover—Your dog deserves a break from his routine of eating, sleeping, and walking. Consider this: Arrivederci Rover, the world's first travel agency for canines. Imagine your pet on a tour bus or an aircraft that caters to his needs, complete with complimentary beds, blankets, treats, and toys. He could explore the cobblestoned streets of Europe, the crevices of the Grand Canyon, the rainforests of Costa Rica. Optional tours might include an evening at the opera to hear Pooch-ini, or reservations at select restaurants such as Bone Appétit.

Car-panions—These are life-sized, lifelike male dummies sold to women who drive alone at night, especially those traveling on dark, remote roads. A car-panion is placed in the passenger seat, and the driver's hand-held switch can activate his head and hands so he looks real. A car-panion can thwart carjackings, assaults, and other crimes that could target women who travel alone.

Anesthesia Airlines—This new venture caters to fearful flyers. Passengers are given full anesthesia prior to their flight, timed to wear off just after the plane safely lands. Passengers arrive refreshed, as if waking from a long nap. As an added bonus, if the plane should crash, the flyer would never know.

It Could Be Verse—This custom poetry service offers a personal, literate alternative to mass-produced greeting card messages. Clients select from a variety of poetic forms (sonnet, haiku, free verse, etc.). All poetry is crafted by experienced poets. Advertising copy promises: "I love you, happy birthday, congratulations, goodbye./ Whatever the message, it shouldn't be terse./How to say it? It could be verse."

My phone lines are now open for calls. I hope to hear from you soon!

CHELSEA MORNINGSTAR
BUBBLES

very time I put the gold eyeshadow on—once, twice, a week—I think about Bubbles. I think about how she was a figure skater once, and how they only keep you so long, and you still have to make a living. I think about how loud she was, and rowdy, raunchy, and how the young men, usually with only ones, didn't know what to do with her. I think about her doing Sturgis, unafraid, posing on a motorcycle, always laughing. And how at a rest stop out in the middle of nowhere in the Southwest, the knife in her boot saved her life but not before the one he had slashed up all she had to sell. Her boy waiting in the truck, twelve years old, learned to drive that night through the desert. I think about how only two of her remaining friends knew her real name. And of her sitting in the dressing room, no longer raunchy or rude, touching up her eyeshadow, how she was all gold and tan and platinum, a starlet, looking not a day over fifty.

DANIEL MUELLER
ANTIVENOM

In San Antonio, my father met us at the airport in his commissioned officer's uniform, brass caducei pinned to his lapels, and drove us to El Tropicano, a hotel with a lobby, gift shop, restaurant, and bar. It was happy hour, and our third-floor room overlooked the swimming pool where, below my sister Karen and me, two women wearing bikinis under terrycloth robes sipped cocktails brought to them from a thatched hut by a waiter in a red tunic. Their laughter over conversation not meant for the ears of a six-year-old—this discernible from their hushed tones—wafted up through the rattling palm fronds.

In a blue Ford Falcon rental car, my mother had driven us from Greeley to Denver where, in a cafeteria before boarding our plane, I'd bumped into a soldier's table and knocked his cup of coffee onto his lap. He was black, and I hid my face in my mother's skirt. Holding our tray of food in one hand and my sister's hand in the other, she apologized for my clumsiness, in the midst of the chaos extracting from her purse two dollars that fluttered between nails I'd watched her file and polish the night before.

"Now, now," the officer said, standing up from his table and revealing the full extent of the stain across his jacket and slacks. "The little man meant no harm."

"Please," my mother said, "take the money. Your uniform will need to be dry-cleaned."

"You think the army can't afford its own laundry bill?" He laughed and adjusted his garrison cap. A big man whose roundness was betrayed by starched angles at his chest and shoulders, he took the tray of food from my mother and led us to an open table. "Now you and your children enjoy your lunch, ma'am," he said.

She thanked him, setting milk containers, apples, hotdogs, French fries, and vanilla puddings before Karen and me. As we ate, I kept looking at the man as he blotted coffee from himself and his table with a napkin, then sat before his cup with the napkin stuffed in it, his animation subsumed by gloom, the crescents beneath his eyes weighted and blue.

I thought about him later as I held my sister's hand, imagining lowering her on a rope and pulley from our balcony into the bed of anemones and flamingo flowers where, concealed by the foliage, she could record the women whose conversation I strained to overhear. Inside our hotel room, my mother recounted her day to my father, who lay on his back on one of the queen-sized beds with fingers laced behind his head. She told him how well behaved I'd been on the flight, how I'd looked after Karen, letting her affix flag decals to their corresponding countries in my *Flags of the World* activity book and explaining to her that despite how springy the clouds looked from our airplane window she'd fall straight through them if she tried to jump on them like she did on her mattress at home.

"Norm likes when I..." one of the women said, but a breeze passed through the palms and I could not hear how she finished her sentence. "Of course, he does," replied the other.

My mother made no mention of the soldier on whom coffee had spilled, and while I was grateful to be spared the attention, even I could tell that her omission was meant to protect something that no longer existed if it ever had.

If only I could hear what Norm liked, I'd share it with my mother, and maybe my father would like it, too.

FOR THE THREE weeks left in my father's basic medical officer training at Fort Sam Houston, my mother, sister, and I lived at El Tropicano, ate meals in our room, and spent our days at the pool.

A week into our stay, my maternal grandmother Isadora, a diva wrapped in shawls of organza and tulle and partial to turbans from which sprays of her orange hair erupted at odd angles, came to visit us with her second husband Leo, a rangy Texan from the Panhandle. An oilman for most of his life, he'd retired to Los Angeles where he and Izzy had fallen "in cahoots," by which he meant they lived together in the yellow brick apartment building he managed three blocks off the Miracle Mile. Photos of them on the front steps between blazing pink azalea bushes in concrete urns abounded, she pumpkin shaped and ethereal, he leather skinned, silver buckled, and gritty. "A real pair," my father called them behind their backs.

In the afternoons they were our lifeguards, and their laissez-faire approach was a pleasant change from my mother's hyper-vigilance. While they relieved her to get her hair done, shop, or lie down for an hour in the afternoon, I dove for quarters Leo plucked from an avocado coin purse, and Karen bobbed around the pool in a Type II boating vest, her blonde hair and ever-reddening face a Janus set adrift on an orange raft. For hours she'd be as placid as the Buddha, alternating between herself and Cousin Itt, until a combination of hunger, thirst, sunburn, and boredom wormed its way into her cerebral cortex and she'd wail as if attacked by hornets, her mouth all quivering uvula, her eyes squeezed lemon wedges.

While I could've fished her out myself and placated her with bananas, Leo made such a big production of unsnapping the snaps of his Western shirt and draping it over the back of his chaise longue, unfastening his watchband and setting it on the table between their whiskey sours, all the while saying, "You aren't really going to make your step-granddad get in the water, are you? You aren't really going to make old Leo perform a rescue?" that I assumed he enjoyed our daily ritual as much as I did.

"You're a lifeguard," I'd say. "Saving lives is what you do."

"It's what young lifeguards do," he'd grumble. "Old lifeguards train young lifeguards to do the actual lifesaving."

He'd put out his Salem in the mound of butts and ash that rose from the ashtray and, in his swim trunks, straw fedora, and aviator sunglasses, venture down the steps into the shallow end where my sister's intermittent gasps promised a return to tranquility about as well as a machine gunner's pause to reload.

"Will you nab her, Leo?" Izzy would call from her chaise longue. "I can't take another second of her caterwauling."

"Your wish is my command, sweetheart mine," Leo would reply. Not until Karen was swathed in arms tattooed with anchors would she desist in her keening.

Indeed, she'd stare up into the shade of his hat brim and giggle.

"Now will you look at that?" Leo would say as Izzy applauded, making all her many parts jiggle.

"My gallant prince."

It was as if each afternoon were choreographed and perfect. Once all of us were out of the water, Leo would wipe off the table with a napkin as Izzy shuffled a deck of playing cards, on each a color photograph of a mostly naked woman, for the ongoing game of gin rummy they'd been playing since 1963, the year they'd met and married. With the coins I'd collected from the bottom of the pool I'd pay for Shirley Temples and a bag-a-piece of cheesy popcorn for Karen and me. "English tea," Leo would call it, and draped in hotel towels Karen and I would pretend we'd been kidnapped by royalty.

The day before they were to start back to California, Leo wanted to change the oil in their Bonneville, and Karen and I were left alone with Izzy. In tan coveralls, Leo placed his coin purse in her palm and, whistling "King of the Road," headed for the parking lot. But once we were in the water, nothing was the same. Izzy wouldn't leave her chaise longue, and the pennies and nickels she picked out from the quarters often wouldn't make the edge of the pool. While I was happy to climb out and throw the money in myself, I could see that I'd never collect enough for a single bag of cheesy popcorn much less the "English tea" we'd come to expect.

Sensing a diminished return, my sister began to whimper before the sun reached one o'clock, and Izzy commanded me to make her stop.

"I can't make her stop, Grandma," I replied. As if to prove it I swam up beside Karen and beneath the water yanked one of her feet, which made her cry even harder. "Besides, you're our lifeguard."

"I'm much more than your lifeguard, Buster Brown," Izzy replied. "I'm your grandma. And you're too big for your britches."

I threw a nickel into the deep end and swam after it. When I came up with it in my fist, Karen's crying had become a squall. The only sanctuary beneath the water, I thought of myself as a dolphin, rising to the surface only for air, and each time I did Izzy was closer to the edge of the pool. The water mortified her, but could she not see that the only way to mollify Karen was to confront her fear? Even as my sister's mewling made my teeth hurt, I was rooting for Izzy. Did she not want the same delight Karen had brought to Leo's visage brought to her own? With eyes above the surface and ears below, I watched as water rippled up her gold polyester pants to the waist of her leopard print blouse. As she waded toward Karen, her taut lips were those of a fledgling aerialist afraid to look down.

Once beside Karen, Izzy spun her around by her life preserver, and I swam to them, not about to miss the change in my sister's demeanor that would bring about a corresponding one in my grandmother's. Maybe, I hazarded, I'd even get credit for it. But once embraced, Karen looked up at Izzy's sunglasses—pearlescent cat eyes!—and screamed even louder.

Izzy snapped, "You stop your blubbering right now, child, before I wring your rotten neck. Is that what you want? For your poor, old grandma to wring your rotten neck? Because I will, child. Don't test me."

Izzy was hyperventilating, beside herself with fright, which in turn frightened Karen, whose exasperated shrieks echoed off the sliding-glass doors of hotel room balconies seven stories up. "Here, Grandma," I said, "let me do it." I towed Karen to the steps, unfastened the straps of her floatation device, and freed her from the constraints. I peeled a banana, cut it into rounds, and placed them before her in a plastic bowl. Only then did her bleating turn to sniffles. Wrapped in towels, Karen fell asleep in her chair.

Looking up from her word-search puzzle, Izzy whispered, "I ought to wring your rotten neck, Dan." Beneath her chaise longue the pond she'd brought with her from the pool was retreating from its shores, and her pants and blouse were mostly dry. By this time tomorrow she and Leo would be cruising West in their sea-green convertible, likely with the top down, while Karen and I would again be under our mother's supervision and without any prospect of an English tea.

I asked Izzy if I could use her deck of playing cards to build a hotel. The air was still, and El Tropicano, towering above our oasis on four sides, would be a challenge to replicate.

Izzy glanced at me over her puzzle, her smile conspiratorial but inscrutable. "You want to build a hotel of cards? Not a house but a hotel?"

I nodded, and she handed me the deck, still in its original packaging, on the front a color photograph of a lady riding a stallion in just boots, chaps, and hat. If on each card a female model wore accessories in lieu of clothing, to me their worth lay in what could be built with them, and soon a rectangle of lean-tos linked apex to apex by cards lain horizontally across them rose from the tabletop. The first floor done, I began work on a second, and at the north end a third. By the time my mother had finished her errands, I'd used up all the cards but the jokers, and my replica was only three-fifths complete. Without another deck, I could not go on.

"Will you look at your son's marvel of architecture and engineering?" Izzy exclaimed to my mother as she set down her department store shopping bags on the grass and moved a chair into the shade of our umbrella.

"Wow," she said, "that's the biggest house of cards I've ever seen."

"It isn't a house," Izzy corrected her, "it's a hotel."

"Not anymore," I corrected them both, turning the last two cards into a steeple. "Behold, a church."

By then Karen had awakened and, jealous of attention directed at anyone but herself, pulled a card from the ground floor, and three dimensions collapsed into two on the beveled glass. I wasn't upset, proud of the concentration and steadiness of nerves with which I'd used every card in the deck, knowing from experience that a single, misdirected breath could raze an entire structure.

My mother snatched Karen's card, glanced at it, and said, "Dan, take your sister back to our room. The key is in my purse." Her tone one I'd heard before, I did as I was told until Karen and I were through the gate and hidden by the wooden fence that surrounded the pool.

"God damn it to hell," she said to Izzy when she thought we were out of earshot. "Do you want them to grow up to be as trashy as you? As us? Is that what you want, Mom?"

How dare she talk to her own mother that way, I thought. Izzy's feelings were hurt, and I felt ashamed of myself for having forced her into the pool fully clothed.

"The cards are Leo's," Izzy conceded. "They're our rummy deck. Since we started playing with them, I've gone up a hundred games in less than a year. I think they give him a little thrill." She twittered a little laugh. "You might consider giving Jim a little thrill every once in a while."

"Mom," she said, "he's an OB-GYN. He sees more in a workday than Leo will ever see in a raunchy deck of cards."

"I'm sorry, darling," said Izzy.

"Come on, Karen," I said and tugged her gently away from a bird of paradise in full blossom, thinking myself stupid for not having looked closer at pictures I wasn't likely to see again.

ONE EVENING WE rented paddleboats, a red one for my father and Karen and a yellow one for my mother and me. In a sunset that limned with flame each ripple and suffused with emerald the broad-leafed ferns that cascaded to one bank of the San Antonio River, we raced each other to the cheers of restaurant patrons sitting beneath umbrellas—red, yellow, green, orange, and blue—that spotted the other. Cypress trees formed bridges over the water, and in their canopies, though only July, Christmas lights twinkled. Beneath the surface over which we glided, their reflections twinkled back as if proof that all things had their twins, even us.

At no time had I seen my parents happier. "Pump harder, Dan," my mother cried. "We can't let your dad and Karen win!"

"I'm onto you, Linda," my father called, aiming to cut in front of us and secure a victory for himself and Karen, but my sister's feet fell short of her pedals, and four legs won out over two.

"We did it, Dan!" my mother shrilled as we high fived.

Thieves' gloves contracting in the night, bats snuffed out fireflies whose sputtering paths remained on the retina even after their lives were over. With Cokes for Karen and me and frozen margaritas for our parents, we toasted the end of my father's basic medical officer training, ten weeks in which his time had been divided between combat drills and surgery, the battlefield and the operating room. If in one arena his commanding officers had risked the lives of drafted doctors in war games that prepared them for nothing they would actually face stationed at military hospitals stateside, their orders in the other, often betraying questionable judgment, risked the lives of patients. My father blamed it on the branch's "competing power structures," hating that his practice of obstetrics and gynecology was overseen by a decorated colonel and *podiatrist.*

"The clown's never performed a vaginal hysterectomy in his life, never removed an ovarian cyst, performed a tubal ligation, or even delivered a baby, and he feels qualified to tell me what to do?"

During the one night a week the army granted my father leave to visit us, my mother did her best to console him. "At least you're not going to Vietnam. You're two and through, Jim. After two years, they have to let us go."

"That's if I live through this, Linda," he'd say and remind her that he was allergic to the antivenom used to treat viper bites. During field exercises the men regularly encountered rattlesnakes, cottonmouths, and copperheads sunning on the shelves over which they climbed and hidden in the grass through which they crawled, grenades detonating all around them, bullets zinging over their heads, no one sure if the ammo fired was real or not. Loaded with blanks, their own weapons were useless against a poisonous snake reared to strike, and some of the men had the fang marks in their battle fatigues to prove it.

But my father wasn't one of them, and the threat of a deadly snakebite was but a distant memory as our waitress nestled skillets of fajitas between Talavera ramekins of guacamole, salsa verde, and sour cream, and tortillas kept warm in foil.

"Tomorrow Fort Hood," my father said, and my mother explained to Karen and me that the army had waitlisted us for a two-bedroom house on base. In the meantime, she explained, we'd live in a two-bedroom apartment in Killeen.

"It may not be God's country," my father added, "but it'll be better than this."

"Who'd have thought," I said, "we'd ever tire of hotel life?" I hadn't—El Tropicano's endless supply of miniature boxes of Cap'n Crunch and Apple Jacks that opened into their own rectangular cereal bowls; the maids Carmela and Rose who stepped around my Hot Wheels raceway, thirty-two feet of orange track, start gate, stop gate, and daredevil loops I'd set up between the beds, when they changed our sheets, relieving my mother of housework; and suspended on brackets from a wall of our room the Magnavox color television so much fancier than our old Zenith black and white—but had fallen under the spell of my parents' hopefulness.

Neither had seemed happy in a long time, and though I'd looked everywhere for the reason, browsing magazines and books in the hotel gift shop, watching soap operas on TV, and at the pool and in the lobby eavesdropping on couples I thought in love, language, whether spoken or in print, presented a second riddle I could not unravel.

But maybe, I thought as they joked and laughed and kissed in front of us, my misgivings had been for naught, and everything was fine.

OFF THE BEACH

Ocean driftwood fires flicker especially marvelously, the salt burns green and blue

At the end of the continent in the fall equinox evening light there is an amazingly constant arrival of cars and campers from all the way back to Maine and the Maritimes just to be, just to be there, at the end

Would watch them years ago from my eighty-dollars-a-month apartment on Ocean Boulevard at Pico and still they come

Since about J. C. Fremont in the 1840s they have been striding across the sand purposefully agape to take their shoes or boots off and walk in

Shutters, at One Pico Boulevard, a seven-hundred-dollar-a-night hotel, exactly absorbs the site of my old Vicente Terrace place

At the western edge, the grand Pacific façade

Could not recognize where we crossed the Coast Range, hoped for the Angeles Crest and the San Gabriels but those ridges must have been back in the San Bernadinos

The Basin's vastness, Cajón to the ocean, a stretched-out glide path from over Riverside

The first few times was hitching or driving Route 66 in from Needles and Arizona

Once heading toward Needles at night from the East, rattlers by the dozens were stretched out on the warm asphalt in the black-night desert chill

Then before cars and trucks had AC were the big sweating water bags hung on a bumper or a door handle in the desert

People then pondered whether to wait for dusk before starting across from the river or to gamble on their tires and radiators to venture it in the Mojave day

In the desert to Barstow from Arizona is more than a hundred and sixty, another sixty over El Cajón down to San Berdoo

Coming off the pass into the San Gabriel Valley citrus groves was a triumph then, as significant as making it to the ocean that was still eighty miles ahead

Cascade now of LA's time-distance-sequence phosphenes, trolling in the past, jagging in and out, the future-past

And down to earth at LAX to rush into it already there, back on the Pacific's edge

In Marina del Rey out to walk in the Venice Beach evening felt like being home

Willets on the swash common as the sanderlings

Half a dozen Venice Beach fall-plumage ruddy turnstones

Pothunters used to call them horsefoot snipes

And dramatically, humpbacked-stitching along while feeding, were more than two dozen marbled godwits

Working both directions in the plum yellow sunset

Magical godwits

Earlier this fall watched a lone Hudsonian godwit at Cape May

It was missing a foot but doing fine

Gently voluble Southern California people, mostly alone, walking behind the uprush

Serene but alert with that unmistakable California placidity

Falafels and beer supper at dark on Washington Boulevard at the beach in South Venice

Strike across the city toward the Angeles Crest with Guoxiu and her husband up from Laguna in the morning

Her hair a beautiful wavy gray

Last time when she got out of our Shanghai taxi to catch a train her hair was bobbed and not gray

We take the 10, the 5, through downtown, the 2 to the Crest Highway that just up from La Cañada is barricaded from slides after the huge Station Fire that burned out the Arroyo Seco in September-October 2009

Since the fire the only car route into the forest from the city circles around the foothills on the 210 to Sunland and up the Big Tujunga that is closed to Clear Creek, so then Shortcut to the Crest at Mount Sally below Windy Gap

All the old still-remembered roads and ways

Guoxiu and Xinzhou, urban Beijingers, stunned at the distances and the emptiness of the Coast Range's barren ridges and canyons

And the Station Fire's burn drapes over the low mountains of the Big Tujunga like cloud shadows

It took almost everything deep into the high country beyond Horse Flats

Still the nakedness, black snags, ashy duff and singed chaparral

Out on top and on the Angeles Crest itself before Chilao

We stare down into Devil's Canyon toward the river where my West Fork ranger station used to be

In Chilao the one-room school is still painted Forest Service bayberry green among the boulders and manzanita before the camp itself

The giant-coned Coulter pines where the fire didn't make it up into high Chilao and Charlton Flats

On the narrow road into the fire camp a masonry monument with four bronze plaques to Forest Service people, three of whom I knew

George Lopez, who once let me take the stick of his Bell helicopter before we landed at Barley Flats, who two fire seasons later crashed a Hiller and died over on the desert side

Tom Reginator whose Red Box patrol adjoined my West Fork one so we would tie in at Switzer's in the canyon to take our lunch break together leaning on the hood of his truck or mine, killed with his neck caught in the shrouds on a jump on the Sequoia

Pete Trujillo, a Taos Pueblo chief and superintendent of Chilao, who saved my life once firing-out on the Sequoia, called me Judge, died three years on alone in his truck at night going over the side on Ladybug Curve down below Red Box

The fourth plaque for a name I didn't recognize, someone way after my time

The Chilao crew now with many Hispanic names, all frank and open friendliness showing off new equipment and listening to me on the old days

Three or four women now part of what was all male when I lived and worked out of that very special high-country place

Forest Service hotshots then were like crusader bands of the peaks and canyons, self-celebratory of our abilities in the tall timber and the chaparral, of how fast we could hike in after we were dropped off helicopters or crew trucks, how fast we could cut line, how good we each were with brush hooks, Pulaskis, fire shovels and McLeods

It must be like that for those lean, earnest, good-tempered Chilao people now

There was no time for boredom up there and it was a totally mountain-man life around camp, not even conversationally misogynistic

Chilao didn't nourish the usual men-alone sex talk, no boastful stories about what any of us did down in the city on days off

Virtually asexual except for a little Winslow Homeresque grab-ass when after a fire we would strip down at some high-country river off the fire line to clean up and swim

No lack of uncomplicated eager enthusiasm about what we did and there was less mind-game undertow than in any place I've ever lived

We would sit outside the barracks at dusk on the steps or on the boulders, listen to the poorwills and talk about our front-country lives and what to do after fire season closed and we were laid off, serene and placidly innocent

Waiting for the next fire

The only women around the Forest Service then were nurses in the first-aid tents on campaign fires, and secretaries in the offices of front-country ranger stations

Rarely an adventurous girlfriend would drive up at night from the city for a sleeping-bag rendezvous out in Charlton Flats

It was remarkable to visit there again, Chilao felt the same, the horseshoe pit, the raggedy Coulter pines, the mysterious dome of the horizon up near the helspot

Having the Forest Service people shaking hands with my exotic elderly Beijing friends and their rudimentary English was purely only twenty-first-century Los Angeles plausible

The three of us drove out the rest of the Crest to Cloudburst Summit to look out into the Mojave over on the San Gabriel Mountain's desert side before we started down

It was getting dark when we made it to the freeways again to ride the roaring torrent of the 5 all the way to Laguna, the El Toro exit

The ineluctability of so much freeway purpose out there in three, four, five lanes, at seventy and sixty-five, nearly wheel to wheel in total anonymity, in the spooky, sodium vapor, halogen, headlight-taillight darkness

Freeway river speed and rumble an hour after sunset the same as an hour before dawn

The latitude and tolerant road skill of everybody to keep it right, everyone on their breakneck way, no margin for wavering mistakes or bad lane-change

Seventy miles on the 5, diagonally across all of LA, La Cañada to Laguna, to take Guoxiu and Xinzhou home and to see their family

Then back to Marina del Rey on the 405

Alone in that fluxing fast-lane changing to the beach with so much awareness behind, ahead and in adjoining lanes merely taillights away, but all of them, those people so near, profoundly mysterious, unknown, all of us moving on

There was still some light over the Pacific, the beach only an exit away

DEBBIE URBANSKI
VERB (USUALLY USED WITH OBJECT)

1. To write letters to someone faraway whom you will never again see.

2. To wish to be alone in some ways but not in other ways; to be a conundrum: *"Are you for real?" he asks, reading over her shoulder at what she wrote.*

3. The narrow and ideally permanent distance between two people; what should, but does not always, exist in that distance: *She does not receive a letter back.*

4. To have no idea, in the context of you, what this verb means.

5. To act how one is expected to act; to give it, as he likes to say, your best shot. *"Come on. I'm right here. I'm right in front of you. Don't you want me?"*

6. *"Of course I want you," she responds, unbuttoning her shirt.*

7. To have a secret, which to him means a physical intimacy in the dark, though to you it means something else. *He tells her, "Do you need instructions? Fine. Kiss me here."*

8. To try and want to kiss someone while, at the same time, trying to want to grope his thigh; to pretend.

9. To wish there were more stories without beds in them.

10. To do what you're told to do in his bed: *Finally, shoving off of her in frustration, he demands, "Why are you just lying there?"*

11. To write a story in which there are no beds; to be, in a story, objectless.

12. In that story to be told, from a great distance, his gloved hands up in the air, "You are who I have been looking for all this time."

13. *"You are who I have been looking for all this time," he shouted at her from a distant rooftop in a story.*

MARILYN STABLEIN
THINKING OF HER

KELLI ALLEN
AN ASTERISK FOR THE WEATHER

I open wider when your hips circle close.
There is no storm, unstrapping its gales,
ruinous enough to hide your body from mine.
Not this night. Not morning, either, knitting
light into shoulder blades exposed, tendons
folding as hands supplicant, fingering,
only bone meeting bone. The sea bean cord
slung around my throat signifies theft. A tongue-
tip remembers salt in all five directions. So,

when you notice the sheets crippled
between cocked knees, consider how long
I wait to admit what a year means. Think
of how many times I offer you the nectarine
sliced even and sure, spread nautilus round
over beveled glass. Your appetite, my chest—
both rising as a fist meant to fit against
the fucked-up keyhole we mistake for wolves'
jaws. Depending on where you release, I might

say your name, and those birds we wept over
the first afternoon will swoop into the country
as though nothing here matters. But, darling—
there is only the width of this bed before
we spill through. I'll swallow what's left,
listening to the way we do anything for more,
thinking we have surrendered just this once.

THE MOUNTAIN LOON TELLS A STORY FOR LOVERS

It's true that the sun did not shine on Jonah more
than she did over Kabir. What does this change
about how we travel toward predication?

Compromise implies swaying, still, but only
as oaks through wind, never night buildings
set against some hurricane. Even lamps bend

their light toward Viking ships when the harbor
fills a window at dusk. We notice the woman
and man tuck a long rudder beneath their bed,

obeying directions for when parting comes.
Herons stand one-legged on poles erected
to mimic shoulders turning firm in affection.

This means swallowing want past tongue and teeth
just before agreeing to board the river boat. Reckless
is for the past selves. I grieve nothing herded at night.

Bellies are for wind burning and perfume. Tell me
how the third body is the one stitched close
every day we agree not to say what the longing is.

DAVID ALPAUGH
SECRET/LIFE

SECRET...

Tattoo. Inside my armpit. The artist had
to shave my hair before tattooing there.
But I'm swarthy, so once it comes back
thick what's etched in my skin will lurk
like a snake in the forest. My tattooed

Secret. I have a public tattoo on my neck.
$E = mc^2$ breaks the ice with the right sort
of women at singles bars. Still, I'm armed
with 5 words of poetry I'll not share—not
even with a future wife: *I have wasted my*

LIFE...

MILES/FUCKER

MILES...

Asked to play piano with the great jazz
trumpeter, I was thrilled. But when I sat
down for our first gig together—you bet
I was plenty nervous. Yes, I was Chick;
and I was good; but, damn it!—He was

Miles! After his solo, I riffed my balls off,
while he stood by the piano *expressionless.*
Then just before he raised his horn and his
lips began to pucker—I was in like Flynn
as Miles muttered *Chick, you're a mother*

FUCKER...

Note: My versification of an anecdote told by Chick Corea at the Masonic Auditorium in San Francisco in 1978. Corea said it was the greatest compliment on his playing that he ever received.

JOCKO BENOIT
FILTERED SUNLIGHT

For a moment we are Any Couple,
trying one color swatch then another
against the stairway wall until
Filtered Sunlight and we say, "Yes"
simultaneously for the first time
in years. And we know our Christian
landlords would love the gentle symbolism
of this mild yellow leading upward
to the skylight at the landing.

So we sand the spackle smooth over
the fist-sized dent I made and head
to the paint store where we will
walk past the rainbow of possibilities
and choose the necessary hue.
We are, as usual, more united by
subterfuge than by passion—the former
enduring more wear and tear.
But when I complain while climbing
the stairs later, suggesting next time
we should get a ranch-style home, she says
she wishes that was all I had problems
getting up and I hesitate, not knowing
exactly how her words are shaded.

ALL OUT OF BUBBLE GUM

I keep cheating on who I used to be.
At first it was with capitalism and her
promise to make me happy, my smiles
from a sticker shock I never overcame.
Religion counseled patience and rosaries,
but once you felt her spine she was
something else between the sheets,
screaming Latin at me until she had
exorcised her demon. I get on the 8:15
zeitgeist every day and use my wife
and son to help me escape my dreams.
Other commuters speak English, but
their lips are moving strictly in emoji.

I feel like Rowdy Roddy Piper's
character in *They Live!*—ready to
chew some gum and kick some ass.
Every time a thought blows humanity's
mind, someone sticks a system in it
like a penny in a fuse box. I may not
be able to read my wife's mind, but
I can tell you what every psychic,
futurist, and economist says next.

I thought if I stayed at a shitty job
long enough it would become art
or philosophy—like Eric Hoffer at
the docks, or *Zen and the Art of Grading
Essays for Last-Minute Electives*.
Time does not deploy air bags. Amway
and Scientology tell me money will be
my reward, but instead all I have earned
is a series of Dantesque punishments
such as replaying that old fantasy of what
my Christmas special would be like.

There are generations of ghosts
crammed in my cranium while all
the gruntled people keep calling
the wrong entity "Frankenstein,"
as if dazzled by this Three-Card
Monte of effects and causes. Here is
a new pep rally Hitler, there is a young
eager Goebbels rebranding the Reich
in a thirty-second ad. The alphabet fails me
so I turn to the Omegabet being acted out
by an Emojesus whose face is a poor
palette for the canvass inside him.

Every happy ending finishes with
ellipses. I sit in my car—a portable
avalanche waiting for one sound
to free me. I am an alien landed
in the middle of a movie of undetermined
genre. I put on sunglasses to cut down
on the glaring contradictions. Soon
the windows steam up and I see the muse's
spread-apart footprints on the windshield.
Her hair smelled of cotton candy,
her skin irresistibly chewable.
She is the only one who leaves me
feeling totally unbuckled.

GODZILLA VS. THE ECONOMIST

When it was Godzilla vs. Mothra
in the ocean, the economist said
he had no dog in that fight. When they
disrupted offshore fishing, he balanced
the lost jobs against the increased
need for imports, and a lower dollar
leading to cheaper exports for a null effect.
As a victorious Godzilla strode ashore,
turning factories and workers into fireballs,
the economist was relieved because this
would raise unemployment, increase
inflation, ensure worker insecurity,
lower wages, discourage unions and strikes,
and feed into shareholder dividends.

Only when the monster lurched towards
Wall Street did he budge. His duty
as economic shepherd forced him to the streets
where he threw high interest rates, a low
credit rating, a sinner's tax at the beast
to no avail. The creature didn't blink when
refused a nest-buyer's loan. The economist
waited for the Invisible Hand to save him,
but he learned too late the solidness
of road infrastructure. Godzilla sensed
something squishy, but moved on because
he never paid attention to the little guys.

ROY BENTLEY

ZENOWICH AND RAYMOND CARVER

Neck deep in a hot tub, Chris Zenowich and I watched
waves, bulb lit and breaking, and he said Ray smoked pot
and so it was to be expected that his characters roll blunts,
as in "Cathedral" where the blind guest gets royally baked
for the first time. We were blazed. And laughing. We were
also plastered on Scotch, and he said writers don't get away
with much since the world has decided it loathes a drunk
in the worst way. I wanted to hear more about Ray Carver.
The writer, not the drunk. But my friend Chris said the two
were inseparable in Ray's case—like weed and good Scotch.

He lit a joint he had carried into the hot tub. Made the tip end
redden in the winter dim that night in Ohio. Jets were sending
silvery bubbles at us from several directions. This was the year
he died, Chris. Found dead at forty-five or -six, I can't recall.
How do you thank a friend for those many moments of wonder
and acceptance that sanction you being yourself and just living?
My hair was long then. Strands at the back froze to the tub edge.
When I moved, he laughed at the hair coming away as icicles.
I read that a seventy-eight-year-old man was discovered alive
in a body bag on a funeral home slab in Mississippi. Kicking

alerted them. I think of Chris, high in a hot tub, talking shit
about Ray Carver who had been dead for a few years by then.
Without a care in the world but maybe entertaining the thought
he might die. I recall the joint flickered in the blacks of his eyes.
And, in all honesty, I was probably a bit bored and wanted a hit.
I lay with my arms out for a moment on the sides of the hot tub,
waves breaking warm around me. I doubt I was thinking of death,
though isn't that what writers would do if they were a lucky corpse
resurrected in Mississippi? Don't they ask the tough questions the
rest of the room wants to, as surprised as anyone to be sitting up?

SHINJINI BHATTACHARJEE
POLAROID

For a while, my throat swells with the secret of a fruit
and dead morning bulbs.
I let them drop—
             soft fall
tipping the insides with what's real.
We hang like a peculiar day, believe that
the bird is the only tool to fold the jaw of the moon,
watch the tired thud of the pears cleansing the grass
of brown rain beads. It begins like this—*I want to place
the quiet and slow of the world inside of me*, watch my snow
fingers paint hummingbirds on our incorrect skins.
A caterpillar wonders if I invented the Earth. I didn't.
Your face plants the wound of the sun and it grows on you,
tugging at the front door. A wet stamp of berries goes insane
on the kitchen floor. The hills pull themselves apart
behind you. Their mouths deep with the secret of little hands.
Sometimes, they cough out an enormous house underwater.
Its ripe arms outstretched to fill us.

PAPER THEATRE

He said: Go back to being the skin
not the salt flower   It is difficult
how the comb bleeds your touch
from my hair   like trees   blooming
gods & time in the white glass jewels
morning writing code in our hands & trying
the nomenclature of the flat crawl of feathers
on the window   Talk to me about the grain in
my palm   to be plump as a tombstone & proud
I am made out of wobbled moon My tongue
astonishes the finished   I met a blind rabbit
sniffing a thumb   a bottle of spoons
we name the edges of the river   fix
them apart so that it can rescue itself
The careful concentration   of grass
we don't mention X-rays   horses
ghosting your breath   how we realize
the stretch of your wound   Instead
we gather rain in buckets   disappear
towns with fingers   dry hourglasses
behind our legs   pause
the breeze that   notices us
The method is quite simple
a small cough inside   the
lukewarm milk   rain knotted to the porch swing
till we learn to strain the light against the color of our scars.

PAULA BONNELL
PARK STREET STATION
Three Weekday Takes

1. FRIDAY NIGHT

The frontispiece is a man exposing himself
near the turn in the stairs.

Not that he's there every Friday night;
he rarely is. When he's not, only the rubble

and clutter of the junk
the CETA workers have not yet swept up

hampers the passage of bodies
through the wobbling turnstile.

But even when he does appear,
offering his limp portion

he's a mere hitch in the flow
of TGIF commuters around the corner.

He'd like to make trouble
not just fumble with this damnable flesh,

but they all pass him by,
the old ones stiffly, the young ones in a loud huddle.

They're onto the platform and into the train.
He's left behind, hanging on for dear life.

2. MONDAY MORNING

the tell-it-all middle
starts off dully enough.
the train expels people
like pinballs, among them
a blonde in a long
white raincoat
with a kick-pleat slit
up the back. last one
out of the last car,
she's relaxed
in the morning interval
before work, daydreaming
as she would
in the kitchen
before dinner. she
heads for the gate
to the escalator, but
just before she
gets there is
clutched
between the legs
by a hand from
behind her.
automatic pleasure
pumps in her crotch
at this soft touch
which her cunt
tells her is her
old husband or
some familiar.
but this hand,
however clever
its warm squeeze,
is no one she
knows. it's a young
moon-faced man
in a bright orange
sweatshirt—nobody
to her. she's
turning, half-knowing

what's happened, that
he's caught her
but good, really had
her on and she's
hot to get back at
him, goes straight
up the stairs for him,
furled umbrella raised,
ready to hit out.
when he then
makes a move
toward her,
she screams, and
gets out the
gate, rides up
the escalator
past the graffito that
says, *we hate them;*
they are not us.
at the top, she
goes back down
the stairs,
enlists the cops.
there's a little
hot pursuit, but the
bright shirt's quick
and hops the train
for Harvard, doors
closing on his
heels. the cops
write it up as
"indecent assault"
and everybody's
heart starts to
slow down. now
she's out to the
sunny Common
and on up Tremont
past the soft green
Granary Burying Ground.

3. WEDNESDAY EVENING

After rush hour, fewer trains, and
you really start to hear who's playing
on the platform between the tracks.
Somehow a wild song's been
pulled down here and let loose to swoop
over all that drab and concrete.
After the song there's a rattle of coins
dropped in the blue velvet lining of
a guitar case, then the train's roar
drubs it all out. Some nights it's a cello,
other nights a fiddle. This time it's
a big young voice flung as clean as
a home run clear to the back wall.
It's outlandish down here, like some
Orpheus descended to the lower-level
platform, singing passengers back
to life. When the train pulls out
he ends the song. Strums aimlessly
as he faces the bottom of the stairwell,
watching people descend, appearing to him
feet first, watching, watching, looking
for her.

ANN BRACKEN
THE MENTAL HEALTH BOX

It must be purposeful—the green container affixed to the wall.
The lid flush against the box, bound with a lock.
Doesn't take up much space.

I feel foolish when I say to the social worker—
Every week when I walk by, I wonder what's in
the mental health box.

I imagine torn pieces of paper—
men filling the mental health box with
furtively written requests, stuffed in as they walk past.

Please don't restrict my visitors.
My cellmate has been in solitary for a year. When's he getting out?
Why can't we have college classes? I need a fan in my cell, please.

The social worker is silent,
then she shakes her head.
"I have no idea what's in that box."

BRANDED

Dad butters my blistered wrist, promises,
She didn't know what she was doing.
Mom wraps gauze over the burn.
My parents know how to tend little hurts,
but my wrist throbs with the white heat of the tongs.

My sister sleeps in the twin bed next to me.
I don't know why she did this.
I pull the blanket tight under my chin and close my eyes.
Like Nancy Drew, I revisit the morning's scene, search for a clue.
Reading the comics in Dad's frayed armchair,

I hear the click-click-click of the gas burner.
My sister calls out, *Jan, look...*
I lower the comics, see her familiar grin.
Still smiling, she grabs my wrist with the tongs
and sears me with a circular brand.

She didn't know what she was doing.
Mom assures me
as she folds up the newspaper
and drops it into the trash.

SHIRLEY J. BREWER
WEDDING DRESS

Engagement ended. Ring returned. The dress
hung on my closet door—a fancy corpse.
Nights, the bodice sparkled like tiny bouquets
or signals from a sister planet.
We fashioned a bond, my dress and I,
in those broken hours after he left.

I wore the bridal silk at home, drifting
from room to room. In full-length mirrors,
I saw a white bouffant cloud
oblivious to the perils of earth.

At last, I surrendered it to a consignment shop,
lingered outside in case I changed my mind.
The man remains a blur. I mourn the dress.

ANNIE O

Phoebe Ann Moses, born poor
in Darke County, Ohio, 1860.
Before she turns one, her father
freezes to death in a blizzard.
Soon she is sent to live
with a cruel family she calls *the wolves*.
Sharpened by grief, she becomes
a hunter—by fifteen a master shot.

Weds a marksman named Frank Butler,
joins his act. Meets Buffalo Bill Cody,
auditions for his Wild West Show.
Known as Annie Oakley, she thrills
the plains with her gun—shoots ashes
off the tip of her husband's cigarette.

This star attracts another celebrity fan:
Chief Sitting Bull. She lifts
his spirits. He gives her
the nickname *Little Sure Shot*,
pays good money for a photograph
of the two of them together.

Oh, Annie, you thrive on fame.
You mesmerize men: Frank, Buffalo Bill,
the Chief—even the Prince of Wales.
Beyond the cymbal sounds of glory,
a whisper of sadness in your eyes.
In soft evening light, you imagine
trading a portion of your wild life
for a few quiet years with your dad.

CHRIS BULLARD
ODE TO STUPIDITY

Thank you for your inability to go from point A to point B. I was charmed by your discursiveness. Thanks for adding two and two and getting five. The world would be so much duller if all the answers were correct. Thanks for mistaking cause and effect so that whatever happens will always amaze us. Thanks for leaving the stove on, the brakes off, and the door unlocked. Now our lives are full of incident. Thanks for standing out in the rain: that's how things grow. Thanks for using the wrong words and leaving the right ones alone. Thanks for failing to understand anything because it lets us drop the whole weary business of trying to explain.

DORITT CARROLL

EEG

so here i am medusa
26 electrodes epoxy-fastened to my head

one for each letter
of the backwards alphabet

that instead of engraving things
on my mind seems to erase them

or perhaps they're being
chiseled out

the tech's taps on her keyboard
do seem to echo like stone

but now i'm thinking of the tangled gray
beneath my skull as cables

the sound engineer will straighten out
and wind around his hairy tattooed arm

that must be the reason i can never find
the word i'm looking for anymore

i've been unplugged
show's over

ANNE CHAMPION & JENNY SADRE-ORAFAI
SPELL FOR THE HIVE

Somewhere, there's a queen
in there, buzzing the honeycombed
tiles to breed a sweetness
you can taste. Save her—
you only have one good sting
in you. Make sure it's worth death.

Watch how the men serve her,
flying in a brainless rapture,
sacrificing until they are mutilated,
erecting the holiest shrine
from their hollowed husks
nosediving to the ground.

SPELL FOR DRAINED PUBLIC POOLS

This will keep alive any animal
living there. What a reverse of
fortune or happy or summer.

This will fill it up, lit sequins
again at night swimming—
the only way for it to ripple.

This won't bring living people
back. They've given up. Deflated
their floats, garbaged their suits.

This won't displace the drowned,
the dead attached. It's not wrong
to do. The water is a cover

they reach for and they reach for.

THE GONE, THE DISAPPEARED

Your faces are age imagined.
Someone's looking

at a shadow, saying yes
it's you. We saw you take

a boat in a black light.
We swing you

home in a net, a room
of jellyfish cushion you.

This spell isn't for you.

It's for families who keep
your pictures pinned

in sacred rooms, who
burn tall candles

at church, who roll
milagros at the dinner table.

ALAN CHAZARO
PIÑATA THEORY #2

Consider the violence
of living. How breath can be
fractured and displaced
while walking. Take bones,
for example, how they are firm enough
for everyday activity
but collapse on impact. I fear
these injuries, knowing
what's beneath, revelations.
Each day is a split in the skull,
a bang in the lungs.

LEAVING FOOTPRINTS ON WATERFALLS

There is a voice telling me to hold chocolate

inside my mouth. I don't know what it means.

Like I don't know how lines can break us

apart. I mean this literally. How borders

are thresholds of the imagination. How

some can be crossed. In dreams I wonder

what is real that isn't shared with others.

How we share memories like sweet bread.

How sweet bread crumbles when shared.

How the word *me* is in *America* and

in *Mexico*. How I am a forest that exhales

through wildfires.

USING GOOGLE TRANSLATION IN MEXICO

I—"Consider very carefully whether you should go"

> What you might expect:
> beers on a beach, tan lines
> and margaritas. The coast
> of Puerto Vallarta choked
> with tourists. Alert, I am
> approached by a street vendor
> selling phone chargers
> and selfie sticks.

II—"Government advises against non-essential travel to Mexico"

> My brother was robbed once
> in Guadalajara, a gun's jaw
> held to his. Summers after,
> I visited. For some reason
> my Levis and Nikes
> didn't loose the devil.
> I ordered tacos, chewed slowly.

III—"Areas affected by the Zika virus include Mexico"

> Do you know what it feels like
> to be the always-American cousin?
> The one who grows
> violins inside his stomach
> after eating nopales in Zacatecas?
> Whose ankles become piñatas
> for mosquitos living in El Castillo?

IV—"Level 2, Practice Enhanced Precautions"

> I don't live with dust in my eyes—
> I have a hobby of getting lost
> in Guanajuato, of climbing
> stairs made of mountain
> stones and daggering into alleyways
> draped in dark.
> I walk with my eyelids closed,
> ask strangers for directions, keep my phone
> on airplane mode.

*V—"Latest figures show the number of murdered U.S. citizens south of border
has gone up"*

> In Tlaquepaque I carried the moon
> under my arm and the stars
> in my back pocket. I dreamt
> of turquoise and tasted silver,
> snorted chocolate and prayed
> inside centuries-old
> churches. I became the clouds
> cottoning skies before rainfall,
> a man riding his bike
> made of bronze.
> I live with electricity in my lungs,
> with wings made of wood to lift me.
> I build bridges with eyes of mosaic
> and fumble tongues in my mouth.
> Do not tell me this is not home.

GRANT CLAUSER
COAT OF ARMS

If we weren't peasants
our coat of arms would hang
above a great family hearth
instead of crumbled
in the junk drawer
with old cell phone cords
and broken corkscrews.
Instead of swords crossed
for valor, ours would show rusted blades
from the lawnmower that needs fixing.
Our family motto would be
a heavy sigh at dinner
after the children have left,
the sound eyelids make
when they half close
at the end of a sentence
so you know the conversation
is over.
Our coat of arms would bear the wag
of restless dogs,
the cries of mocking birds,
and the silence of cars
leaking oil in the driveway.
No one would wear it
on armor or a shield
into battle or a flag
flown over a keep,
but our arms carry it now
like groceries from car
to kitchen cupboard.
We feel it always
like a dancer walking home
from the practice studio,
blisters and tape
on her feet,
pain and pride
bound together.

ODE TO THE HALF-DEAD BEAR ON THE WAY TO DEFIANCE

Chained to the axle of a rusted F-150,
bald spots on his sides where he worries
the rind raw, not to escape, just to feel
his tongue roughing blood from his skin.
This road through Ohio's dried swamp
is corn and soy for eyes' miles,
the sun takes hours to set, searching
for the last place it called home.
The hunter who caught him as a cub
in Michigan pumps gas for travelers
who took the wrong road to Toledo,
believing straight lines wouldn't bend,
believing the river was just ahead
where the horizon melts into corn silk's
towhead gaze. This is how he breaks—
the gas jerk tossing scraps of meat
to the Ford's rusted shade, eyes
forever curved toward the dust of cars
pulling out into the road, and one front leg
curled into a crook that never grew
the way it should, the way a dam can turn
the river east, letting water mute
all the land's furrowed voices.
And this is where he'll die, bruised
shadow from Skanee, gumming his paws
until blood is his only memory,
the time he mauled the boy
and watched him crawl away—
the taste that keeps him warm
at night under a moon he doesn't know.

KATHARINE COLES
FINE DINING

Totting up exes with an old friend
Over a dinner we can afford now,
Accounting things we used to take for granted
And thought were normal and continuous

Like how I've always fainted with a fever, or when
Suddenly standing up, or falling little deathlike into
That delicious and complete evacuation
I thought took everyone the same

Until much later. Nobody spoke of it.
I admit, this is an older woman's poem,
Though really not much changes: you learn
To keep your feet under you no matter what

Even when your tights have bound your ankles
And your back is shoved against the wall.

ENDURE

I don't know what I would want more
Than a body to open

The sky with its eyes, taste
Its own salt, feel the Earth's

Weight in the soles of its feet
Pressing down. I wrote "souls"

Though I never believed
In place of our hardened heads

They used to count the ethereal stuff
We invent longing

To bear. I've outlived my own
Likelihood, given how

I've lived, and I will not
Last. Is the trouble. Is the joy.

ROBERT COOPERMAN
THE NEWLYWEDS

They moved into the apartment
next to ours, their bedroom adjacent
to the one I shared with my brother.
Mom welcomed them, washing
and drying her hands koshering
our Friday supper chicken,
to shake with them both and smile.

"We have new neighbors," over dinner
Mom nodded in the direction
of the apartment that had stood vacant
for months, word somehow seeping out
to renters that the woman who'd lived there
had been murdered by her husband,
while the whole building had slept.

"They seem nice," Mom nodded again.

Later that night, Jeff and I were yanked
from sleep by screams, shrieks: a woman
on the edge of terror; no, way beyond it.

"Mom! Dad!" we ran into their bedroom
and knocked and knocked, until they stuck
disheveled heads through the slit-open door.

"He's killing her!" we shouted, "Stop him!"

"Go back to sleep," Dad grumbled,
his pajamas nowhere to be seen.

KATHLEEN CORCORAN
CURES AND CHARMS

Granddad soaked his feet in a tub of Epsom salt.
He said it cured his nerves, but I thought it was sugar.
When I stole a handful from the cupboard,
the sour taste was worse than the cod liver oil
I had to swallow each spring when the first robin appeared.

Skinned knees full of cinders from the playground called
for the blue medicine my father swore by, lent to him
by Johnny Mosco who used it on his horse's wounds.
I cried at the healing sting and had to go to school
where children laughed at bright blue knees above white socks.

I feared the vaporizer that chortled through the night.
mocking my sore throat. When I said *Ahhh*, Aunt Lila
saw red spots, then painted my throat with some
concoction on what she called her magic wand.
All winter the Milky Ways I ate tasted bitter.

I tried to hide the warts that multiplied on my feet
like mushrooms under elm trees after rain,
but Mother took me to Minerva Peck who mumbled
and scraped the scaly growths with a safety pin, then stuck
it in my collar and said to leave it there until they disappeared.

When I had a sty, Mother removed her wedding ring
and rubbed my throbbing eyelid with the tiny diamonds.
I closed my eyes and heard her chant a future
full of cures and charms, and sure enough
years later my love and I linked arms and wandered

down a country road made narrow by hedgerows.
When nettles bit my ankle, he knelt and stroked it
with a green leaf from a roadside Docken plant.
Docken Docken in and out, take the sting of the nettle out,
he said, and a soothing juice cooled my burning skin.

BARBARA CROOKER
MARTINI

Look how the olive green sun
slowly slips into the cold shimmer
of a glass of gin, the evening sky
beginning to glow red as pimento
behind the blue hills. Clouds spread out,
delicate as cocktail napkins, and the birds
begin their scat of warm-up trills,
vibratos, little snips of phrases.
I can hardly wait to see
that evening sun
go down.

WHY I LOVE BEING MARRIED TO A CHEMIST

after Andrea Potos

Because he can still cause a reaction in me
when he talks about SN2 displacements,
amines and esters looking for receptor sites
at the base of their ketones. Because he lugs
home serious tomes like *The Journal of the American
Chemical Society* or *The Proceedings of the Society
of the Plastics Industry,* the opposite of the slim volumes
of poetry with colorful covers that fill my bookshelves.
Because once, years ago, on a Saturday before our
raucous son rang in the dawn, he was just
standing there in the bathroom, out of the shower.
I said *Honey, what's wrong?* and he said *Oh,
I was just thinking about a molecule.*

Because he taught me about sublimation, how
a solid, like ice, can change straight to a gas
without becoming liquid first. Because even
after all this time together, he can still
make me melt.

GREGORY CROSBY

WALKING AWAY FROM EXPLOSIONS IN SLOW MOTION

It's all you can do. The world is always
behind you, the catastrophe of time,
the exchange of air & fire, the wave
of force raising the hair on the back of
your neck, a rivulet of sweat unseen
by all the eyes on your unseeing gaze,
the blank face that says *I'm walking away,
I'm getting away with something*: all those

opportunities to find your body
framed by boiling galaxies of flame,
untouched by shrapnel, not above it all
but out in front of it, like the *future
itself*, walking *away*. Fucking *badass*.
Fuck no you don't look back; you can't look back.
A cinder in your eye might ruin the shot.
A world might suddenly taste of salt.

DANA CURTIS
BEDROOM LIGHTS

A stack of mattresses
imagining a princess: the first is
of feathers, the next of nails,
then hair, then fruits and nuts,
rivers, night lights, her dream
of sensitivity; they never
end. She's looking down
at the whole world pretending
distance is a virtue.
She hopes her love will arrive
towing basilisks and bedside
tables made of bone. The reading
lamp illuminates her hands
over her eyes. There is
a knock on the thickening
door. He offers her a golden
tray of food she can't eat,
flowers she can neither
see nor smell. Let us
rejoice at the marriage
of inconvenience and
entanglement; promise
quiet, love.

JIM DANIELS
ELEGY FOR PHONE BOOTH

Upright coffin of human odors—sweat, mostly. Hopeless ashes of old smoke.
Metallic moist panic. Piss, often. Dried spit on scratched plexiglass. Emotion
emergencies. Muffle and echo and clank of receiver dangled. Steel cord
spooled so you cannot cut it. Walk away and talk to God on it. Impenetrable.
We bleed all over it. Come pick me up. Accident. Beat up. Abandoned. Need.
Need. Nothing casual about talk in a phone booth. Is it raining? Is anyone
watching? Anyone waiting? Can I help you? They cannot help you. Operators
in a safe dry room with a bag of Fritos and a Coke. Family photos. Inspirational
sayings and pictures of cats. You watch cars slosh through puddles, blurring
the world, rain rattling off your public cage. Where to begin? Where to end?
Whose numbers are memorized and why? Hers stuck in there, as if scratched
with a key. What would she say now if you called? Would she hang up? Laugh?
Would she say, *funny, I've been thinking of you?* Could you warm your cold wet
hands around her voice? Start your car with it? Drive across three states, pull
up out front, and announce, I'm back? Close your eyes and press your head
to the greasy smear of somebody else's head. You have one minute left, you
have 5 seconds, 4, 3, 2, 1. How can I help you? How can you help me? Where
to begin in that false light, in that true darkness? Coins trembling on the metal
tray. Insert to continue. Buy a few more minutes of bewildered anguish. Tell me
about your sins and I'll tell you about my penance. The empty coin return. The
clawing fingers.

PHONE BOOTH, EIGHT MILE AND RYAN

near Top Hat, our White Castle knockoff,
warm inside, cold out here, eight lanes
of midnight blurring past in slush freezing
to ice, and you with the hunger of habit
that can't stomach cheap burgers, stepped-
on drugs, arbitrary inflation, manufactured
shortages, threats not idle, Top Hat open
24/7, always hiring, greasy exhaust
of hamburger, exhaust of idling cars,
exhausted resources, exhaustion
without drugs, exhausted by the search
on Eight Mile, sirens passing toward skids,
black ice midnight, loaded salt trucks
arriving late, you dial and dial
for a lucky number, on the other end,
busy signal of nobody home,
in Top Hat windows, a shooting
gallery of drunks watching you
watching the siren blur, or just
doing the Eight Mile stare, exploring
options, making bad coffee last,
you wave to no one, your tank
on empty once again and always,
an arrangement of coins vibrating
on the metal shelf in front of you,
and you keep repeating *I'm good,*
I'll be good, in lieu of a voice
on the other end, your voice
chanting a present and future
fortune depending on what
god you're praying to
in the phone booth
at Eight and Ryan
cold hands cupped against
air hissing through bullet holes.

MARK DECARTERET
NERVAL

The plan was always to finish the backwash of ale,
left-out slaw, and then nap for a century or two

maybe have myself dry-iced and shipped
somewhere shop or alp-lined, security-cammed

where I'd dine in the most posh of dumpsters
and then walk off all those *New Yorker* poems

still punk-decaled and acne-d, my theme song
undanceable, later shifting from one claw to another

as my infant pal, instantly plopped on the ash and straw,
lays down a salable beat with a slap of my leash.

NOT TO ONE'S TASTE

My lips are still sick of not speaking—
ape-kissing the ether or silently reading up
on nuclear storage tips—*please don't staple notices...*

and yes my eyes are envious of each other—
one seeing only those detonations of veins
and one everything I thought saved for the future.

Through the forest I hear a father
shouting "Throw it to me" in Russian
a thousand times over the afternoon.

Either my fingers are all here
or I'm grasping death's version of me—
an indictment I can't tell from this page.

But what's felt often lets the self off too easily
until so soft-hearted and given-to-fits
even one's tongue will be sold on little else.

THE ONE ABSENT FROM ALL

No, not the same butterfly as the last poem—
that blue I'd referred to as "a heaven twice-sacked,"

this silver I'd dubbed "a butler-shined knife,"
or the feverish prying at a bud I had bluffed through,

the asthmatic heaves and uneasiness I flubbed—
measuring up against my own unsurety, strife,

or worse, used as a case study for my sanity's sake,
this relic I'd sworn to and cared for in line after line,

would continue to dust off all those damnable flowers—
so mad about their beauty, so adamant it was mine.

BARBARA DECESARE

POEM EMPLOYING SOMEWHAT CHEAP METAPHOR TO DESCRIBE MY ANXIETY ABOUT PUBLIC PERFORMANCE

The squid shoots ink when sensing danger
peels back an eye, assesses threat.
It obfuscates its narrative,
it gets away, it goes.

It blackens out, it putrefies,
it bows its arms and pushes off,
it leaves the ink, the cloud disguise.
It obfuscates its narrative.

The squid selects the ending option,
the squid expels a magic potion,
the squid peels back an eye—alarmed,
it pours out ink, the cloud disguise.

The sea is dark, there is no question:
Leave a mark? A good impression?
A food chain makes the worst first meeting.
A coward sprays her ink when fleeing—
An inner terror guides her nature
the squid shoots ink. It senses anger.
It gets away. It goes.

OTHER SON

She hamstrung you fresh, as soon as you foaled:
We've had enough Bushes
not counting herself,
then gave you just enough support
to show there was support to get.

What embarrassed reminder are you
of soft voice and hands,
with brown wife and children?

Could you be the ghost of her
nobless oblige Christmas past
when she'd share the bomb shelter
with anyone knocking?

And now she is the bomber.
Brings favorite meals because she loves you.
Oversalts the plate.

This mother makes a beggar of her child:
The one who comes in trickles and promise,
who drives the art of ownership.
It's she who says you can have nothing
and still won't give it 'til you say *Please.*

MATT DENNISON
BARBARIANS

After my mother's death my elderly
English teacher—half-Spanish ex-inmate

of the state hospital, it was whispered
in the halls—asked me to her apartment

at the bottom of the hill. I went and sat,
feeling the cramp of the place, a few rooms

I had imagined would be soft and musty
like my grandmother's house, but were lacking

history—cut off, somehow, from the past.
But *she* was lively, her dark face talking

and talking for what seemed hours as she
brought on the cookies and soft drinks,

slowly wearing me down until I could not
maintain the current between us and when

the backed-up waves of surrender rioted
the giant hand of my yawn across the room

she stopped, opened a book and carefully
spoke a poem: *Waiting for the Barbarians*

about which I remember nothing but her voice
as she read, her hands closing the book, and her eyes

meeting mine for the first time all night.

DEBORAH ELLIOTT DEUTSCHMAN

THE LAST GENERATION BEFORE ZYPREXA

The last generation before Zyprexa—
The Abstract Expressionists: Pollock and de Kooning,
Rothko, Mitchell, Gorky, Riopelle...
How much of their lives spent going through hell—
Before Zyprexa, Risperdal, Seroquel, Geodon:
The new generation of drugs, of atypical antipsychotics
(In the 1950s there was Perphenazine,
A mild soothing pablum in comparison).

The last generation not on psychotropics—
They went spinning away, bashed and pummeled, crashing
At top speed, untethered

Out in terra incognita in feverish throes,
Exposed to the maelstroms of self-annihilating debris
Striking them blind and paralyzed
Without warning or reprieve.

Today what would they be?
Tame and docile, sedated
On customized pharmaceutical cocktails:
Zyprexa, Risperdal, Seroquel, Geodon?
When the panic took over *(The show's opening next week—*
You don't understand. It's horrible—It's all awful—
I've got to work round the clock,
Put together a whole new show in a week—)
A new molecular formula would simply be added
To the already individualized potion.

Is that what the script would be today?
And order and calm would be restored,
As they would be brought back in, from those lost worlds
Where chaos had been unleashed, and back to reality:
Pliable, willing to see reason, and accept whatever
Dictates and limits thrown their way—
The way they never could or would?

And at the Art Court, they would know their place—
And could be relied on to say the right thing,
Finesse the philosophical modalities
Of constantly fluctuating rates and dictates
In the cultural currency
That is the lingua franca of mental commerce—
As opposed to flying off the charts, in free fall
Beyond-Time-Space-Continuum-Incognita, the way they had
Before Zyprexa, Risperdal, Seroquel, Geodon?

NIGHT LIBRARY:
MARCEL BROODTHAERS

Into the Library at night Marcel Broodthaers goes—
in the eerie silence of the mausoleum dark,
past the guard, half-asleep at the front desk—
and into the Main Reading Room
with its different sections clearly marked he can see,
by the low-glowing nightlights: Art/Business/Fiction/
History/Philosophy/Physics/Poetry...

Systematically, Marcel Broodthaers goes
up and down the ladders to get to the top shelves.
He lets his hand trace along the books,
touching them lightly, as dust motes of stars float up
in the semi-dark—occasionally, switching on his flashlight,
he opens a book to take a quick look,
skims a few sentences or lines, searching for his favorite words and images.
And they come drifting out
from art books, history books, novels, poems.
One by one, they leave the pages,
flee the confines of the books they're in.
And he gives those books a slight push, urging them on
so that his favorite words and images can escape faster:
Eggs, Mussels, Camels, Palms, Eagles, Scepters...
The *Mona Lisa*, the Sistine Chapel, *The Night Watch*...

And Broodthaers appropriates them
and incorporates them into his own work:
reproductions of great paintings—from Western culture,
old prints, photographs, posters, manuscript pages...
Portraits of Eggs in shells—whole as well as cracked...
and Mussels—the national dish of Belgium (his country),
pots and pans brimming full of Mussel Shells...
and scenes with Camels and Palm Trees—dated exotica,
flash cards for Colonialism/Africa...
and emblems of Eagles and Scepters (from Rome or Napoleon I),
as in Imperial Power or Totalitarianism...
And the *Mona Lisa*, the Sistine Chapel, *The Night Watch*...
An installation show—fleeing
out of the Library, and out into the night city streets—
waking up the sleeping world.

LIZ DOLAN
WHITE SPACE

How often had I taught you
how vital it was
on the page.

But I never really understood myself
until one day
I entered your aerie
and before me lay
      a
    white
   marble slab
    with
    thirteen
 green
      bowls
  and   vases
you had thrown yourself.

    Exquisitely
    placed.

And you standing
in front of a window
hands   outstretched
your black skin backlit
radiant as an angel unaware.

M. SCOTT DOUGLASS
FINDING IOWA

You don't like to ride at night when
bugs are bigger, people dumber.
You remember a night ride years
ago from Findley Lake to Erie.
A June Bug kissed your forehead
at sixty-five miles an hour and
nearly knocked you off the bike.

You come to Iowa late, but
sunlight angling across the road
says there's still light left to wring
from the day and cool evening air
is a comforting contrast
to blistering St. Louis traffic.

Somewhere ahead you will park
for the night, unhitch the dry bag
you bungied to your seat, drag it
to a dark room, and crank the AC.
But you haven't found that exit yet.

The ramp for Mt. Pleasant loops around
enough land to grow corn for a Third
World nation and ends at a road sign
with two arrows: one for Mt. Pleasant,
the other for Ottumwa to which
your mind attaches the subtext:
Home of Radar O'Reilly and you
wonder about a town that owes
its fame to a fictional character.

A herd of hotels huddle here
like bison on a winter prairie.
The Best Western is out front like
an old bull, its lot full of RVs
and pickups—some parked on the grass.

A guy in a John Deere cap sits on
the front lawn in a green and white
folding chair made of woven
nylon mesh. In one hand he holds
a 2-liter bottle of Coke,
in the other a spatula
to flip the burger he's cooking
on a mini charcoal grill.

You decide to pass on the Best
Western, imagine bonfires
and pistol popping might also
be part of the evening agenda—
not the ambience you desire.

A Comfort Inn is tucked behind it.
You roll up beneath the awning,
park and drag a numb leg over
your leather saddle, shake it back
to life as you walk to the lobby.

No one is manning the counter
at 8 p.m. You holler but no one
replies. Tap the bell and notice
a commotion in the breakfast
area: a swarm of seniors.
Maybe someone there can help me,
you think, then turn back to the desk,
startled to find someone standing there.

You ask for a room and she says,
"Aw, hon, there ain't a room around
for a hundred miles, but I could
get you something in Iowa City."
Iowa City, another
two hours of highway riding.

You thank her, decline the offer,
and turn to the door. You'll call your wife,
have her book a room for you somewhere,
but before you leave you turn back
to the clerk with an urgent need to know:
>   *why here, why so many people stopped*
>   *at this tiny dot on the map?*

You ask, she answers, "Oh, honey,
there's a big tractor pull tomorrow,"
and you realize you have entered
the *Twilight Zone*, another dimension
of space and time in a parallel universe
where vocation and recreation
have somehow become confused.

You call home to another time zone,
wake your wife, ask her to find you
something cheap, easy to locate
in the dark, climb back on the bike,
back onto the highway, head north
into darkening Iowa night, where
a faint scent of shit paints the air
as the sun slides away, revealing
a world you never knew existed.

MATH DON'T LIE

You should have gassed up in Louisville,
before you crossed the Ohio, before
the blank stare of southern Illinois
forced you to consider distance

versus tank reserve. You know math
always wins these matchups and math
now says you should have stopped
in Louisville, but traffic was polite

as rush hour loomed. You could steer
clear of the gnarly wake commuters make
on their way home. You were certain
a cluster of fuel and fast food options
huddled on the far side of the river.
You passed them your last trip through.
Or was that a different road? After
a while, some stretches look so much alike.

Southern Ohio, southern Indiana,
southern Illinois, each has its own
Mt. Vernon with mileage signs to match.
Here the road sign said one hundred

and sixty-seven miles. Your reserve
said one hundred and seventy, close
but there had to be at least one station
on this section of interstate, surely

a savvy entrepreneur reasoned
a pit stop between Louisville
and Mt. Vernon was a certain
moneymaker. *If you build it,*

they will come. So you twist open
the throttle in southern Illinois
where wide treeless plains leave nowhere
for stealthy cops to hide. It's just you

and the long haulers you fly by
at ninety-five miles an hour. You,
fresh air, sunshine, open road:
What could possibly go wrong?

After an hour of full throttle,
a road sign says sixty-nine miles
to Mt. Vernon, but your fuel gauge
now says fifty-eight. Math has turned

against you. You saw the map before
you left: nothing between Louisville
and Mt. Vernon and now you
can testify to its accuracy.

Math says: speed kills fuel consumption,
so you slow to seventy, scour
every green sign, every billboard
for hope, but there's nothing and your gauge

continues its constant rate of drain:
fifty-one miles of road, forty-six miles
of gas. You slow again. Truckers you passed
an hour earlier now pass you back.

You swear you hear a snicker in
the tone of their exhaust, a laughing
confirmation that they've been this way
before and always refuel in Louisville.

You wonder how long it would take
triple A to reach you if your tank runs dry.
Could your cell phone get a signal here?
Would they have to come from Louisville?

Twenty-nine miles of road left, twenty-three
miles of gas. You imagine yourself coasting
down an exit ramp outside Mt. Vernon,
rolling in neutral until inertia deserts you.

A Flying J down the road raspberries you,
taunts you with a mantra you've heard
in your head for the last sixty-nine miles:
You should have stopped in Louisville.

SUNSET OVER SUBURBIA

A hint of color tangles in trees
as the sun falls over the far side
of anonymous rooftops.

Here the last gasp of light
bounces between prefab windows
until all that remains of brick

and siding is muted silhouette.
Soon workers will return home,
close the doors and blinds, confine

the warmth of their lives behind
the silent sameness of this
final destination. For now,

light fades like the muffled voices
of children ending playtime, or
a lonely dog barking, like the whine

of tires swerving toward night
or the clumsy snort of day drifting
into full, indifferent snore.

YOU KNOW THESE ROADS

Sometimes you think you could travel
these roads blindfolded, close your eyes
and find your way home or somewhere
familiar, a street name you know,
a billboard that hasn't changed
in decades, a diner parked
conveniently close to the road
with a neon sign that says *Open*.

Exit signs you pass post the names
of towns, roads, route numbers etched
into your memory in DayGlo paint,
a distance in miles you translate
into seasons, events, years gone by;
people populating pages
in an unscripted journal
of an unplotted journey
toward an unknown destination
with mile markers as captions to hint
at what came before or waits ahead.

Each road sign implies one thing,
your rearview mirror another:

    Town where you were born
    Town where you grew up
    Town that closes at 5 p.m. and all day on Sundays
    Town found when lost on an ill-advised shortcut
    Town with no gas station
    Ghost town
    Town where Matilda, your '65
        Ambassador, cracked her block
        and was put to rest
    Town where you left your wallet and didn't
        discover it missing until the next time
        you stopped for gas 200 miles away
    Town where your grandmother was born

Town where you experienced your first
        passionate kiss and second orgasm
        (maybe third)
Town where you left your first love
        forever
Town where your best friend was married
Bean Town
Town where your roommate's father died
        of a heart attack
Town where his son died from overdose
Town where your son was born
        and his son
Town with a pond and clock tower
        in the main square and boarded-up
        buildings all around.
Town where the fan belt broke on the old
        Chevelle along with the water pump
        at 10 p.m. on a Saturday night
Town of rocking chairs
Town with bears in bonnets and sunglasses
Town with three colleges
        three golf courses
        three microbrews
        three sisters
        and bike lanes
Moose town
Town where a pair of flats meant sleeping
        in the bed of your truck in the rain
Town where you pissed in the underground walkway
         because it smelled like everyone else had
Town where you slept with spiders
        under cardboard, behind junipers,
        against a brick wall
Town where you ran dry on the exit ramp
        two miles short of a Chevron station,
        in the middle of a state trooper
        dragnet for escaped prisoners
Town where an old black man excused himself
        when you walked past him where he sat

Town where a store clerk refused you service
        when you asked another patron, a hunter,
        a black man, what his favorite game was
Town of marchers with picket signs,
        of broken windshields and tires shredded
        by sharpened jacks
Steel town
Town where you got a ticket for parking
        in an unmarked handicap zone
City where your mother was arrested
        as a teenage runaway and locked up
        with prostitutes
Town where you ran away and camped
        on a hill for two weeks in midwinter
Town where you hitched a ride with a guy in a Nova
        you were convinced (later) was a serial killer
Town where you were exiled after burning
        too many bridges at your previous stop
Town where you were caught on the wrong side
        of the Rockies in a late May snowstorm
Windy city
Town of broad shoulders, boxcars,
        double trailers, and toll roads
Town where two guys tried to rob you,
        then bought you a beer when they learned
        you were more broke than they were
Town where Barney Fife pulled you
        and a cute blonde over for speeding,
        but only tagged you
Town where Johnny Carson was born
Town that barely made the map and smelled
        like cow shit because it had fifty times
        as many cattle as people
Town you cut through at 2 a.m.
        on a Halloween bender to find
        a haunted house and were escorted out
        by local cops
Town where you jumped a moving train
Town where you broke your foot in three places
        jumping off a moving train

Town with the same name as twenty
    other towns in twenty other states
Town where you learned how not to ride
    a bicycle when your friend was skewered
    through the neck by handlebars
Town where you witnessed your first violent death,
    a bicyclist hit by a drunk driver,
    his body wedged into a split against the curb
    with one leg twisted behind his head
Town where a Pomeranian defended
    its owner's shrubs from a bull elk grazing
Dream town
City of bright lights, beautiful people
    and highways
Town where you wish you could live
Town where you hope to die.

GEORGE DREW

ROMANCING LAMENTATION ON THE IDES OF MARCH

—John Amen

Understand, I know it isn't him, my dead amigo,
the man holding a gold award plate over his head in the ad
for a National Latino Writers Conference,
not unless the ashes I took part in scattering on a hillside in Pennsylvania
were really those of someone's pet—all part of a conspiracy, what else?

Which would mean mi amigo's alive, maybe living under another name,
somewhere in Iowa or Indiana in a poet's Witness Protection Program;

which means he orchestrated the whole damned conspiracy;
which means he wanted to disappear, damn his soul,
leaving his wife and sons and dogs behind—and me. Of course,
that's nuts, and I know, even if he were still alive,
he couldn't pass himself off as a Latino.

But jesus, that guy in the Latino ad sure looks like him—bushy beard, big belly,
spectacles and out of style jacket, shirt and tie, mismatched colors.

Understand, I *know* it isn't him, but just for one quicksilver moment I
stood beneath the balcony of grief and lamentation and pointing at yon ad
believed he really had been just asleep and once the herb wore off, awoke.
Even on the Ides of March the heart, that heartless beautiful dupe, dupes us all.

DAVID EBENBACH

NOT LONG AFTER THE WAR, THERE WAS ANOTHER WAR

Luckily we hadn't taken
our ribbons down, our
extra flags on the lawn.
The young people were
probably about halfway
through their dinners, big
welcome-home dinners
with something to carve.
But there were explosions
on the television, which
was on because the
young people had missed
watching television
with dinner. The head of
the table stopped in the
middle of a slice. Waiting
for the young people.
Who balled up their
napkins—cloth
for the occasion—
and left them on their
plates. Their mothers
always hated when they
did that; it was like
spitting in the food.
Though cloth isn't like
paper. Outside the
house, at the edge of the
bannered lawn, something
burned. The young people
buttoned their collars
stiff, went through the old,
familiar door, and
forgot to close it.

BE THE CHANGE

He was sick of pretending he was good,
so he stopped buying those sweatshop clothes
and with the money he saved
he sponsored three Bangladeshi children to come to America
and he wore them instead. Two girls—
one hanging on his back sort of like a kid
who had slipped and the other hanging in front—and the boy
wrapped around the man's hips
and everything, which took real strength.
He fed them well—they played apron
when he was at the stovetop—and they
cleaned up easier than a decent sweater would.
It wasn't easy for the man, either,
dragging the kids, who were growing.
But he didn't want easy; he just wanted
to be warm.

HANUKKAH

This year we spangle the place, the door
wrapped like something we're giving away,
the whole living room wrapped,
coffee table a jumble of wind-up toys
and candy dishes,
the seam of the wall into ceiling
a braid of lights, illuminating
plastic chunks of holiday
kitsch. The bookshelves, the rug,
everything is plastic now, is sequins, is
glitter. Stars and dreidles, dreidles and stars.
Everything held up with tape. Even the way
we open the gifts: we use an elbow, we
refrigerate them, we use

the Force. The gifts are completely
underfoot. And sure we make it
dark, lightswitch by light switch, unplug
the string of bulbs, let the candles
make their quiet points.
                              But then we
plug the strings back in,
and tap the uncooperative set
until it works.

DISAPPEARING CITIES

Even packed in ice, even preserved in salt water,
it goes like the others. The old lighthouses, only there
for show, won't be showing. And the bed and
breakfast where we were feverish until the morning,
where there were cats we didn't know about. They
closed that bookstore a few years ago already,
even though my name was written on the
back room wall. There was one day when I put it
together, that Congress Street met State, there at the
Longfellow statue. Or when Edwards connected
to Brighton, which ran out to River and then you
turned on Chute to find that now-empty house. Though
that was always way outside the city, the town. But
there was a Thai restaurant by the old paper mill;
pizza ovens next to the water. It was so cold, so
many times. For a long while this was the furthest
possible place, though later we drove through it
on our way to Canada and came back grateful for a
hot meal. And now even that's done and the town—
Old Port, the museum, my mother went to those
craft fairs—like chunks of ice, it all breaks, floats off,
looking for the white part of the map. The edge.

KARI ANN EBERT

I CAUGHT A TRAIN
TO DUBLIN ONCE

after Louis MacNeice

Your empty fists, your broken smoke,
your wooden strength
sift themselves into wisps of thought
carrying me about and seeking to give me more,
though more cannot be gathered up.

My sinews and marrow evanesce
into trails of shadow
passing through landscapes of slanting rain.
Long ago I yearned to translate
a kiss, to distill the joy in laughter, to
navigate the wandering path
of a hand.

Now, looking ahead past the waves of wheat,
past the rolling sea,
past the whitewashed walls,
I follow the tracks of your alchemy
and open my ears to the gold we breathe.

BY CHANCE ONE NIGHT, I MET A MAN NAMED SUNDAY

His legs,
thick and sturdy,
were great cedars holding up the world.

Some say smoke follows beauty,
yet his candlewish paused
in the air. Inert.
Lifeless.

Your children
shall be my children;
your family—my family,
he murmured.

But the gilded Paris moon interrupted his plans.
He kissed the side of my hair
surprised by the turn,
and I stood still—
dead still—
like the
smoke.

MEG EDEN

PURITY CONFERENCE

I.

We are ushered like cows into the sanctuary.

Noelle and I never talk about boys, let alone sex. Our mothers brought us here because *it's better to learn young and not the hard way.* We are in seventh grade and talk about *Lord of the Rings*. Men are elves and dwarves and hobbits—strange, distant, only in our minds.

The speaker says: *You are all treasured like princesses!* A squad of volunteers kneel at our seats and massage our feet, the way that whore washed Jesus' feet. Instead of tears, they use generic-brand lotion, scented like craft store roses. I want to tell the girl in front of me that I don't like people touching my feet, that I don't like the texture of lotion, but she's working so hard, so sincerely to remove the dirt between my toes.

II.

Before we can leave, we are lined up to get our souvenir—a plastic pearl, made in China, *a reminder of your worth in Christ.* In my palm, the gloss begins to peel.

III.

The speaker holds up two cups: one paper, one china. She asks, *Which would you rather be?*

She explains: paper cups are used then thrown away, while teacups are washed and treasured.

What she doesn't say: teacups sit on a shelf, displayed but never used. Paper cups are crumpled, but can be uncrumpled and used again. Drop a paper cup and it stays whole. A teacup shatters.

Inside my head, I tell her: Let me be paper!

NORTH CAROLINA HISTORIC HOME FESTIVAL

Three white middle-aged moms
bellydance in a local park, their coin skirts
clanging like aluminum cans. In bejeweled
yoga pants they move to Elvis Presley hits,
hips clumsy and off beat.

While the single dads and married men
hold up cameras "to remember the moment,"
my father turns to the houses, which carry
the sort of beauty he can appreciate:
those vintage soffits, dovetail joints, colorful
awnings—my father imagines building
and rebuilding these homes with his hands,
deciding where he might put a movie room,
whether to cover the fireplaces in stone or brick,

and my mother beside him has a beat
in her step—not quite a dance—but she was
a dancer once, and for once I want to see her dance
in the middle of this street in front of everyone,
for my father to turn his head and look at her fully.

CATHRYN ESSINGER

NAMASTE

For Dinty W. Moore

We are stopped on I-75 behind a line of idling
motorists and a semi that has jackknifed
in the construction zone, an accident that
has been waiting to happen all summer.

I am reading *The Accidental Buddhist*, a book
found in the trunk of the car, left over from
a rummage sale. I am definitely "in the present"—
construction grit dusting my windshield,

police lights throbbing, red and blue, August
heat beginning to shimmer along the dash.
We have been here long enough to meet
the driver behind us, who is beginning

to regret the Pepsi he drank at a rest stop,
and the young woman ahead, who has reclined
her seat so her mahogany hair now hangs
luxuriously over the back of her head rest.

She is not meditating; she is texting her boyfriend,
while I am letting go of appointments, shutting
down anxiety, attaching myself to nothing but
this book and the cadence of southbound traffic.

A trucker walks the guard rail, tipping his hat
to strangers, looking for conversation.
You Buddhist? he asks, and not waiting
for an answer he adds, *I tried meditation.*

*Got so relaxed I almost fell asleep at the wheel—
not like this idiot, who can't even read*, he says,
flipping a finger at the big rig still hunched
like a crippled animal over the median strip.

Namaste, I say and hand him the book. I tip
my seat back and from behind closed eyes
can still watch the evening sun calculate the best
way to blind as many motorists as possible.

DAVE ESSINGER
POETRY → BEARS

Poetry is like bears,
I tell my introductory creative writing
class: It's more afraid of you
than you are of it.

They look skeptical,
but in the front row, a girl
with a ribbon in her hair
writes: "Poetry → bears."

A fly lights on her ribbon, then
buzzes away, and I think of the Old
Masters' still lives, obsessed with death, finding,
even in vitality, decay. But I want to keep

my students imagining bears,
and I tell them they must,
when in Poem Country, carry
a can full of stones or coins to shake,

so the Poems know they're coming.
A surprised poem, I warn them,
can be dangerous. Because maybe I've
misjudged, and the problem is,

they are not scared *enough* of
poetry. They need to know
how an angry poem can rip your face
off. Even an immature, otherwise

mediocre poem can really
fuck you up, especially
if it's mating season.
I look at them. The girl with the ribbon

is drawing a daisy in her margin. The boy
next to her leans over, pretending he's forgotten
his textbook, to ask her what page we're on;
and this, this is when I stop talking.

The fly has zeroed on
a ceiling light, buzzing toward
crescendo. There's so much these children
can only bear for themselves, all of which

I can never tell them. And surely some
beast stands at my own shoulder now, raising ponderous
mauling paws, breathing its hot rotting breath
into my ear.

JEAN ESTEVE
BUBBLELAND

I don't question that there's Hell, I don't belong there
and Heaven's certain. I've met certain saints.
What I can't envision is that bland place
—maybe yellow sand against off-white amorphous skies—
that cannot rise or dive, but must hang somewhere
untouching and untouched, where they herd trivial souls.

I've been known to paint gold polish on my toes
while listening to the anchored, anguished news.
The titans out there flounder, musclebound,
their puppets clap and dance with fatal bluster.
I read the funnypapers and make catscradle
and wonder if it's time to nosh or doze.
I've not prepared myself for heat, nor virtuous cold,
nor grit, nor gossamer, nor reds, nor blues.
I've packed my grip with a B for Bubbleland
where I can go, gold polish on my toes.

CRESCENT

When will you notice
my immaculate hands?

The cuticles I cure myself,
the clean slice of nail

and, under the membrane,
glistening orange? I open

my eyes, my body hums
its debt, junk car in a crowded

garage, I fall apart and arrive
before the bathroom mirror

whole again, sallow. More
and more, I primp myself—

clear, vertical strokes,
crescents clipped, collected

between tiles—for love
I make with ghosts.

GARY FINCKE
CONTAGIOUS (A SEQUENCE)

DANCE MANIA

Within an early chapter
In the thick biography
Of hysteria, Frau Troffea
Suddenly lifts her arms
As if she's hanging laundry,
A spread-wide sheet. Hallelujah,
Perhaps, but then her feet
Skid into the swerve of dance,
Limbs chattering out of sync
With any tune her neighbors know.
There, in the sixteenth century,
Spectators gather like guests
For the first dance at weddings,
But she carries on for days, tranced
By some phantom partner
Who leads until someone joins,
Then another, so many more
In this weeks-long fit of dancing,
That ballroom fills four hundred strong,
Twisting to the inaudible,
The song on repeat, the pit keyed
To a frenzy of thrashing,
Each dancer with room enough
For solitary violence.
Nothing can end this except
Exhaustion or, for many, death,
The manic choreography
Famous for casualties
Who endured to the heart's collapse.

MISS HARTUNG EXPLAINS "CONTAGIOUS"

Twice a week, during public health,
Miss Hartung filled the room with fear
While we sat in perfect rows marked
By small spots in the wax, the ones
That revealed restlessness, that shamed
If they showed like lace-edged slip hems.

The contagious, she said, leave filth
That lives on buses and streetcars
And seats at the Etna Theater.
What's worse, you'll never know who's been there
And given you the itch and fester.

The contagious, she said, shout words
You mustn't say. They seed their yards
With bottles, cans, and tires; drip snot
And never cover when they sneeze.
They wipe their noses on their sleeves
Where crusts collect like scabs that bleed.

The contagious borrow combs, touch fountains
With their mouths. They gobble food they've dropped
To floors. Not setting rings of paper,
They squat on public toilets, never scrub
With water that's been run to scalding hot.

The contagious are everywhere,
Common as flies. Splattering stains,
The contagious spread like lies.
Look around, you'll see what I mean.
Eyes open, class. Keep yourselves clean.

CHILDREN'S TELEVISION

In Portugal, a children's soap opera produced mass hysteria, symptoms
of the script's mysterious disease showing up in young viewers.

Epidemic waits like the rocks
Below the cliff-carved narrow road.
It hums the synonyms
For inevitable, arranges them
In sentences slick with speed.

The script opens its sack of symptoms
To teach the country's children,
Each episode completed
Like homework. One mother fears
Permanent pockmarks; one follows
Her son's geometrical proof
Of cough and rash and fever,
Afraid of its solution.

All of them watch until the script
Declares an end to epidemic.
But after every child recovers,
After school reopens, parents
Learn that a child, next season,
Is crushed inside accident's car,
And all of them refuse to drive.

THE DEVIL'S CHILDREN

"The sins of your fathers," Miss Shaffer said,
"belong to you," and she listed the ways from drunk
to unfaithful while our Sunday school class
constructed heaven and hell, silently
attaching the future for all of us
onto the church's new bulletin boards.
Melanie Truman, whose father was gone,
cut narrow spaces into heaven's gate,
forming a grate so we could see inside
where white wings we drew floated against
a cloudless blue sky. We shaped a purple robe
for God and a loose, white cloak for Jesus,

their faces turned away because we dared
not look upon them. "The whirling of those white wings,"
Miss Shaffer said, "looks like it was created
by the sweet, benevolent breath of God."
All of us designed the black wings for hell.
Dick Wertz, his father arrested, scissored scarlet
triangles for eternal flames and left the green door
to hell wide open for the paired hands we made
by tracing ours. We forecast weather for hell,
heavy rain, every drop vanishing above the flames
because not one would ever reach us when
God saw into our sinful hearts that year
before boys and girls were separated
for Sunday School, before we began to learn
the sheer sins of lust and envy, using the sin
of falsehood to deny how we abused ourselves
and blasphemed, counting the commandments
we broke each day although Miss Shaffer made us sit,
one by one, beside the dark, detailed face
of Satan she drew, learning, each Sunday,
how it felt to be the devil's children.

THE BUG-BITE COMMONALITY

*In 1962, dressmakers in a textile factory blamed the bite of an
unseen bug for the illness that spread among them.*

The dressmakers grew faint,
Unionized by the venom
Of a bug so elusive
The foreman had to search
Like a safety inspector.

Claims fluttered their small,
White wings until, at last,
Owners started the strip search
For evidence, bodies bared
For a physician's house call.

What, among insects, left
No mark as it poisoned?
Ask us, the dressmakers said.
Go ahead, and they answered
As if they'd taken vows

During suicide videos,
Each of them displaying
Scissors and needles,
Wearing a white mask
Over the nose and mouth.

When one of us dies, examine
Your flawless flesh. After the next,
Open her sewing machine
Like a music box, and its song
Will emerge like a spider.

MY MOTHER LISTS THE THINGS
THAT ARE CATCHING

Measles. Mumps. Chicken pox.
The flu. The common cold. Strep throat.
Whooping cough. Smallpox. Tuberculosis.
Head lice. Ringworm. Impetigo.
Poison ivy. Poison sumac. Poison oak.
Comic books. Television. Rock and roll.
Lying. Stealing. Cursing. Idle hands.

THE CRUSADES

One Sunday, just before we were moved to the next "higher" class, Mrs. Shaffer
said the Crusades were the pinnacle of holiness. "Imagine," she said, "a host of
armies fighting for Christ." She told us about Peter the Hermit, the hero who
preached so well Christians everywhere joined up to rescue the Holy Land
from the heathens. "Because the struggle never ends," she said, "so many
Christians wanted to march to Jerusalem, there was always a next Crusade. In
1213, there were 30,000 children who marched. Imagine that, boys and girls.
Imagine them being willing to be martyrs for Christ."

THE TRESPASSER CHRONIC

Because my sister had walked home
alone eight Fridays that summer,
this time carrying the green skirt
she'd sewn at 4-H, mastering
a straight, invisible seam,
she took a shortcut through the yards
of tiny, floodplain houses
bunched like a small, silent herd.
She was eager, in August,
to enter that skirt and a dress
in the county fair, girls' novice class,
hundreds of preteen outfits
laid out for three shades of ribbons
two weeks after she identified
which loose dog, possibly rabid,
had bitten her as she crossed
that neighborhood of the unleashed,
so hesitant, when she'd narrowed
the choice to two, that both were loaded
into a van while the owners cursed,
the rest of that pack of dogs
barking as if they were
marking her, as if, next time,
they'd make sure she'd never tell.

TULIPOMANIA

In the early seventeenth century,
in the Netherlands, tulips from Turkey
charmed everyone. They loved Holland's soil.
New breeds were coveted. The price of bulbs
went up. There were mornings when so many
people woke to what seemed like paradise,
the rich had to own the best of those bulbs.
Speculators in bulbs made huge profits,
and buyers, eager to be rich, bought bulbs
on credit. At last, the price of a bulb
rose to as much as the equivalent
of two million dollars. When the bubble
burst, the deepest believers were ruined.

UGSOMENESS

n. (archaic) loathsome

On television, politicians
Lift from disaster's leaves like starlings,
Their thick-flocked chatter sending shudders
Through the room of held drinks and hors d'oeuvres.

Somebody suggests, "Fear and loathing,"
Producing applause as if a book
Will follow that allusive title.
Ugsomeness, I tell them, the tough,

Archaic word better suited
To measure the circumference of rage,
And not willing to explain, I walk
Out the door and stare at the still life

Of the neighbor's house, time slowing down
Like accident's traffic, this loathing
Setting flares before it lifts its paws.
After a while the inside voices

Begin to smear like an overstrike.
Loud talk infects the living room, turning
From politics to the poor and dark who,
Quite frankly, they're tired of hearing about,

Someone shouting "ugsome!" and receiving
A spontaneous round of laughter.
For now, alone, there's a sensation
Of stillness that I understand is

The hell side of immortality,
This loathing so lame in familiar
English, yet extending as far as
The infinite integers for pi.

THE SPACE-JUNK PREMONITION

One autumn, my son searched the sky
For the first sign of space junk tumbling
Precisely toward us, sleeping downstairs
And walking eyes-up, expectant.

He researched each satellite,
Its size and orbit. He prophesized
At school, at last infecting
Boys and girls with binoculars

Who, for hours, scanned overhead,
A pinpoint of hysteria
In Selinsgrove, Pennsylvania
Where they anticipated craters

As if they were following
Invasion bulletins. Each of them
Slept in their basements, and each woke
Believing a terror of fragments

Had torn apart someone they loved,
A skeptic in an upstairs room.

A CITIZENRY OF BIRDS

Tarantulas leave behind footprints of silk—Harper's

That neighbor, shortly after sunrise,
Says he loves to hear English
In the morning from his backyard birds.

They're citizens, he tells me, born here,
So many generations
With us, their accents have disappeared.

His mouth flexes. The pink horizon
Has nearly vanished. We are
Surrounded by the bright eggs of May.

My nod, meant to be neutral, narrows
The distance to empathy.
Only our lawns show the paths of shoes.

Suddenly, along our street, houses
Are raising flags, becoming
The embassies of allied countries.

When a siren opens full-throated
On the nearby county road,
I try to translate its accident.

Squalled from his architecture of leaves,
Vowels seem a needle's cry
Seeking a sample of suspect blood.

Some of the letters cannot be sung;
His lawn displays the sparkling,
Bent admission to his blue-rimmed door.

A MONTH OF CRUSADERS

March 29th   Moscow, 2 women detonate on the Metro, 40 dead

March 31st   Kislyar, two bombers, 12 dead

March 31st   Khyber, Pakistan, one car bomber, 6 dead

April 4th   Baghdad, three car bombers, 42 dead

April 9th   Ingushetia, Russia, one woman detonates, 2 dead

April 12th   Mosul, Iraq, one car bomber, 3 dead

April 19th   Peshawar, Pakistan, one bomber, 26 dead

April 23rd   Baghdad one car bomber, 11 dead

April 26th   Sana'a, Yemen, one bomber, 1 dead

April 28th   Baghdad, two car bombers, 5 dead

POSSESSION

In the 17th century, in Loudun, Mother Superior Jeanne des Agnes claimed
the spirit of Urbain Grandier, the parish priest, visited her at night to seduce
her. Soon other nuns reported spectral foreplay, moaning in ecstasy at night,
convulsing and speaking in tongues during the day. Exorcism followed, but the
nuns remained possessed by the demons Asmodeus and Zabulon who had
entered the convent with a bouquet of roses thrown over the wall by Grandier.

When possession went public, crowds of thousands come to watch. Out of
the nuns' mouths flowed public blasphemy. From the files of the exorcist came
the contract from Asmodeus himself, signed in blood by Grandier, a host of
demons, and Satan himself. That contract has been saved for centuries, so
that long after Grandier was burned at the stake, those nuns recanting and
regaining their holiness, we can witness Satan's pitchforked signature and the
decorative names of the demons.

THE MARTYR IN OUR TOWN

The martyr in our town is scouting
The public places where we gather
In great numbers. He enters our malls
And notes the busiest stores; he scans
The food court's longest lines. Fridays,
He watches football at the high school;
Saturdays, a blockbuster film.
Sundays, there are churches to attend,
Sitting with families on wooden pews.

The martyr in our town studies
Prophecies and commandments. He reads
Only the holy translations. At last,
When winter justifies his knee-length coat,
He thickens his waist with dynamite,
Develops a nails- and ball-bearings paunch.
He enters the one restaurant where
Every diner has three forks, two spoons,
And wine on ice, ticking as he gives
His reservation name. He decides
That the tables nearby are perfect
With use, steps forward as the hostess
Offers a complimentary room
For his heavy coat. All this, he prays,
Will spread, go airborne, a pandemic
Contagion. She employs the word "sir"
Just as he triggers himself, ascending.

JARED FRANK

THE FOLLOWING PROGRAM CONTAINS THEATRICAL RECREATIONS

I am watching late-night crime shows,
tanning myself in pale blue LED.

I wonder if you can bury a body
under the dust on a TV screen

and if *corpus delicti* still applies
should the body be replaced with a duplicate,

made up to look so smooth and edgeless,
because even we who choose to engage

death quite willingly only
eye it sideways, displacing it

from our lives like water from
a body in the desert one full week.

The family of the disappeared is saying now
that they are certain the unlikely best will occur

we think this too, that we can cast our fears off
on those that have already gone

dressing an idol in their clothing
and letting them burn somehow believing

that paranoia is an unrenewable resource and that
we will someday dredge our ponds and

find our bodies were not there after all

THE GROWING SEASON

I did not bury your body
I told myself I had no desire
to insult you by implying
that your rot was not beautiful
that I was the sort of friend
who would leave before the decay,
a coward who would deny
that moss and mold are greenery too.

Instead I had you sit in the garden,
next to azaleas and milkweed. It
cheered me to see you so calm.
I found a praying mantis egg case,
an elegant lumpy honeycomb thing,
and placed it in your hand, stiff-clawed,
waiting to hold it. The nymphs crawled
over the hollows and havens of rib cage, and found
you suitable. From your remains grew
strong stalks, leaves so sharp,
they could cut like mandibles.

In time you were obscured,
glimpses of dirty eggshell off-white
against the soil, then
nothing.

Forgive me for my use of you.

CHRISTIEN GHOLSON
BODIES, WAITING

1.

I work in the medical records department at St. Ignatius. White corridors, no windows. Every morning, on my way across the parking lot to the employee entrance, I pass a row of bio-hazard barrels, and every morning I have the same thought: are those the same barrels that were here last week, the week before, last month—since the day I started this job? I can't tell.

On my lunch break, dirty snow clings to juniper shadows, chamisa shrubs dot the distant hill. I eat almond butter and jelly sandwiches on rye. I'm allergic to peanut butter and wheat. Sand blows across the parking lot from the west. On my way to the file storage room, hunting down some old record for an insurance claim, I sometimes see the bodies, waiting on gurneys outside the morgue door.

A hospital is about bodies—living or dead—waiting. Bodies wait in the emergency room. Bodies wait for their records in the records department waiting room.

2.

Records always tell the story: how a girl was raped, over and over, tearing her apart. How she was sewn back together, became addicted to painkillers. The records reveal a junkie, body broken, who keeps returning to the hospital, again and again. They open her up, take things out, put things in, give her more drugs. The drugs mingle and mix.

She's on the phone with me right now, demanding her records. She's searching for clues. She's slurring, drunk. The phone slips from her fingers a few times, drops to the floor. "They're tearing me apart," she whispers. It's her secret. I've seen the records. I know what they've done. They have cut more and more of her away, replaced her body with something else. She is on the phone, looking for her body. Her body is waiting for her, somewhere. I want to tell her it's not here, that she must find it somewhere else. But I don't. I can't. I'm a professional. I am bound by law to her secret.

The phone rings the moment I hang up—an insurance company. The phone rings again—a law firm. Claims, checks, HIPAA law, almond butter and jelly sandwiches, bio-waste. When I finish with the asshole ambulance-chasing lawyer (who wants his request expedited RIGHT NOW), I begin the request of the woman-who-has-lost-her-body, copying her records for her, knowing she won't remember our conversation, will stare at the package on her doorstep for hours when it's finally delivered, immobile, wondering what it could possibly be.

JOB INTERVIEW

To be a successful customer service technician requires personality, enthusiasm, and a proactive attitude.

The manager asks me: "Why do you want this job?"

Sometimes at night, my hands become anglerfish; bioluminescent antennae trawl the dark. I am not saying this from inside a dream. The light is real. I have seen this dim green-yellow light cast shadows across my bedroom wall.

Ideally, customer service technicians will be confident in customer service techniques, be highly motivated, with a strong focus on upholding the company brand.

"How do you think you can contribute as an associate in this company?"

Let me tell you about the face that once appeared to me through charred bark; a bear god, a black mask; the curious eyes of the long dead.

You will need to focus on achieving the highest standards of productivity, quality, and efficiency, as well as looking after our stock accuracy. Key Performance targets will be set and you will be expected to achieve and improve on those.

"Why do you want this job?"

I know a live oak that explores the death of those that walk beneath it. Invisible fingers pull at you until something terrible you've forgotten is revealed.

Here at (fill in name of store chain) we reward those who show initiative, delegation, empowerment, transparency, accountability, mutual respect, collaboration, innovation, recognition, and passion.

"Why do you want this job?"

When I was four I was swarmed by a hive of bees. My head and shoulders were covered completely for at least ten minutes. Blind, deaf, my lips trembling, I stayed still, so still. They eventually flew away, not one sting. Is that a question? If so, what would be the answer?

SID GOLD
POINT

Pozo's red scarf signified his allegiance to Shango. Christianized Visigoths ceded their rule of southern Gaul early in the eighth century. I'm not the slick, stylish guy people take me for, shrugged Karpanty. Bats are the only mammal capable of sustained flight. A splendid season for mutual congress. Do stars fall on Alabama? Every print came up matching those of Pork Chop Lewis. Phantom pain may also affect a paralyzed limb. Yet evergreens do know how to keep a secret. Not circumstance but circumcision. Not imposter but imperative. So, Alex inquired, is she syncopated enough for you? Pernick strolled down the boardwalk with five grand in hundreds stuffed into a back pocket. There's no sense in mourning the passing of doo-wop. We shall be the nourishment & the poison. The Benin Bronzes are actually brass. How many fezzes, she wondered, can anyone go through in a year? Zukofsky refused to endorse Pound's economic theories. A flock of black shorn sheep strayed about their shepherd & his dog. Discourse is our most important product, confirmed the ombudsman. Oregon or oregano? Bedlam or Berlin? The Inuit consider Eskimo pejorative. In this way, we came to Ballyba. The plan is the body. Yes, the plan. And the body. Mance prefers being seated below the salt. GT is gran turismo. O is omologato. A busy day of constant rotating. Just this once, I'd like to get it right. The Nova Express no longer stops at St. Louis. Vultures may circle, but they do not point.

THREE

Daphne was saved from Apollo's grasp by turning into a tree. The repeated use of cocaine results in impotence. No one had to encourage Ludlow to throw his weight around. Evenings, the fir trees take the fog. Rodin was first of all a modeler. Old tires can be put to a surprising number of uses. At that time grave civil disturbances broke out among the inhabitants of Tours. Vivian wanted toast. She got toast. Who sweeps up the dust in industry? Who pitches the tent in tentative? Other echoes inhabit the garden. I'll have no truck with narrative, grumbled Martinson. In the seventeenth century, the Church struck back against the Reformation. Steeple day lime dove sir tardy. Rahv well understood the limitations of the New Left. You may find yourself sitting in that courtroom a long, long time. So shone the fresh young maiden amidst her servant girls. Some varieties of oranges can be grown only from grafts. Bud first walked into Minton's in 1941. The thirty-six hundred seconds in every hour. Swoop or swipe? Tunnel or toenail? Only the Evil One, Mara, rejoiced not. When the leaves turn red, orange, yellow & brown. Merely escaping insignificance was enough. Her glance insistent as a splinter. For they perished by their own madness. Saying he was heading downriver was the best lie he could muster. What occurs at night happens at night. Normally ravenous, blues will readily take both live bait & lures. I hesitate to say it's fiction, he said with uncertainty. No, it shouldn't be very hard to remember three little words.

DREAM

The bow & arrow arrived at the end of the last Ice Age. Cheap, ardent spirits were said to be the bane of the British working classes. Don't blame me, protested Professor Mondo. I'm merely curious. They hadn't had many rewarding experiences involving tunnels. The eye of the hawk dims at dusk. The Prince of Mercy occupies the twenty-sixth degree. Van Gogh returned from Arles with nine completed drawings. A dolphin is not a dance. A beetle is not a baked good. I'd find a way to handle it, suggested Hadley. Sources have Hengist defeating Vortigen in 457. Somehow the piano ended up in the pool. An arduous trek through the new Eastern Europe. Where have all the girls come from?, wondered his drunken buddy. Dryden claimed there were twelve knights, but Scott names sixteen in all. Felicity insisted on Calvados. Nothing but Calvados would do. The Aztecs performed human sacrifice on a daily basis. I can't forget that look in your eye, Darnell crooned. The ends of the rope shall have a whipping finish. Not loss but lost. Not placate but playdate. What art can wash his sins away? A skillful general does not load his supply wagons more than twice. Waltha kept a close eye on his anaphoras. Alecto's fiery torments never cease. Crockett vehemently opposed the Indian Removal Act of 1830. There are but five boroughs. The challenged chooses the ground; the challenger, the distance. All year long, the shofar hoards its piercing blasts. Later that morning, she suggested we go chasing tornados. It is no longer my turn to dream.

ERIC GREINKE

SUMMERTIME BLUES

"There ain't no cure..." —Eddie Cochran

It's a hazy summer night
for an outdoor blues concert.
The small green stage is set
on a hot asphalt parking lot.
The drummer takes off his shirt.

The bass player adjusts his ball cap.
The rhythm guitar unzips his jumpsuit.
The crowd is alert & ready to party.
A local DJ introduces the band.
They open with "Johnny B. Goode."

The frontman is yellow
after his recent liver transplant.
He no longer drinks alcohol, but
he can still play pentatonic scales
all night long or even in his sleep.

Two drunken biker chicks
sway-dance up front by the stage,
over a hill neither saw coming.
Their bleached hair looks tired
despite pink & blue streaks.

Most of the men wear black, with
greasy leather chaps & vests, &
big trucker wallets chained to belts.
They're in perpetual mourning,
afraid someone will steal their money.

The beer line is long, but
the lemonade man has no takers.
The older bikers sit on lawn chairs,
& arrive in cars or trucks,
but they dress like they still ride.

The younger bikers stand or sit
on or by their big Harleys,
keeping them always in sight.
They stay on the periphery,
where they almost feel comfortable.

But, the band sweats it out
& the crowd gets the beat.
The oldsters sway in their chairs
while tipsy dancers rub the stage.
Grace notes rise to the pink sky.

A slow blues hymn ends it
like a cool unexpected breeze.
Bike engines roar on the edge.
A wet encore soars aloft
in the sanctified sunset.

JIM GROSS
THE LET GO

For Herman Gross

simple phrase uttered by my father
taken out of context
from our final conversation

worried
I was losing cellular
connection

             (trying to push for last ditch Dialysis)
"Da ad, y u're break ing up ...I
don' know why...I...don"

"Y u're brea kin' up !"

"Well, I hear you very well..."
dry staccato throat saying:
      "Don't worry, I got yah"
      (calming, playful even)
                "I **-got** yah!"

& me not sure
        After he'd passed—
what I'd heard
checking the tape / his magnetic words transposing
thru computer to CD:
        Why the phrase uplifted me so?

family friend Sam recapitulating
the question,
"Why'd he say it like that?"

        "Don't worry, I **-got** yah"

in the night
it caught me
long flautist fingered hands
      behind my bicycle steady-ing
            the let-go fear

THE LIGHT APPLAUSE

For Polly Podewell

in Lounge
coveys of Executives
unwind their blue serge feathers

pinstripe America after cocktails
gesticulating cold mania economics
like olives on toothpicks

few notice "Skylark" landing
by her piano
        settled to 3rd Set:

sanguine voice
cut above whispers
of efficiency quotients

sweet Lady— beauty always gets
the light applause
in such rooms

ONE FOR THE PH.D.

we drove thru high desert
from Colorado
to get her a
San Francisco Abortion

I was delegated with
holding her nervous hands
in demure Frisco Bay
waiting room:

the friend who'd go on to be
        a PhD in Higher Education
sluffed her & one growing
Fetus on me

I saw him pull his wallet—
slow-count her 68 bucks
        "for the Procedure
        it's all I got—" he lied,

with broken shoulder
in cast after
motorcycle accident

he stayed behind in Denver—
        managed to shift
his scrotum into gear
for the next bitch

ONE FOR BUKOWSKI

For JW

he reads aloud
all the bad rhyming
Dead poets

Video on YouTube
affected rhythmic inflections
reaming his vocal cylinder

when asked to buy my book
he balked... Messaging:
"That must be quite some book
  for $335.00 ! Wow, congratulations"

hollow sarcasm noted
I texted:

> There's a tradition
> of the Art of Handmade
> Books—
> that goes back
>
> I chose that particular
> mode to help
> express in the physical
> Book, what I hope—
> quality parallels
> in the contents

no answer forwarded,
Message Delivered;

less pull on the wallet
when the poet's
a corpse—
            I figured,
he'd stuck with the Dead Ones

MICHAEL GUSHUE
ENNUI

I fell in love with Boredom. It didn't work out. Then I met Ennui, who was French, and I married her. It was wonderful. We went to the theater, the opera, museums, sports events. We traveled to South Africa, Brazil, Iceland. Ennui hated all of it. So we became homebodies. She would watch TV for hours and she could spend an entire afternoon eating a single pomme frite. Her hobby was standing in line. She practiced at banks, DMVs, unemployment offices. It's true she had some odd habits. Halfway through cooking a meal she would stop and walk out of the kitchen. She'd hang up the phone in the middle of a conversation. Still, I was always delighted to come home from work and find that she had not moved from her chair the entire day. Maybe it was because she was French, but being married to Ennui made every day special and nerve-wracking. One evening, I told her how happy I was. She looked at me with that blank stare of hers, her full lips in a slight frown. When I came home the next day, she was gone. There was a half-finished note in French on the kitchen table, a teacup with an unused tea bag in it, a half-eaten sandwich.

HEDY HABRA

OR HOW COULD HE EVER WIN THE HEART OF ANY WOMAN?

After Remedios Varo's Dead Leaves

She shuffled seasons at will, carpeted her floors with grass and wildflowers, picked the first man who showed her a spark of kindness and carved his heart at her image. Words danced in vibrant hues over the pages of her diary, giving life to a silhouette hovering in half tones in midst of the grisaille. With an empty stare, she'd sit for hours, see his shadow kneel in front of her, listen to his fading merman's song.

She'd redress his crossed eyes, bent shoulders and slight limp, or else, how could he ever win the heart of any woman? She thought of Beauty and the Beast although he was no beast and she was no beauty. Until the day she flung windows wide open, let gusts invade the rooms, let her skin bear the colors of dead leaves, and knew time had come to pull the thread, unravel the feelings spun around his heart.

VANISHING POINT

After Juanita Guccione's Surreal Board Games

Under a dark moon that has decided to keep silent, I wander along the street of chance, staring at the vanishing point, uncertain of the odds of being, but with the certainty that it leads to the sea. I walk like an automaton among passersby, gliding as faceless pawns. A couple of black horses pound the pavement, wavering between going forward or backward.

I wonder what lies for me at the end of this road lined with lamplights and palm trees. Fan-leaved branches stretch, unfolding an animated deck of cards turning into murals that grow in size. Shuffled and reshuffled at each step, some cards flip into a hall of mirrors in which I lose myself in my own reflections, as though in an old photo album where the faces of those now buried are fading.

> *we're crossing the bridge of death to leave behind*
> *the madness of the civil war...black sacks stained*
> *with blood...stillness...snipers...*
> *a heart skips a beat.*

I walk faster, look sideways: some things are best forgotten. Let's fold the night into light. I pass a couple of young men who seem to get closer to me, then recede and peel off the murals, disintegrate like antique parchments at the sight of an imposing woman in Tyrian purple, a younger version of my mother who takes me by the hand and whispers in my ear: "There isn't a minute to lose."

ALAN HARAWITZ

ETERNAL PARADISE

She gave us the grand tour in the silence
of a battery-operated golf cart,
weaving in and out of the vast acreage of gravestones
like a camp director guiding us to the ball fields,
the archery range, and the lake where the children
would frolic all summer long.

Only those residing here
on this Florida plain of death would frolic no more:

The final resting place chosen by all
these Jewish doctors and lawyers, scholars and teachers,
bookmakers and gamblers, heroes and scoundrels.

And now my father would join them
surrounded by his neighbors
in the strangeness of this tropical paradise
of eternal summer and heat, palm trees and golf courses
they so eagerly gravitated toward.

And he would be happy to know
(as I learned from my tour guide)
that Seinfeld creator and comedian
Larry David's mother was buried just a few rows away.

SEXY NAMES

Whoever called it fellatio
                                    must have been

a poet.

And cunnilingus?
                        An anthropologist.

JOHNNY HARTNER
ATTACK OF THE
50-FOOT WOMAN REDUX

Every cheating husband's nightmare is
to have his wife grow fifty feet and
come chase his tired old ass
out of the local bar where he sits slobbering over
Sally Slut. Naturally, let's throw in the local drunk
on the side of the road singing "Genevieve" to himself
until he sees her walking by—probably wondering
how the towel got as big as she, wishing she were
completely buffo—and ends up pitching the bottle of rum,
swearing to go back on the wagon.
          Now what would she expect anyway?
Trips to couples counseling would result
in some Dr. Ruth type who would only propose
that to sexually satisfy her not only would
his organ have to go in her
but his whole body.
          Smothering would be his climax.
          And how could he afford the food bills
when the whole supermarket would be bought
every time she got hungry? How many towels
would serve as one Tampon? Who would deliver their
giant kids? What state would hold all of them?
Despite her anger, divorce was in the picture.
          What *was* the message of that movie?—
That one in a slew of many where radiation answered
how the creature got fucked up in the first place?
It was more important than the others
with giant ants, scorpions, preying mantises, tarantulas
even talking crabs. We even had a giant tit in that
later Woody Allen movie.
          Sad times were the fifties when women
had to grow fifty feet to get revenge.
          Now what's only needed is a half-pint lawyer.

WELCOME TO MY KIBOSH

We're dressed like droogs with bowlers
in my dream following my reading *The Metamorphosis*.
Donny Normandy and I are having a duel of jokes
on a scaffold in my backyard.
Every time we say a joke, if the other doesn't laugh,
the wood cracks and the failed jokester is plummeted
to another plank below. Punishment for bad humor.
"We're paintless painters," I say,
"no brushes, no cans. This is absurd." The friend laughs
and I am spared the wood splitting
beneath my knees. "Your mum's gonna have a hissy
when she sees we did this," he replies. I don't laugh.
The wood splinters; my friend's arms flail in the air
like Robert Preston waving madly
in *The Music Man* and I start singing "Then we *surely*
got trouble   right here in River City!" He laughs;
I'm spared again. Back and forth this goes and finally
when my friend is on the bottom, he says I won.
"But like Gregor Samsa, I'll wake up a six-foot bug," I say.
I sail through the planks to join him on the ground.
        Nearby, Judge Kafka says, "That's no joke,"
pointing to his cap. "Welcome to my kibosh."
From his black robes, he pulls out a can of Raid.

TIMOTHY HOUGHTON
HOARDING

startled

Always the clutter, the dust on things, the stuffed things,
the ranks, too, of porcelain birds,
contemptuous owls. The television goes beyond
the normal meaning of loud. I can hear it outside the window.
Agile rhinos are charging a Jeep on the screen
as she sleeps in a chair. Hanging from the ceiling light,
a mobile of Viking ships barely moves.
Maybe I should try tapping the glass, or knock again on the door.
So little space between the knickknacks, the birds,
the stuffed rabbits and dogs. They can't breathe—from where I stand
they are a dense entity, a projection. Half awake now,
she strokes the cat on her chest like a baby, her hands a brown bark
that's been in the rain—a little shine, a little give. She is happy.
Down the hall my brother's been sleeping as well
after the late shift at the hospital. How much of him, I wonder,
is here. Can sameness be richness? A deficiency
keeps me outside her contentment. Back to sleep she goes.
There's my brother now—just woken. He stands over her,
as he told me once, to make sure of the soft movements
that indicate breathing, as I watch for a moment, then tap the glass.

J. HOWARD

APPLICATION: MORE THAN THE SUM OF THINGS

"Two chairs, one dish and a dog
Will go to my wife
who cannot read nor write,"

claimed pensioner No. 13511.
One child, Isham, farms the cotton
with the grandchildren.

"I have no trade beyond farming
but for fighting: Brandywine,
Germantown, Pennsylvania.

I've trod the old, riven roads,
forded rivers iced and hard:
I've watched cannons bring down

rows of men, and gangrene eat
the limbs of survivors. I took
my place in line and would serve

Again. If you'd take me—
seventy and deaf. Not dead.
Years ago, Old Daddy lost

my Auditor's Report, so
I hope you'll audit this: I
fought with Virginia's best men,

Served under General Washington
For frozen weeks at Valley Forge,
returned to reap and sow years

and what I deserve, you can't
measure by money, but I'll
take what's due me, do you hear?"

NANCY IANNUCCI

MY LOVE IN RING YEARS

I spoke to you
in omens,
held your veiny
hands; warned you.

I watched you
drain chlorophyll
from your skin;
I raked death
in the cold
& buried
it for you.

I stroked your
elephant skin,
weathered &
carved
in Croatoan
codes by
roving lovers
who fucked
at your
feet.

I kissed your
Piculet
mutilations
after they
tapped in
black cloaks
so rhythmically,
so savagely
& then
sucked
the living
sap out of
your body.

I loved you
more than
those who lusted
& you trusted
me—
*Why didn't you
listen?*

I smother those
I love.

My teeth sawed
you in pieces;
I cut you down
& reconstructed your
broken self into
a Wicker Man
statue in
my shed.

I counted
our years
together
through your rings,
which I couldn't see
until I saw beneath
your tender cambium.
You loved me
for so long,

and I felt no remorse.
I carried you inside
to the cast iron fire
& threw you in,
one by one.

And as you
struggled to speak
in spit & crack,
I consumed
you still,
inhaling your
last maple-scented
breath.

DONALD ILLICH

TEMPORARILY HUMAN

We sleep in the closet, hanging upside
down like bats. When we take off from
the room, we flap our arms, seek out fresh
fruit. Our sonar keeps us from running
into anyone, but people still seem bothered

by our high-pitched screams. At work
we've turned into butterflies. Floating by
coworkers' cubicles, we drive them so mad
they swing at us with nets. Escaping,
we settle at our desk, letting our wings

tap out the memos, hitting number keys
with our antennae. When we've finished
our day, we swoop to the elevator as a cardinal.
People remark on our beauty, but we do not
let it influence us. We'll still devour all

the seed in their bird feeders, sneaking
into their backyards when it's dark. Before
they have a chance to shine a line on us,
we've disappeared into the darkness, a raven
that perches on windows. "Nevermore,"

we caw, "nevermore." Our spouses wake
to shoo us away, but by morning we've
already plunged into our clothes, eating
Grape Nuts, temporarily human, though we'll
always believe we're a creature that soars.

BRUCE A. JACOBS
PERFECT GAME

"No one has ever bowled
a perfect game with duckpins,"
declares the balding husband
of the slimly sheathed woman
who has been steadily rolling her huge gray eyes
straight into mine, like a she-wolf with a hobby.

In our three games at the duckpin alley,
we are two couples plus me,
the straggling stag,
the one with no reason
to not return the two-hour gaze
of the lithe wife
as she avows again and again—
while harvesting me with those eyes—
that I am just *bound* to be a better bowler than she.
She wears little black shorts, a spotless white T-shirt,
the red Krishna-like logo and name
of a beach resort pulled tight across her breasts.
I wear jeans that would boast my high-school waist
had I not covered it with the tails
of a loose white shirt hung from my workout shoulders.

I like show-off clothing on her.
I like draped clothing on me, the kind
that sends her eyes prowling,
her smile all incisors.
There are times for a man
when being hunted by a woman,
seeing the undergrowth parted
by the wildness in a woman's eyes,
makes him sit up and make a rustling sound
that says, "Over here. Push
to the left through this thicket and I will
have no escape."

She cradles the hand-sized duckpin ball,
the size of one of her breasts,
in her right hand, releases it side-armed
onto the cherry-wood lane,
her bare legs springing, stopping short
at the painted line that cannot be crossed.

"It's just too hard with duckpins," continues
the husband. "The ball is too small
to get the pin action. The all-time high score
is something over 200. It sounds
unbelievable. But it's true," he says,

while behind him, she bends in her black shorts,
offers her right arm on her way
to another release.

Some assertions require proof.
Others you have no choice
but to believe.

PLAYING FOOTSIE

After I have bent to kiss a woman
who I know only by her first name
at 4 a.m. after the two-block walk to her place
from the basement bar whose windows revealed only
the shoe soles of pedestrians outside,
and she maneuvers away from my advancing face
as expertly and wordlessly as a figure skater—
after such a missed midair kiss, even her second-floor studio
—with its alley windows and its scrap yard
of dirty sneakers, T-shirts, and jeans heaped on the floor
as if James Dean exploded here—
becomes transparent. We hover,
she and I, above her unfolded laptop,
where she taps up videos of animé rap songs
one by squirming one. A white-faced pop wraith
with lips like a split tomato
puppets her own mouth in Japanese
from the computer's hinged jaw
which hangs open between the two of us.

Donna and I bend together over the music.
My hand is very near her face, almost touching
the fringe of her hair banked into a curve
by the electric curler on her vanity.
We have talked ourselves into quiet,
having debated, since two in the morning,
whether people are selfish because people are selfish
or whether people are selfish because the people who taught them to be people
have taught them to be selfish.
Either way, I am selfish:
My hand is now an inch from her brown cheek, the cheek
that moves just a little as she tells me that she is a lesbian,
that she likes women.
My hand replies, "What a coincidence. I like women, too."
Her hand says nothing, but holds my left shoulder and pushes,
with a softness like kindness,
to shift her face away

as I lean in to kiss her.
So now Donna and I have made this
a *silent* film, even with the pop diva
piping loud vowels from the screen.
As if subtitles had not spelled it out for me at the bar:
Perfect, a lesbian, an intellect, her recoil soft as
a trampoline. Our talk can fuck, our fuck can talk,
we can love in exclamation leaps that drop us back at our
point of departure, where we can slip our feet back into our shoes.
It will be like it was with Carla and Tracy and Mona, only years shorter,
the impossibility guaranteed upfront.
I will be both loved and alone
in no time. Perfect.

Our two mouths do a stunt flyby.
We look both at and past each other,
the way pilots veer their way
out of a near-miss at altitude.
The possibility of words fades like a vapor trail.
She and I have talked for hours, and the eyelashed black hairs
on her forearm make no sound when I graze them with mine,
and the cube of an apartment with her empty sneakers strewn across the floor
rubs us both like a room-sized eraser until our chalk bodies vanish
except for our feet:
her bare toes in their flip-flops
walking me to the door, mine riding in my black Oxfords
down the escalator, as if these two shoes
are my only eyes.

RELIEF

Your insides press you outward against the world
And you fear your skin will not hold.

But do not worry:
The world pushes back, enveloping
Like a mother, her mouth full
Of you. This is how you scream
Without breaking. In a galaxy blanket
wrapped tighter than you. A vise
holding your shatter into one piece.
A tension that frees.

Go ahead. Say it. Claw at quiet, feel
Your voice saved in grasp of greater throat.
Freedom of compression.
Tourniquet of ease.
You do nothing but rest against the universe
And it holds you in all your exertions.

Easy now.
Moan into its hand.
As if sadness were possible.
As if you could ever be alone.

BRAD JOHNSON
BUDDHA LOOKING THIN

I've always found undue comfort in knowing
so I ask the woman standing in line
at the Boca Raton Marshalls wearing
yoga pants and Buddha T-shirt to which aspect
of Buddha she most relates: the wealthy,
aristocratic pre-Buddha Buddha or Buddha starving
for nirvana beneath the Bodhi tree? I ask
if she believes a T-shirt manufactured
by exploited labor violates the Eightfold Path
or if she feels Americans make choices
and once across the river on Buddha's raft leave
the raft behind, free to embrace consumerism
but she looks at me like I'm a weirdo
for commenting on a shirt she probably bought
on sale and never thought about again.
I'm not sure if that makes her more enlightened
or less and wonder if there's a scale anywhere
that's accurate in measuring such things.

JEFFREY N. JOHNSON
THE IMMIGRANT

While on holiday in America he missed
the revolution. Thirty-three years now
on tour, crossing the bay to Cape May,
he gripped the cold steel rail as the wind

parted his gray Persian hair. He had already seen
all the cities, he declared, and for a moment
I did not doubt he had seen them all.
Now he was driving up the coast,

the nearness of water his only guide,
to see his son somewhere in New England.
He kept no schedule, made no reservations,
no deadlines to heed or tickets to punch.

He didn't know of the ferries until well after
Cape Fear, when he came upon a clumsy-looking boat
to Ocracoke. I like the ferries very much, he said,
dwelling on this simple exodus from land to land.

Would you go back home if you could? I asked.
He only stared out to sea where the occasional
dolphin broke the waves and plunged just as quick
like a rare glimpse of hope submerged.

Would you like to join us for dinner on shore?
No, this was not possible. He would make Atlantic City
by nightfall, then set out in the morning for Long Island
where he hoped to find a ship to ferry him to Providence.

RICHARD JONES
THE HAYRICK

When I was seventeen I took a ten-week battery of psychological tests at the local college to help figure out my future. Most kids waffled between medicine and law. The baffled doctor apologized when my final results counseled "hermit" or "monk." I'd never considered becoming a long-robed monk and didn't think of "hermit" as a legitimate occupation. I forgot all about careers when I crisscrossed Europe with my childhood sweetheart. Though we were poor, Europe was our oyster. We lived for the moment—Amsterdam, Paris—and our minds burned with all we saw—the face of the Matterhorn, the fountains of the Alhambra. We slept in youth hostels, converted monasteries, and convents with separate dorms for girls and boys. Lying in a dark monk's cell, I couldn't see the future—the heartbreak that would shatter me, the ruinous breakdown. No, I believed in love and bright mornings and couldn't see past summer's end, when we went in search of the Holy Grail and King Arthur's castle. We crossed the channel to London and took the train west to Tintagel. Under a windswept sky we spent the morning hiking barren cliffs; in the afternoon we followed the footpath signs into deep woods. In the woods lived a hermit in a shack by a waterfall. Bearded, gaunt, and wild as Tennyson's Merlin from years of solitude, the hermit fixed his eyes on me, put a finger to his lips, and bid me listen to the rapturous water endlessly falling. That night there were no boys' beds left in the hostel. I knocked on doors in the village, but there were no rooms to let. I slept in an open field of hayricks on a bed of straw beneath a sea of stars. Beneath the black cliffs, I could hear waves crashing. I dreamed of Merlin and the naked babe born to reign. I dreamed of a wave all in flame, so that the child and the wizard were clothed in fire. *And presently thereafter followed calm, free sky and stars.*

GEORGE KALAMARAS

TONIGHT AT THE FIVE SPOT

So, I'm listening to Kenny Burrell
and Art Blakey tonight at the Five Spot.
The recording's opening cut, Dizzy's "Birk's Works."
And I'm hearing the other music
in the background—applause after each
solo, clink of glass, the tabletop
tones tapped out by a stranger's grooving
hand. Bobby Timmons lays the keys, tells me
piano notes are possum tracks back to late summer
nights, 1959. Whose birthday
was the 25th of August? And did she feel young
again when Blakey stroked the skins, safely
tucking her into the marsupial pouch of night?
Now the treatment of a dump truck pours sand
back through the spider-webbed throat of a guy
at the bar, hunched from the load work left
dented into him. Late, though too soon for home.
What was missing in his life, sucked upon
in Scotch on the rocks sipped slow between tracks?
Kenny must already be missing
Sonny Clark, though he wouldn't overdose
for another three years. He could read future
sorrow each time he bent back a chord,
as if a tarot of notes charged toll,
the strings of his guitar like the digits
on a mortician's hand counting out
all the Lee Morgan dead—those hard-bit cats
who tried to kick the horse but got kicked
in the head instead, crueling their duel
with youth. All possible dead air this night
are lungfish wallowing in the mud
in Tina Brooks's sax. Five-fingered count
says he'll only record two years more.
Says the Five Spot is a Mr. Lincoln palmed

from a friend but also the waiting dead
already there in the background awe
of the crowd's applause. How many patrons,
even, are still alive? Did they dodge disease?
Did they marry again, or even at all?
Were they given the death of a cat?
Did they return to this joint night after night
to hear their lives slip past? This five-piece band
reaches beyond the grasp of death's hand, saying,
Spot me five. Let me buy a nickel bag,
my brother. I got the itch, and tonight there ain't
no junk. Let me calm myself, buy some time
with five tokes through the five steady steeples
of the hand. What is the sound of one brother
dying? What are the tones, the minor notes,
dizzying me tonight from a café across country,
fifty-five years late? How can this music
keep slipping me some skin from the hard life
of these sorrowful men surrounded by fives
at the Five Spot, on the 25th
of August, in 1959—
not in New York but Indiana this time,
in the almost-light of 5 a.m.?

SO MANY ROADS

for Otis Rush

So, I'm walking the mountain roads tonight,
Otis. Livermore, Colorado. So many roads. Some in. Some

further in. That's how your blues fastens me—soulful—
to the Milky Way. To the stars. The fiery orange bend

in Jupiter says you too have eight fluid moons. That your sun
sign, Taurus, gave you a home—far from Neshoba—steadying you into the orbit

of Chicago's South Side. Your slow, sultry sound. Your long, bent
notes. How could your recording of "I Can't Quit You Baby"

possibly be as old as me? 1956 is a long life away.
In hearing those riffs, perhaps I, too, fell from the stars,

unable to quit the world. As the Buddha said, we all come back,
time and again. You arrived this time to open our hearts

to the happy-sad that matters. Like the left-handed practice of certain yogis,
you flipped your guitar strings upside down to say what we thought

was right could be better said from the opposite end. Like wearing
your cowboy hat on Chicago's South Side. In Bronzeville. You playing Buddy's

and L.C.'s Checkerboard Lounge in the '70s, just under four miles from where I was born
in Englewood a couple decades before. Did you pace the hospital

corridor, convinced you'd have a white-boy poet as a godson from the stars?
Did you hand out cigars and say, *One day he'll carve my bluest blues*

into poems and unto the world? Now you are struggling, Otis. Wheeled
from this venue to that. Your Gibson semi-hollow 355 is quiet. Still,

that happy-sad. Electric cowboy that you are, I always thought you'd take
one of those *so many roads* and ride off into blistering riffs

of who and what we do. There are sunsets and moon-glow. And sometimes each
is the other. The sun quavering the strange quixotic color of the moon. Like the lightning

light of your left hand bend bending into Peter Green. Into Eric Clapton.
Mick Taylor. Into Bloomfield, Gravenites, and Stevie Ray. I can't quit you, Otis—

whether in Chicago or Colorado or Timbuktu. And neither
could they. So many roads, and one of the roads they took was you.

BREAD ENOUGH / LANTERN-LIT / LOST HEART OF THE HOUND

Sometimes there's bread enough for Raven
to die from bloat. Other times, we wake
with the heart of a lost hound pounding
through the shin-oak hollers of the chest. Where
did childhurt go when we remembered
the fish whose skeleton burned the book?
If you ask me the exact stance of jazz,
I'd say it's Ornette Coleman inside the throat of Miles

burred in the belly-burn of Thad Jones. Even my mirror
complained my face doesn't stay put. I corrected it
to *maybe*, to *might-if-it-could*, and the mirror got mad.
There's a book of Chinese poetry following me
frown to frown. Thirteen poems mention geese and not one
has a hound dog howling the misty peaks
of Fujian Province. But I have tea enough
to stake Raven from its perch, open the wool

of a lamb three days dead at the river. Tea black
with the mabbled motor oil of the world. Oolong tea
the scent of pines beneath which we could stand
to draw on their energy and send regret up the selfish ass
of guilt. I'm talking terms of surrender approaching me
from the mirror above the bathroom swirl. The skirl
of jazz is in me tonight, and now Mal Waldron is in
the piano keys of the rain-soaked night. It could be

the turkey vulture feather, which outweighs all the stones
of Egyptian loss. If we have left one person in this world
to miss us when we leave, then we are redeemed. Or is it a crow
feather? The feather of a Raven, shiny from preening
the muck out of the world? I don't feel redeemed
except when I drink tea—black as midnight's
mustache, or oolong as if Chinese gold in a cup, the simple *this*
of amber, the *that* of jazz. We ease into our brain. Rain enters it

slantwise through the throat. Trane at the Gate, brandishing his sax
as if publicly displaying my spine. What is open
and what is closed in Raven's beak are the lost stops of my hound
heart. A hound dog, simple of ear and snout, sniffing
out what might be dead in the wet-smoked leaves
of dogs / baying men / hollering lanterns lit
seemingly by what is lost in the shivering
our shimmering leaves.

JUST WHEN I THOUGHT I'D FINISHED DESCRIBING ALL THE PHOTOS OF THE PRESIDENT'S HOUNDS, I COME ACROSS THIS SHOT OF A REPORTER AND JOHNSON'S DOG, *HIM*

Based on a photograph of President Johnson's beagle, Him, *lying beneath a picnic bench,*
upon which a reporter is taking notes, during a press conference, August 2, 1965

The guy is smoking a cigarette on the 1965 White House lawn, as if Kentucky or
Virginia expanded, the rows of tobacco burning long the soft grass of his lungs.
The hound crawls into some Washington shade beneath the reporter's bench
where August is autumn, and it's a sliver of the day's darkness—not the moon's
worms—that saves us. So many other shades, like Edison standing near the
gray silk of Topsy, the Southeast Asian elephant electrocuted decades before to
demonstrate the dangers of alternating current and put Tesla's theory to bed.
Tesla, unable to sleep, pacing rows of troubled cages to stroke the gray-tipped
wing of the last passenger pigeon. The mud-cloud of my little-boy mouth
decades later—as if I'd just been raked from moon-wash of the Wabash—pouty
in my own 1965 photo, anxious to return to my backyard mimicking of the
batting stance of Ernie Banks at Wrigley. How many cigarettes a day did the
White House reporter smoke, and what brand? His ash long, barely attached,
four seconds from falling. A hidden flame in the roots of grass waits to blaze.

Did he lie awake, puffing a Tareyton or an Old Gold Filter, sussing the answers the President did *not* give? Was the Gulf of Tonkin—a year earlier to the day—a bight of ocean in the turbulent turning in the reporter's chest? A slice of himself in the man and woman divide he could not bridge with his own wife? Was he somehow aware that my cousin George would go MIA four years later, moments after departing the chopper? A jungle of Southeast Asian elephant grass burning at the pace of a Virginia tobacco field reaching all the way into Indiana and Illinois. Ernie Banks and the Cubs, I knew, could not save George Avgerinos. Nor, even, could Jack Brickhouse—the only one who could call the game just right. Did Johnson sleep? Did he lie awake counting the blood-hairs on Oswald's balding scalp, moments after he was shot? Did he wonder whether Jack Ruby really loved the business of owning a strip club, or whether he was addicted to the alluring curves of Little Lynn and Tammi True? Was anything these days after all, he thought, really little *or* true, as he lay in bed, inches from Lady Bird, back turned to her and cuddling the dogs—both *Him* and *Her*? Perhaps the smoke pouring forth from 6600 volts and 72 seconds of current in Edison's elephant still perfumed the country, as if the cables of 1903 smoldered inside 1965. The great inventor still trying to prove that one has to kill something large in order to demonstrate swift manly weight. Was my cousin George swift, as he disappeared into the tall almost nothingness of elephant grass, wind-bent from the blades of the chopper? Was the reporter, mindful in his character count? Did his editor cut one hundred words and give him just one hundred fifty to say what the President refused? Was the beagle-hound proud in those days of mostly male reporters to be *Him* and not *Her*? How did he know to loll beneath a bench of men as the only seemingly sane place to seek relief from all that burned in the burning White House lawn?

STEPHEN KESSLER
ON BOOKSHOP SLOPES

Gary Snyder jumped off the shelf
and onto the floor at my feet
in the poetry section—
     surely a sign
        from graybeard uncle
to pay closer attention
when I'm reaching for Mark Strand collected poems
     with cover art by Steinberg
and knock Gary's off
so that's the one I must buy

and take to the terrace of the art museum
which used to be exercise yard of county jail
where inmates hung on the chain link
shouting to pedestrians below on Front
     asking for cigarettes
        or some babe's attention
and open and read a few poems
and am reminded of Gary's clarity
his teacherly wit and scholarly street smarts
     to impart skills around the homestead
        or library or campfire or mountaintop
or jumbo jet streaking him from one continent to another
to transmit what he knows
     to those who care

I'm not sure whether what I care
matters anymore
or what if anything I have to teach
but Gary's in good shape for someone his age
and he can still write
     so he's a role model

pages flap in coastal breeze
the succulents breathe
the sculptures in this garden look comfortable
but the fountain is off and I miss
     its watery sound

GARAGE ELEGIES 22

How do the new dead blur
in the streaks of tears down the bereaved faces
grieving in disbelief the sudden impossible losses,
what forms must mourning take to serve their memory,
what plain joys and pleasures measure up to the absences,
the missing persons.
Consider the beautifully robust young bodyworker
at the farmers market, tall and strong
with the flushed cheeks of the recently orgasmic,
whom you mistook for another brilliant girl
you've never met and you struck up a conversation
and now she is in your office working on your wife—
what kind of luck is that?
Or lunch with another woman elegant in her silvering,
or a friend whose marriage is almost as strange as yours,
or coffee with a couple of lovely lesbians
worthy of Sappho's lust in their fresh appetite for the physical,
all evidence that amid the neverending atrocities,
buds of breastlight, flashes of eyegleam
elevate heartbeats and remind you of what is everpresent
even while forever out of reach and beyond recovery.
That sound she made when she came,
your first taste of her tongue,
what touching her felt like—
those are pleasures you never lose
even though you will never know them again.
You must notice every platonic signal of correspondence,
every sexy nuance, and when a fox looks in
through the French doors as you are eating breakfast
you must trust it is a gift and not a mirage,
small measures of grace against the enormous horrors.
Jack Gilbert, one of the unstrung lyre lovers
who left one delicious light green brick of a book,
wrote somewhere that we must savor what sweetness we are given
to overcome the refugees' sufferings, to counterbalance,
counteract the victims' violated bodies, the shredded lives.
The cruelty of the aggrieved cannot be comprehended,
and the tenderness of affection never denied.

GARAGE ELEGIES 8

The nurses have arrived to comfort the afflicted,
bringing prescriptions and stories of their own ordeals
under the influence, and the suffering one takes it personally,
self-absorbed in a network of electric nerves.
This is what you were trained for in madhouses all those ages ago,
to negotiate altered states, inmates on incompatible trips
at odds with prevailing paradigms. You are now cool,
with help from your preferred medicine like everyone,
inoculated, and have learned to recommend your own regimens
according to existing conditions. The all-night tremors,
the shivering ripples, the heebie-jeebies of the mumbo-jumbos
whispering sweet-and-sour everythings in ears
where the cranio-sacralist has left her seeds
to sprout fresh imaginings in your flesh—
these phantom spirits know not what they speak,
they are subcutaneous yet without teeth, swirling like smoke
from the goofy ancestors' long-since-extinguished cigars.
We are doomed, no doubt,
but not yet, taking the waves day by day,
holding close at night the sweet warmth of the beloved
in whatever shape of lost sleep. Bad dreams may come,
and redeeming spells to expunge them, ineffective as elegies
to rescue the dead, yet almost magical in their mourning.

ROSE KNAPP
POIE E SISTA

Compose
　　　　Construct
Conscribe
　　　　Conform
On the spot
　　　Sign the y line
　　　　　　No knot om the x)(ॐ௫

HARPER'S POEM #1

An esquire sent in for
　the hottest wasteland.
　　But Johnnie only walks on
　　　black raposado water.
　　It's Christ Ole Mass
　　time for time, iq,
titles, toys, tits.

LUISA KOLKER
ARTEMIS IN TAOS

Artemis
Artemisia
Artemisia Tridentata,
three-pointed leaves
of big sage
that purify, protect
and heal.

I look like a jogger,
in shorts and a T-shirt,
but I am running, fleeing
like an injured animal
on the
dusty, dry roads
of Taos.

I stop to breathe
and cry
in front of Taos Mountain.
I press my face
into the scrubby artemisia,
one of millions
that protect the desert floor,
and I breathe a prayer.

Goddess Artemisia:
Hunt down my broken
heart.
Please don't kill it.
Bring it back
to me.

D.H. LAWRENCE MEMORIAL

Frieda condemned your ashes
to a cheerless concrete slab
for all eternity.

As an afterthought,
she adorned your tomb
with a sunflower and a phoenix
to lift you up.

This confusion we call love.

WHITE SHELL WOMAN

(Ojo Caliente Hot Springs, NM)

Wanderers in need of water,
in need of new life,
have always sought
the springs that rise
out of the dry earth.

White Shell Woman,
White Shell Woman,
I need your help
to heal my heart.

White Shell Woman,
White Shell Woman,
I am drowning
in empty spaces.
I need your help.

She is well-known
to the Zunis, the Navajo
and all the ancient ones.

Years ago,
I heard her name
from my friend Steven
who said she lives still
at the sacred
healing springs
of Ojo Caliente.

On my fifty-seventh birthday
I need to visit her,
so I drive northward
to her sanctuary
of waters
surging from the earth..

White Shell Woman,
White Shell Woman,
I am surprised
that I speak to you
and instantly you
appear to slake
my thirst.

You show me a pure,
dry, white shell
embedded
in the cliff beside the spring,

a tiny shell
empty for so long
and exposed to the
parching heat of time.

White Shell Woman,
White Shell Woman,
I offer you my shell.

What can you do
with this dry, brittle
bowl that once was
filled with life
at the bottom of
this desert ocean?

White Shell Woman,
White Shell Woman,
you hold me and
offer me stillness
in the amniotic rhythm
of your healing waters.

White Shell Woman,
White Shell Woman,
I feel you loosening the
old life still
clinging to my
shell.

And now you speak to me:

*Old shells become
new homes,*
you say.

*Old shells become new
homes.*

THE TEARING APART

Before life can begin
there is the tearing apart.

There are graceful,
romantic ways
to describe
birth
but the truth is
it is a ripping apart
of union
and there is blood
where there once
had been fusion.

Persephone,
joined in perfect
merging with
her mother
Demeter,
is torn apart
from the world
she knew,
blood red
poppies
still
clutched in her
milk-soft hands.

She is abducted
into the
Underworld,
which is
sometimes
the only way
you can leave home.

LAURIE KOLP
BUMPER STICKERS

Boobies. That's what the pink bumper sticker says. My youngest starts to giggle. *Do you see that?* It's no laughing matter, I say. It's about breast cancer, awareness of it. Of *B-O-O-bies*, he giggles. Sometimes they have to remove them, I say. The silence hangs like a pair of old socks that don't want to stay up when it's cold outside yet you need them for comfort. It feels uncomfortable, the stretched-out silence, and I don't want to be having this conversation right now. He breaks it. *I have to ask. What do the doctors do with the... B-O-O-bies—* (giggle), his giggles are deep from the belly kind of giggles, the kind that make you want to laugh, too. *Do they put 'em in jars?* I can't help but giggle. No, they usually remove one, the one with cancer; but sometime it's both, I whisper. With luck it's just a lump. My mind races to an alcoholic-bottom time I won't forget the day Mom told me she had breast cancer. I thought she'd die and she thought I'd die. We both got worse before we got better. My son turns to me, his face a question mark. *So their shirts go like this?* Hands across the chest, one quick out then straight. No, I say, they usually fix it up. No way am I going into breast implants with him. *I see,* he says, *the skin stretches out. I guess they have to eat a lot.* What can I say?

BETH KONKOSKI
WINTER ROUNDS

February you beat me this year
with magnetic fists and a ballerina's
precision. No glancing blow or
blown circuits, no half-dark shadows
where threads of light could dangle
and my eyes take a moment, but
adjust. No, this hammering and lustful
catastrophe held me long past
the ten count. In fact referees
called the fight while I bled and begged
on the canvas. I hope the champion's
belt is real gold, hope the victory
was worth its price. While you
may not be at fault, you could show
a little less joy in my defeat, could
offer a hand to pull me into March,
but you don't. Muscles flexed,
eyes apprised and on the prize,
you circle the ring while I crawl
toward my stool in silence.

LYN LIFSHIN
FROM LIPS, BLUES, BLUE LACE: ON THE OUTSIDE

Born in Russia, my father had many qualities
typical of Vermonters: he was quiet, frugal, taciturn.
Maybe it was that lack of warmth, that withdrawn,
brooding, often depressed mood, a dark coldness
that endeared my father and Robert Frost to each
other. I used to see Frost wandering around Middle-
bury in baggy green pants, carrying strawberries. He
bought those pants in Lazarus Department Store, my
grandfather's store, and he would only let my father
wait on him. Afraid to take a creative writing course,
I submitted two of the only poems I'd written and
one was published. My father, without telling me,
got a copy of that poem and showed it to Frost who
wrote on it, "Very good sayeth Robert Frost," and
told my father he liked the striking images and
wanted me to come and visit him, bring him more

UPSTATE NY, IN THE HOUSE I'M IN RARELY THESE LAST 12 YEARS

a box of notes from
Robert Frost to my father,
ticket stubs from when
my father, estranged from
his family, as Frost was
from his, hitchhiked
to Amherst for a memorial
celebration. What linked
these two men, links me,
wondering what they talked
about as my father sewed
green cotton pants as if
linking the straw farm in
Russia where chickens
slept in the house to
Frost's house of alien
women. My father, who
never went to school but
read, to Frost's green
pastures, his aloneness in a
house where no one talked.
My father with his notebook
of grievances, the cost of
life with a family, always
worrying about money,
stingy with it, with love as if
like Frost "Love of the lips
was touch... /And...that
seemed too much." Two
bitter and burning men,
sorting thru stacks of simple
cotton. No fancy clothes,
no fancy words, who might

have been as happy being
tramps in mudtime. A life
pared down, a separateness
from those they could touch
but wouldn't, choosing "to
scare [them] selves with their
own desert places," trusting
trees, the dark trees, and
as I have, the words for them

NOTHING GOLD CAN FLY

the palest petals on
the apples near the
metro, eight
small trees, the
boughs, floating
lace. I learned
from Frost early
on late freeze
could swallow. But
for as long as you
hold your breath, a
cloud of milk petals,
so thick you can't
see bark. Ghosts, a
white face
blending into
blackness

HOW UNLIKE
FROST'S COUNTRY,
VIRGINIA SQUARE

and unlike mine. Sitting
near Starbucks on a
brick patio, too early
for ballet after an
early morning eye
doctor appointment,
metro bus, the metro,
people on their way
to Reagan's lying in
state, crammed flesh
to flesh. Hardly a
slashed green. No
cows, no horses,
apples, wheat. Only
a small dog on a
leash. The potted trees
aren't doing well.
Few speak English,
let alone Vermont-ese,
flat with A's a little
southern. If Robert
Frost walked by he'd
be dubbed a street person,
especially in those over-
sized green pants. High
rises blot out sun, at
least this early and yet
if isolation is what
you're after he could
pull up a wrought iron
chair, let the fountain
drown out other voices,
imagine the spray was
ocean air and let the
words, as Frost taught me
they always do, take
him into another world

HOT MUGGY AFTERNOON ON MAIN STREET

fans shirring in the
long deep department store
in the bookstore smelling
of hot damp wood.
Church bells from the
congregational church,
always a little late while
later boys waited at
the First National Corner,
dared each other to
walk on the stone bridge
over Otter Falls. Slow
days, Robert Frost
lumbering thru Main St.,
I sat in the lilac room
wondering if I'd ever be
pretty, have anything
to write about. Summer
droned on. On the hottest
days, my mother packed
salmon croquettes for
Branbury Beach where
we stayed 'til darkness,
came back to rooms
that still hugged
the day's thick heat.
Whatever mattered,
seemed about to melt.
When I wrote a poem
about that, which the
mythic white-haired man
would never see, write
saying he liked it,
seemed as impossible
a pipe dream to
hold onto as the
lemon sherbet I could
almost taste slipping
from the sugar cone to
steamy pavement

ON THE DAY OF THE BOMBING

one boy called his father,
excited, he just found
out he would be playing
goalkeeper for the first
time and asked his father
to bring him some gloves.
"But," the father said,
"I was working and
couldn't leave." As soon
as his shift ended, he
rushed to the store to
buy the gloves. He heard
the explosion as he stepped
out of the store. Smoke
was rising from the direction
of the soccer field

THE MAD GIRL DREAMS OF MOROCCO

of the toucans outside
her window, how she longed
to see the rooms where
Paul Bowles lived, the
desert in the distance, a maid
hanging up clothes, singing
to herself in Spanish. She
remembers the children
being led out of school
throwing stones at the pale
birds past the bodega
under the sun where she
stopped, lured by a carpet of
turquoise and mauve where a
man brought her apple tea
like a ticket to love

THE SADNESS, THE BEAUTY OF WHITE TRILLIUM

In spite of days in the
trunk of my Mustang,
jounced from VT to
Niskayuna the flowers
kept blossoming. Dug
up weeks after my
grandmother died on
my mother's first
motherless Mother's
Day. We traipsed thru
soggy woods for the
white jewels. Each
spring they brought
back my mother's laughter
at our treasure. Seven
or eight beauties
spread to almost a
hundred with a blood ruby
trillium tangling with
pachysandra, columbine,
hepatica, May flowers
until the snow plower
ruined half of the plot and a
year later left his van
burning to wipe out the
rest. For years I tried
to replace the plants,
ordered white trillium, my
knees ached trying to
plant them, hundreds, but
nothing took. It was
as if somehow they needed
the magic of that sad but
beautiful afternoon
in VT to flourish

EDWIN MADRID

YOUNG LADY AT LUNCH

Although a poem is not a girl eating, it happens that food
and girl enter inevitably the unbounded world of poetry.

ANY OTHER FLESH

On the wide kitchen table, a big-eyed thin-skinned fish
awaits its dinnertime journey to the interior of Miss Claudia,
who won't have any other flesh, judging it to be a sin.

TURKEY DEAD FOR LOVE

A turkey with half a bottle of wine inside can't walk two steps straight, he stumbles
around like a feathery basket. He doesn't watch his step, his feet tangle up and slip,
they stumble, fall, they can't find the way to sanity. He seeks the world of salads,
the freshness of lettuce, the moans of a walnut or the absurdity of a gravy who will
love him. He is an erotic turkey ready to lie on any loving table.

WORD PEPPER

Pepper burns what is most private; it is lip-deep fire, a territory on the tip of the tongue
spitting words black and insane. Red river from mouth to mouth like flames scorching
all until they reach the syrup fountain; and words become chunks of beating flesh
and climb up to the mind, to that heart of the tongue, where it burns hotter than a
thousand words extracting the taste from the dream food.

—*Translated by Julia Velasco*

SAUNDRA ROSE MALEY
ALL THE SUN IN A GOLDEN CUP

for Ezra Pound

The Cantos, incomprehensible,
    perverse and mystical,
    a macaronic chaos—

      You—   find   me

          —in fragments

The light, the song, God's fire, shaken
    with new music,
    luminous and strange

        like the fiddle of the wild Tzigane,

Contrapuntal, vertical,
    harmonic, hysteric
    at times, demonic

    this music,

        Intellectus est

      a solid object, an edge
            melodic

Notes as facets
      of air,

and the mind there,

      before them,
        moving

—this high-wire act—

MISS AMERICA, 1951

Yolande Betbeze Fox,
a convent-educated, Alabama-born
beauty queen, entered
the Miss Alabama contest
to get out of the South—
her aria from *Rigoletto* charmed
the judges in Atlantic City
and won her the tiara
but when she refused to pose
in the Catalina swimsuit—
I'm a singer not a pinup!
one sponsor stood up
and started to fume—*I'll run you*
off the news pages. *I'll start*
my own contest. *You'll see!*
So he founded the rival Miss USA—
People can thank me
or blame me for that,
she would say.

She did perform her other duties, though—
once babysat a bottle
of Hudson River water all the way
to France to be poured ceremoniously
into the Seine—*oops!*
the bottle leaked on the plane
so she topped it off
from the hotel tap and next day
poured to the memory
of Lafayette, the Statue of Liberté,
and crêpe suzette!

After her reign she ran off
to Hollywood where
she turned down several movie roles
and left for New York
to study at the New School
for Social Research—
she was nobody's fool, read
Schopenhauer and Hume—
at a party in Manhattan she met
Matty Fox, a one-time wonder boy
at Universal Studios, he was
stout and twice her age—
I can't pass a delicatessen window
without putting on weight, he laughed—

Yolande loved the way he danced
so they married and moved
into a Park Avenue penthouse—
were friends with Marlene Dietrich
and Elizabeth Taylor—
Matty bought Yolande a rooftop theater
in the East Village over
a bagel baker's union where
she produced plays of the Bard
and Aristophanes—once cast herself
and two other Miss Americas
as the witches in *Macbeth*—

She was an activist, too—
stood vigil outside Sing Sing
the night before the Rosenberg executions
always did her own thing—
there's a 1960 photo of her
in the *Times* carrying a sign to picket
Woolworth's segregated lunch counters—
I'm a Southern girl,
but I'm a thinking girl—

Meanwhile Matty tinkered
in a political game that led
Sukarno to power—Matty denied
all charges—and later, quite
unrelated, invented a goo
kids used to blow up big
Wham-O plastic bubbles
with the pipe he invented, too—
soon after, at 53, Matty's heart
popped like one of his bubbles
and his young widow moved to D.C.—
into the Georgetown home
that had belonged to Jackie Kennedy—

For a minute Yolande contemplated
running for Congress but didn't
and settled *into* the society scene
and eventually *down*
with a dashing Algerian diplomat,
Cherif Guellal, who helped his country
gain independence from France—
he was her enduring love, though
they never wed—for years
their lavish parties were legend
with the international set—

At the pageant's 80th birthday bash
Yolande told a reporter—
I can't write a memoir, just yet,
too many people still alive—
and so am I—there's life
in the old dame yet!

STEPHEN MALIN
MORNING DRILL

Programmed drapes snapped wide, on time; early
tray arrived, Morning Post, ironed, lay flat
by juice and coffee—Kopi Luwak,
one ninety eight Fahrenheit degrees.
Ten minutes marked redeployment to
the atrium's koi pond as he strode
unslowing to reach both waterfall
and adjacent lap-pool where his wake
washed thirty metronomic circuits,
concluding in a thick Egyptian
robe that dried him for the spa's massage;
then, head shaved and gleaming, he returned
to claim his rosewood chaise for blood-rare
steak, careful eggs and new-brewed coffee.
Prudent when networks' Mid-East tensions
upstaged news of Fossoil and AllArms
stock splits, he closeted self and smile
to don a tailored set of modish
summer cottons, Gucci case proffered
along the walnut hallway as he
approached his car, olive tones subdued
in burnished depths, fender flags uncased,
aide in uniform holding the door.
"Morning, Getz." Their eyes met, did not change.
"Good morning, General. The office?"
"Ah, yes. Fine day for soldiering, Getz."
"Yes, sir." He sat back, eased by lambskin.
For that day's War Room docket he would
again confer on drone strikes. He hummed.

AOIFE MANNIX
RECONSTRUCTION

We are back in that waiting room
with the weird tapestry of lost Londoners
straggled across the wall. He says
"some women don't mind being flat chested."
And I wish I was one of those warrior types
tattooing myself with dragon defiance
and bearing my scars to the world.
But the trouble is I have never wanted
to stitch my story into skin, to ink myself
with mysterious symbols of deeper meanings.
I just want to look like everybody else.
Boring, normal, T-shirt and jeans,
swimming in the summer.

I remember when I was thirteen
asking my mother to buy me a bra
because all the other girls had one.
She laughed because I had nothing
to put in it. I suppose it was vanity then
and it's vanity now. But when you said
the scar's looking great, I felt as if that's all
my body was. A gash across emptiness.
A horror show nobody would want to touch.
My skin stretched far too tight, a lump of plastic
that chaffs against who I used to be.

It's just flesh, it shouldn't matter.
But when you turn away from me,
it's as if I'm sliced open to the bone.

HOW TO GO

A ladybug slowly crawls
across the front windscreen
of the hearse. We joke
about musical mixups,
how she blasted "Bat Out Of Hell"
instead of the song her mother loved.

I think don't let me be a scattering
of blurred photographs, a video camera
trapped behind a crematorium curtain,
a corpse dressed up for three weeks
in the funeral home.

Let me be those orange wings
taking flight just as the wiper
sweeps down against the glass.

PARANOIA

The man at the table next to me
is wearing the most brightly polished
white leather shoes I have ever seen.
He is also talking to himself
and filling sheets of A4 paper
with large, loopy writing.
At first I think it's the same phrase
over and over, *Shining* style,
then realize it's not, though I can't read
what it does say. Perhaps he's only
having a bout of creativity.
But I get up and move away just in case.

At Baker Street the tannoy
is repeating "due to an emergency
would all customers please leave the station."
No one seems to be hurrying.
One bloke near the entrance
is complaining loudly
that he just bought his ticket.
But I quicken my step, not running,
but moving fast because since
they told me the tiny lump
that was nothing to worry about
is, in fact, cancer, the world suddenly
seems full of psychopaths and terrorists
and lightning bolts from the blue.

SIMPLE DIRECTIONS

Take your purple ukulele and tune in
to letting it go as you check the timetable
once more, not forgetting that the schedule
changes with the coming and going of children,
the chasing of foals across a field.
One of them rolling on his back, feet kicking the air
as you spot the single decker weaving round the bend.
Remember how you worried how long it would be
till you'd be well enough to make this journey again.
Pay your money and listen to the weather songs of old women
as a strange man offers you sweets. Settle into glimpses of sheep,
the castle with its music room, until you reach the cross
from the nursery rhyme. The lady on her fine horse
cast in bronze and clicking her heels. Ding the bell
and alight with thank yous before turning back
the way you've come past the pub of broken dreams
and the Polish surprise eggs till you reach the corner
with the money machine and the iconic public toilets.
Turn right into the howling glitter ball wind
and the endless scaffolding. Ring the lower door
and identify yourself as a collector, not a kidnapper.
Listen to a warm review of wolf dancing in French
before walking past jigsaw puzzles, toy cash registers,
racks of small shoes, and into the inner sanctum
of the nursery where a little boy is listening to a story.
His face bursting into song when he looks up
to see you are here to take him home.

MICHAEL MARK
GOODBYE TO THE TECOPA PUPFISH

What kind of life was it anyway?
Grubs and maggots for breakfast, on a good day
a worm? Yes, it's quite something
to live in 120 degrees but that's too hot.
Even if you had gotten used to it over 10,000 years—
and isn't that long enough for any species to exist,
a hundred centuries?
Somewhere in the Middle Ages you must have completed
your evolutionary agenda, though what that could be
is unclear: swimming around, surfacing
for a sip of arid air, submerging again?
Would have thought you'd die of boredom.
Palatinate blue boys flitting about tediously striped girls,
not going very far.
Cute name, though, Pupfish, we'll remember that.
More than Cyprinodont.
And you can rest in perpetuity knowing
you were first on the endangered species list
to go extinct—you're on the internet forever!
Inch to icon quick as that.
What you have to know, though it's a little late,
is man works so hard. The city is a cauldron of its own,
and those soothing sulfur springs were just
what the doctor ordered.
Nice long soaks after a long drive to God
forsaken nothingness. Put on a little Dead, light up a doob,
marinate in Mother Nature's briny bubbles.
A man could get revitalized, feel his strength rise
from those depths in a too-short weekend.
Then it's back at it. The grind, the rat race, the relentless
real world—you know what college costs? A gallon of gas?
Our water bill is murder! And the baths
are bone-softening medicine—I know
it was your little home. Little wonder it became so popular,
masses of sickly flesh and bushes of hair rubbing
against saline and suds and more reddish flesh—don't blame you
for not sticking around, not one bit, Pupfish.

RICHARD MARTIN
PATHETIC LOVE POEM

I'm so far away from touching you
I could be in the next room,
On a planet shaken from its orbit,
Careening freely in space.

It's a numbers game
Of walls and darkness, isn't it?
As if you could respond to that question,
Find a drill or telescope to see

Where I might be, hiding perhaps
In a dream of the past,
Imprisoned by a dialogue with the moon
On the nature of romance.

This afternoon I purchased an avenue of birds
And stoked old flowerpots to life
With magic inherited from rain.
My mind works this way;

It sends messages throughout my body,
Surreal ones, really,
Open to ridicule and false accusations
As if nature took its cue from Lazarus

And unqualified hope.
Once I was covered with tattoos of sunlight
Because you kissed my lips
With vigor, hired musicians

For the absence of garments.
We entered nakedness like we knew
What we were doing—sommeliers of flesh.
Your beauty broke the clock on the bed stand

Into a single moment.
"Work with that," you said,
As if I could grasp eternity
In the sweat of bodies.

If love had a brain, things would be different.
It would appreciate the way life and death
Lie side by side in embryo,
Aware of the odds.

SUSAN H. MAURER
ORLANDO 2016

From the pile of corpses,

the persistent ring of the cell phones.

MILES DAVID MOORE
MAN ON TERRACE WITH WINE, RECALLING A LINE FROM HERMANN HESSE

What happiness to dream when, drinking wine,
You notice beauty that you never see
When sober and at work. Late summer vines
Glisten with purple fruit. Serenity

Drifts through the willows, buoys the scent and sight
Of lavender and baked earth. Tenderness
Wafts from the hills and permeates the light.
You get it by the bottle or the glass.

You can't prolong this feeling, yet you must.
If life itself could only be your wine!
You feel not dulled, but heightened. Even dust,
Waltzing in sunlit motes, seems rich and fine,

And you feel you are better than yourself.
The mountains are your friends, the grass your home.
Why must this soaring pleasure be so brief
That, sooner than you've reached your car, it's gone?

Birds hop on empty tables, pecking crumbs
And tipping beaks into abandoned dregs.
Vineyards and flagstones steep in Napa sun—
A benediction, bright and plain. You beg

To live completely and a thousandfold.
Where are the vineyards when the way is rough?
If, deep inside you, there's a place to hold
A drop of stillness, will it be enough?

ELISABETH MURAWSKI

PORTRAIT: MADEMOISELLE BOISSIÈRE KNITTING

She is a guest in these rooms
of chintz and highly polished furniture.
A nephew's flat, perhaps.

Her needles click
like dripping water in a cave.
Mourning becomes her

complexion, weeds
bring out the rose. Her lower lip
protrudes. No angel

stands guard, preventing
her return to paradise.
Caillebotte

paints her like this, alone
with her knitting
in a world of gaudy wallpaper,

head down, forever
bending to her work
like a mare who's been broken.

UNEXPECTED POINT
OF INTERSECTION

From the top of a building or a mountain
a woman dives into a river.
She is wearing a long white dress
and the water is so clear
one can see the high heels of her white satin shoes
kicking her way through the water.

If she is a bride, she has lost the groom
and the entire wedding party.
If she is a nun wedded to Christ,
he is spectacularly absent from the scene.

Historically, any number of women
have drowned trying to swim
in voluminous skirts.

I admire her courage.
I honor her journey
as she works her way down
to the murk and silt
on the river bottom:
the braid and jowl of her fear.

I honor her
kicking her way deeper
in high white heels,
leaning over her fear in the dark,
no candles underwater.

I would like to believe
she does not drown.

That astonished by the light she found
many layers down,
the radioactive flexing
of her heart,
she surfaces, silvery
as a fish.

SHERYL L. NELMS
SUMMER WAS

Marysville, Kansas in the '50s

listening to the
KFAB Livestock Report
at noon
on Gram's Philco

eating bologna
sandwiches
with horseradish mustard

in the cool
north room

then hot afternoons
in the front porch swing
sitting
toe rocking

shelling green peas
thumbing
them
out
down the pods

air full of lilacs
thick and sweet
as sorghum syrup

brooding calls
of nesting
turtledoves
floating easy
through the mulberry trees

holy spirits of summer

AMANDA NEWELL
ELASTRATION

pooh the appaloosa
his favorite
could work any bull calf
away from its mother
he banded them
in the farmhouse kitchen
days later their balls
just dropped in the grass
hay or mud—
he said it was humane
no need to feel bad
they were too young
to know pain was pain

THE BLACK AND WHITE OF HIM IN HIS WETSUIT

Thin, cigarette
loose between
his fingers. It was

the day of Sicily.
Of frogmen
and the Mediterranean.

Of blue tattoos.
Before the Playa
Girón and whole

team gone.
Before blasted spine
and barely alive.

Before *go to hell*
on checks sent
back to the government.

If I had known him
then, had even been born.

ANNETTE OXINDINE
ON MATTER

*"[T]he difference...even between sentient and nonsentient matter...
is a question of degree more than kind."*
—Diana Coole and Samantha Frost, New Materialisms, *2010*

Everyone is talking about things
as if they were new planets.
Our microwave and French press,
unnatural allies, are interrogating us
about the new atomic clock. Make it stop,
my love, and pull me into the just you, into all
that won't outlast our new vase,
paid for because I use words
like *subjectivity* and *materiality*
instead of words that imitate matter:

Watch the light move across
                              then leave
                                        just one face.

Even the French press knows this, getting its liminal on
in the half-light of early dusk, making the whole
kitchen bend to its onlyness. The flowers, too,
the musk of still water like a dirge too soon.

JANUARY PEARSON
COLD EASE

Tissues white and puffed around my hips
    golden lozenges and candy-pink
        pills strewn about,

I am the spirit of someone
    once useful, floating
        above this color and motion—

papers rustling,
    backpacks zipping,
        eggs scrambling in a skillet.

Such a pleasant view
    from this cloud,
        not a clock ticking.

You, clinking forks in the sink,
me, a drugged queen slurring requests.

How I love this afghan,
    its drowsy wool,
        and the sticky sweetness of honey,

no rushing
    no shushing
        no tart remarks

just the pucker of lemon,
    the cool mint of eucalyptus,
        and the small ache

in my back from lying flat.
    I think of the sun-warmed sidewalk,
        the garden lavender no longer wet,

but I'm cozy in this fog,
    drawn away by my tea still steamy,
        light and wispy, swirling

through the den, out the window
     past sparrows and swallows
         and the blue, planet blue

to the star-smeared
     milky way
            of space.

KATE PEPER

LOVE IS AN AIRBORNE THING

—Gerald Stern

All I want is to sit cross-legged once more under our square grand piano* and hear the felted hammers rain music over my head as my mother's bare foot— her toes with a pink shimmer of polish—pumps the pedals. "House of the Rising Sun" is her favorite and though I don't know what that means, I think a house named after dawn is beautiful, just like her knees that bump the piano's edge every time she presses down and has to lean forward on the broken stool, the heel of her left foot raised for balance. Her nails never stop clicking the keys. During the loud parts I press my palms up to the instrument's belly and feel the wings of birds lift in one chord, and I no longer have hands but feathers. Everything—piano, mother, me—is risen.

---

* The Weber square grand piano was manufactured in New York in the late nineteenth and early twentieth centuries. It's known for its rosewood body, which was carved in the Victorian rococo style.

WHAT THE WITCH TOLD ME

I know how to find treasure, she said. Your *treasure, only for you.*

How? I asked.

Follow the birds. They'll be black. A murder of them flew east, where youth lives, orange and foolish. Wait until they roost, then put on your X-ray glasses. Look up into their bellies. Be sure your pocket knife is sharp. While they're cawing, slice the biggest one's belly open. It has to be the biggest.

I did what she said and trash scattered on the forest floor. I poked at it with my blade, some of it papery, some of it snagged in clumps. The dead crow rolled its eye and spoke, *Look closer.* Early Girls on the kitchen sill. My brother hinging a stamp into his collection. All the pets buried behind the pool. My father's hand I held after he died, the warm spot in his palm, size of a nickel. *This is not a dream,* the crow whispered.

MICHAEL PONTACOLONI
HAPPY BIRTHDAY

What a creek-side log to sit on,
this warm and easy freedom of adulthood.

Up to my ankles
in mud like cake batter.

Heron imitates a floor lamp.
Nickel of a beetle on my knee.

This water has melted before
and it will melt again.

Green warblers.
Staring contest with a turtle.

BARBARA ANN PORTE

WHY OLD WOMEN LEAVE THEIR MONEY TO ART MUSEUMS

Here's the thing—
if you die young—youngish—
say in your fifties,
life seems swell,
the children are grown,
gainfully employed,
at least most of them, with children
of their own, every one of them
adorable, and way above average;
naturally, then, when you and the hubby,
not yet deceased, draw up a will,
you have all their best interests at heart,
children's and grandchildren's, plus yet to
be born posterity—so many things haven't yet happened.

For instance: none of the children have yet gotten divorced,
moved on, on account of finding partners they like better,
with whom some of them have new children, though by now
they can no longer afford even the old children,
having nonsensically quit their well-paying jobs,
with benefits, to start up businesses of their own,
requiring huge and never-ending infusions of capital,
in the end, failing, as you could have predicted,
but didn't, not wanting to be accused of negativity.
So, now, on your own, you redraw your will,
your grandchildren's best interests at heart, plus yet to
be born posterity—so many things haven't yet happened.

For instance: none of the grandchildren has yet been arrested
for dealing in pot, or jailed for the same, or explained to you
how in Colorado what he did would be legal, or insisted
that a *General Equivalency Degree*, earned while incarcerated,
is just as good as a high school diploma; nor have any grandchildren
yet dropped out of college to become professional skateboarders
(with no health insurance), or a song and dance girl
in a nightclub in Shanghai; or a Sikh teaching English
in an Indian ashram. Nor have any yet had children of their own,
more or less the same ages as the newest grandchildren,
making some aunties and uncles while still toddlers, all of them
well above average and adorable, all of whose parents
expect you to babysit, while the parents go off to get
therapeutically essential, not to mention expensive, massages
and facials, or to "destination spas" for *Rest* and *Recuperation*.
"A person has to look good to feel good to be a good parent," they tell you.

"Yes, but what about me?" you say,
back aching from so much lifting of infants,
from low-to-the-floor, portable cribs, great- and
grandchildren all needing to be changed, comforted, fed.
"Well, there you go. Too late now," the parents tell you,
giving you hugs, as if to show they're only joking.

But old women know better. They redraw their wills,
leaving their money to art museums,
where once, long ago, they spent
so many tranquil moments.

ANA PRUNDARU
AWAY

again morning unravels
endless blocks
breaths cramped and nameless
downtown, someone's touch dissipates
to feathered orbits
planes descend in the neck of thinning harbors
earth clotting to a jar of fish bones
on the rooftop, I thread my homesickness
through purple tulips
stitch just enough patterns to soften
concrete lines to a swoop of sandy hills
because my fingerprints
hang like pendants from telephone wires
is not to say the gust won't take me to a borderless field
that I enter like buffaloes
pavements billow with rising thorns of heads
at night
the sweep of silver-tongued snow
bandaging space as it moves through time
my tulips and I overturned
shifting homeward

INDIAN SUMMER

the pulse retreats paralyzed
walls digging into whalebones
we curl away from the day

frail like straw dolls
dream of disfigured fireflies
purple breaths

electrical fields melting the sad
cicadas, squatting
on our palms

all species dying before
they process the spilled narrative

the end of time
mine versus yours

equates a cacophony of wisdom
pooling
in a stone garden

KATHLEEN M. QUINLAN
RITORNELLO

It wasn't a convenient time,
rushing through central London,
not sure of my directions,
late for a meeting.

How could I have known

...that a sudden, unbidden memory
of your hands—square, balanced,
those little tufts of dark hair
between the knuckles, the warmth
in my hands as we giggled
between mouthfuls of fondant au chocolat—
could conjure
all of you?

...that you would whisper in my ear
amid the red buses on Victoria Street,
fill my nostrils
with that scent of spring soil,
press your long body against mine,
release harmonies
in a new tongue?

CHARLES RAMMELKAMP
SWANN'S WAY

Coming up the airplane aisle,
looking for her assigned seat,
an overhead storage bin,
like a kid at camp, or a refugee,
the pretty Asian college girl
clutched not just a book—
all the others held laptops,
e-readers, ear buds, "mobile devices"—
but a copy of *Swann's Way*.

I couldn't resist saying to her,
from the seat I'd already taken,
"Marcel Proust! Hey, I'm impressed!"

The girl blushed, looking at her book,
then over her shoulder at her boyfriend,
a pudgy white guy, likewise looking
for his seat assignment, overhead storage,
"He's reading it, too."
The boy rolled his eyes.
What's she doing with him, *anyway?*

During the two-hour flight,
I glanced at her in a seat across the aisle,
her head bowed over the paperback,
and I remembered Aika Morita,
a girl from my college days
I never quite worked up the nerve
to ask out on a date.

After we'd landed, recovered our bags,
idled in the aisle, waiting to exit,
I heard the girl, behind me, exasperated,
"All he does is take a walk at Combray,
admiring the hawthorns!"

"No way I'm reading that book,"
the boyfriend declared.
What a douche!

I felt so keenly then how
I could never recover that lost time.

TYRANNY HAS A WITNESS

"What's your ball cap say?"
At the Jewish nursing home
an elderly pair has just joined me
on the elevator going up.
I am here to visit a friend.

Frail as an insect,
his shirt bagging away from his thin frame
like a husk, the shrunken man,
at least a foot shorter than I, and stooped,
points up at the hat on my head
like a birdwatcher spotting a warbler.

"Tyranny has a witness," I answer.
"I got it from Human Rights Watch.
They wanted a donation."
I generally avoid bumper stickers,
T-shirts and slogan-plastered caps
for just this reason,
as if I were suddenly a spokesman
for a candidate or a cause.

The fragile old woman with him
cackles like a radio coming to life.
"It needs more than a witness,"
she declares, a once-shrill voice
gone now to a kind of static-y hum.
"It needs a bomb, or an army."

I chuckle to humor her
My God, this elevator is slow!
That's when I see the faint numerals
tattooed on her bony wrist.

MICHAEL RATCLIFFE

THOUGHTS WHILE SITTING ALONG THE LOWER POTOMAC

Power is in the wind and waves.
Seen as an eagle circles over the water,
felt when easing a hook out of the mouth
of a fish too small to keep.

Days are measured in bushels,
and in the size of jimmies,
rockfish, and blues,
and the ones that got away.

The only monuments
are stacks of crab pots,
piles of oyster shells;
an old deadrise sunk in a creek.
Marble is reserved for the graves
of watermen when they no longer
go out in boats at dawn.

We may think all that is important
lies upriver, along grand avenues,
in meeting rooms and marbled halls,
but everything flows in this direction;
the lower pulls down the higher,
the Way overcomes from below.

ALAN C. REESE

A STATION OF THE CROSS

Yesterday I saw Ezra Pound
in the snow, standing at his mailbox,
his dark pea coat draped over his shoulders
like a cape in a cosmopolitan sort of way,
his hair wild and white as the landscape.
His pointed goatee satanic in design,
his spindly spidery arms reaching inside—
Was he sending hate mail to history
Or expecting a message
of forgiveness from the future?
He turned to look at me as I passed by—
His skull head a pale blossom
on the black bare branch of the metal box.

VIRGINIA SMITH RICE

PRE : LIGHT

red caught in curtains, the first

and only color in the immense
tenuous room

(this is no temporary impairment)

no other tint : no form : no shadow
here, beneath wrists still dissolved with night

even you, next to me, I name
only by your quiet, particular heat

if engines exist, or tires pressing warm
grit pavement, they exist as a sound

tactile as red : a grid quilted (6 across,
7 down) and hung on fat plaster

my body machines and flattens day : it
breaks slowly
                    back to something infinite-

simal and whole : the place inside a seed pearl
clasp lost between floorboards

I bridge the air's static drift
with decades of bright, extraneous detail (6
across, 7 down)

and slip from this stillborn waking,
                      a hook

that lifts me less
and less where I want to go : close and
open : red   open : red   open : red

DERELICT, KEROSENE

No more quiet now that deafness has bent
the left inner ear. Noise folds inward like a rosewood trick box. My body refuses to apologize. Night spirals, a
calliope whine and whurr *:forte* *:piano* *:morendo*   *Repeat.*

At the derelict carousel, that horse and blue plastic saddle—
we were happy then, perched in the stirrups, for whole
moments at a time, mimicking crickets with their dry, vertical
kisses, rain like a catechism turning the warm earth

slowly to mud. Now, November scrubs us kerosene-clean,
baring our Sunday faces. Inside each voice, a bell.
I watch everything and avoid eye contact. Tangled in red

chokeberry, the house is a way of remembering. Brick sponges sun
and breathes heat into evening. Bless this filthy wrist, the bitter
flame thicket, our ceiling stripped, unfinished.

GLASS FLIGHT

Inside the mirror, that sea
filled with mismatched sorrows,

ceilings press us to bring back our lives
and try them on, one by one.

Be careful with touch (you have to)
so cold it burns like snow-melt cascade

and starts an endless internal tremor,
as when you are faced with a limit

the width of a knife blade
that you choose not to press against.

You choose. And the rot, the exhaust,
the rough exhalation of the street

falls away, and you lean
over the rail of a bridge that moves

faster than a body can balance, and empty
your pockets into the green foam

below, because you can no longer stand
the burden of anything,

not even the weight of this skin.

BEGIN WITH A DIAMOND (WELD, WELT)

(Still, there are creatures,
careful ones, overhead.
They set down their feet, they walk
green, red; green, red.)
—Elizabeth Bishop, "Night City"

Look at that! Contorting her way down
Court Street to float a feather in the air—

have you seen her more ridiculous
or singular? And at her age, too,

so determined not to be
sad. Those hands framing diamonds

and triangles, that yellow plastic
handle hooked over her arm.

Everywhere here, there is something to see.
At 3:00 this autumn evening, a man

falling from the sky is caught, skull sheared
by the truss of an iron bridge that spans

the gorge. The rest of him slides, ladder-
saddled, along elaborate trestles, red

buttons on his raincoat sleeve flashing,
gone. His voice stays behind—frozen,

fetal, weld and welt through each metal bent.
The people love it. How novel to have

their own sybil, a discarnate prophetic.
They ask question after question and answer

none of his. What could she do?
Only go to the bridge and mourn with him

his lost body. What could she offer?
Only to keep his voice company in its fade.

All the world's clouds gather overhead,
and nothing tries climbing night

silver anymore to that hidden moonlit hole.
Everywhere here, there is nowhere to go.

(Eyebrights shiver, they blink in the cold—
open, close; open, close.)

WILLIAM RIVERA
IN LOVE

To Seymour Gresser (1926–2014)

In Mexico you fell in love. Sculpture
took you by the lapels and French-kissed
you until the next images you cut so deep they almost
fainted in your arms.

You could have been a rabbi, endured Old
Testament trials. You turned to stone
until dust smothered you at 88.
To the end you consumed bacon and eggs, sausage,
buttered toast, belief in your god's power.

Your carved stones, your wooden panels, pieces
you brought to life. They remain. You've moved
from house to ashes. Life continues
just as you said it would.

KIM ROBERTS
THE FIJI MERMAN

*Mid-1800s, possibly from China, from the collection of the
Zwaanendael History Museum, Lewes, DE*

The fish tail has lost its caudal fins,
the end like the stub of a used cigar.
But a bit of the dorsal fin remains,
standing upright in coarse spikes.
The sailor who made him knew his craft:

the fish tail joins the body
seamlessly. The torso is corrugated,
carved in oak, part rib cage, part wave.
Emerging from the torso are the shoulders,
secured at a later date with black string,

and little shriveled arms: one supports
the body atop its frightful claw,
the other ends in a stump.
Most horrifying is the monkey head,
its mouth stretched open in a grimace.

He has tufts of gray hair
on his scalp and elbows,
and glass eyes round as buttons
that seem to meet your gaze.
He himself looks amazed he's lasted this long.

Brittle, desiccated, his head has hardened
to a deep brown, and the tail to a mottled,
lusterless gray, all the oily rainbows lost.
But that mouth remains open,
little water-dragon in silent protest,

with something beastly like teeth,
stained ivory with a hint of white,
and something human
like a tongue, a hint of flesh
mute as shoe leather.

STEPHEN R. ROBERTS

PINEAPPLE WESTERN WITH SLOW POSSE

A lone tree, twisted into the wind along the horizon,
moves toward the camera under a hankering sky's memory.

The man with the pineapple on his head appears nervous,
yet his pert companion calmly undresses for an encore.

The couple, from this distance dignified and charming,
stands in the shade of an ancient elm convulsed in rope.

Why a peach falls from the hanging tree the moment
the noose drops over a lower limb remains a mystery.

This gotta get solved by sunset, announce the cowboys,
cause our vittles will be served damn cold otherwise.

The man attempts to recall the purpose of his pineapple,
why he's where he is, and how he got in such a situation.

It's all done in flashback, with horses and a handgun—
a six-shot revolver taken off some plugged desperado.

Questions blossom over black branches like death rays
from a sci-fi flick blazing onto the other drive-in screen.

But this is second-tier Western, scarcely B-movie quality,
worth six popcorns once the concession stand closes down.

Now the slow posse rides into town to quell the townsfolk
who cry for justice, or at least an interlude in all the violence.

Seven shots are fired from somewhere out of camera range.
Lucky ones take cover behind pineapples, as the credits roll.

CATHRYN SHEA

A MARRIAGE NEXT DOOR

Let's not imagine the memory foam
of their mattress slowly reshaping itself
from the indentation of bodies,
headboard hitting the wall
the night before. The little death
they both enjoyed.

Let's not imagine her slippers
scaring up dust bunnies,
his flip-flops slapping after her.

Let's not deride her fit, the shrapnel of his stare.
And let's not gawk at her running to the car,
hair wet in a towel. She left
her purse in the kitchenette.

Imagine their wedding day, vows softened
against marble. The grain tossed on them,
sanctity bundled in the seed.
The way they were joined to be lost.

Their studio with its particleboard bookcase,
mismatched chairs and throw rugs,
windows painted shut, a glimpse of sky
over the gas station. Is there a spectacular view
where the mourning doves perch?

Imagine how they now commute to work
through other lives and micro climates.

If I decide to love my neighbors,
it will be when I am late for the bus,
one of them ahead of me bundled in layers
and having skipped breakfast.

May I not forget this world is hurting.

GREGORY SHERL

IN THE DINING HALL
AT THE OCD CENTER
AT CEDAR RIDGE

I ate a snickerdoodle. I loved myself dumb.

In the papers there's a picture of a plane that went away, except it didn't
just went away, it disappeared, except it didn't just disappear, 239 hearts
also disappeared, a black box, tray tables in upright positions, a teddy bear
crumpled into an arm crumpled into another arm, a bigger arm. Who holds the
bigger arm?

Every day a bullet lands in something too soft to ever have a reason to meet a
bullet.

GARY STEIN

THE STUTTERING ANESTHESIOLOGIST

His beard does not distract
nor his thick wild whiskers filter speech.
With much to convey, try to say:
"Propofol and lidocaine"
with your healthy voice.
He says, Open *wawide,*
wawawaggle the tatongue,
now dadadown,
testing for an open airway,
vital tunnel to the lungs.
Before the treasure hunter
snakes a hose up your butt,
syllables and sibilants multiply
faster than computers, and
is that his spittle sprinkling your gown?

Tell yourself a shower helps the harvest
whether peas or polyps. Tell yourself
one shitty day beats three years
of taunts he took in junior high.
He hovers close seeping night
into your veins. Forget
his complicated tongue.
Trust him to guard your sleep
and breathe for you while sharing
a fluent silence, his kind revenge.

TEEGARDEN'S STAR

It's a long commute from Annapolis to the Goddard Space Center.
You can't afford to gaze at the eternity overhead.
Even an astrophysicist must focus on the concrete canyons
and blinking lights—the small glass stars on earthly cars.

Fifteen miles away I can't find my damn glasses again.
Not on the night stand, or in the blue bowl on the marble table
in the foyer where memory placed them, and I don't know
if this is Alzheimer's first kiss on my bald head, the beginning
of the end, and whether I should call in sick again or call a cab
and go to work to provide a lesson in courage for the others.

Meanwhile, you survive the drive and, without even a dime-store
telescope or fancy nuclear-charged satellite equipped with
X-ray projectors, you discover a rare dwarf brown star
undetected although she hung in the universe
for billions of years, just waiting for this date
with you, and like a virgin bride she takes your name,
Teegarden's Star. Delicacy prevents me from asking
about the wild celebration that night.

Everyone knows a light year is a measure of the miles
light travels in one year: 10 to the 12th power times
5.8786625. But your star is more than 12 times further away
than that, a number streaking beyond the outer limits
of my Earth-bound calculator. And I once thought my wife,
a redhead from distant Richmond, was a rare find.

And I haven't found God yet either. Perhaps He's waiting for us
just a few light years beyond your star. And if He's there,
I'm sure he's proud of you for discovering another dwarf star,
drifting unappreciated and lonely for so long, and God must think
I'm a fool for losing those glasses again, in a tiny house,
so insignificant in the cosmos, and for making light of the light
you've shown on the vast interstellar universe, and maybe
He's so pissed off at me, that Alzheimer's is His judgment
and not merely my momentary lapse in focus like when I wore
a brown shoe and a black shoe to that important meeting.

So if you're such a hotshot explorer, how about finding my glasses?
And if that task is too mundane, not elevated enough for a
goddamn PhD from MIT with his own star, then God may be
out there sitting in His heavenly rocking chair, patiently waiting
(just as we have waited for Him), for a scientist like you
with a distinguished beard, much like His, and on his lap
He may be holding your celestial Nobel Prize or
if you're a Muslim, waiting to turn you loose with 42
more virgin stars. And maybe He'll offer you a cold beer
before asking, "What took you so long to find me?"

KURT STEINWAND

PANTONE LIBRARY OF COLOR

Keep the book in the dark,
so ink stays fresh as the day it was lithographed.
Choose an in-vogue tone, a statement. 405 U
taupe for that Lakeshore Chicago trip.
I prefer 123 C honeysuckle, or malachite green,
what Caillebotte would have chosen for his rainy Paris.

I hear about a pill like John Howard Griffin's,
that taken once daily alters the skin.
Pick your ethnicity, or make an entirely new line.
It would screw with statistics,
works like a celery stalk set in food coloring.
Pop in contacts for instant lizard lenses.

A black waitress at a Pensacola IHOP
blinks an azure 292 C, milky marbles in chocolate.
A queen I knew sunbathed for decades
until brown as saddle leather, then his nose fell off.
Rosacea blossoms over my paleness, 185 U
in papules and pustules. All hail the Pink Race.

FREE HUEY

1942–1989

March to the Lower Bottoms of Oakland
to a sidewalk outline where he was shot.
The stencil has since been pressure-cleaned
like renovated Edwardians of the block.

Proud in the photo, muscled tense as apartheid,
spear in his left fist, his right single-barreled,
in a high-back wicker throne on zebra hide.
He couldn't keep from killing, prowled

through Prescott fresh from Happy Time Liquors.
A floating black god by the time he staggered
to 9th & Chester, the corner church in a blank stare
at his body, carved African face shattered.

HOLLY STONE

THE LITTLE SNOW GLOBE PLACE IN OUR SOCIETY

In this time, there was a great stirring having to do with minorities and all kinds of people who weren't in power. As if shaken by some unseen giant, the swirls of this were felt all over the globe: from Tibet, where people immolated themselves like marshmallows in a campfire to protest Chinese rule, to California, where happy people agitated for the right to join lawfully with others like themselves, to Tiananmen and Tahrir Squares, or even Rio, where the ordinary stood up for the right of self-governance, self-expression, self-determination.

But there was another place... where it was as hushed as a windless snowfall. Sealed inside a little noise-canceling universe, tucked away on a shelf in society was a fragile art preserved as if it were opalescent confectioner's sugar in a silent pickle jar. The inhabitants didn't protest their condition. Many preferred their gently sheltered little world.

Sh-sh-sh...! It might as well be a secret society of whisperers in our bawdy democracy. Tiny expressions of beauty would flitter and sift onto poetry editors' desks, to be read, savored, and selected in an unseen shimmer. These worlds unto themselves had a product, beautiful little journals, which they issued unto others in their universe of dainty snowflakes, also scattered across snow globes perched in protected little spots (usually a dusty ledge of a sparkling university or collegial school in an agreeable small town with a sweet stream and a Board of Directors who put their stamp of approval on the idea).

These people were so used to being silenced in the lewd world of the tasteless candy shop that they would never even see themselves as a defrauded minority, denied their right to be read, heard, and discussed as if they were fully franchised members of the culture at large. At last here, they are getting the speaking-up-for they must have, and deserve. It is time to release the poems, unleash them like carrier pigeons fluttering free, cooing as peace-loving doves do. It is time for the artful and softly spoken to be heard.

If one were to lob poetic snow globes into the thick of a political rally, would the evanescence that resulted be like fairy dust and perfume? When the flurry of poems settled, would the world be a more artful, gentler place?

ADRIENNE SU
HOME BAKER

Bread comes to be expected, by yourself and others.
Particulate enters your nose. Art becomes chore,
your hair, clothes, the floor flecked with powder.

Give us this day means ongoing tyranny.
Having baked before marriage for the one you chose,
you pay to the end. Courtship is delusionary,

bread corporeal. In youth it was a nervous pleasure
to set out plates, shop, sip as you kneaded and simmered
for those you'd just met and those you'd known forever,

a sheet for a tablecloth. Now, despite furnishings, a loaf
has the heft of a gift, the hours a miniature life
not spent on a book or a song. Once, the doubling of dough

felt auspicious, as your hands' predictions of tenderness
grew intuitive, accurate. To nurture was virtuous,
the union of salt, yeast, water, and flour still miraculous.

MOBILITY

When I was learning to drive, the family cars were red, white, and blue.
My father drove a white Ford pickup, my mother a blue Honda Accord.
I inherited what the Accord had replaced, a dark red Dodge Dart.

I can remember the Dart's predecessor, a blue Dart,
but nothing before it by make and model. That it was blue
made blue a comfort. Later, when my mother retired the Accord,

she gave it to me, by then a twenty-four-year-old starving artist
in Virginia. It didn't last. The only replacement I could afford
was a used Toyota Tercel, stick, 100,000 miles. It too was blue

and not unlike a rescue dog, grateful, nimble, ready to start
in all weather. It seldom needed repair, unlike the Accord,
and adapted to many states, from its adoption in the Blue

Ridge Mountains to New York, Iowa, and Massachusetts,
where it was displaced by the only Honda CR-V on Cape Cod,
the CR-V being new that year, so there was just one color, blue.

By all rights I should have been shopping for a used Dodge Dart.
I was almost thirty and having just married a fellow writer,
showed no signs of prospering. But my parents, who said they could afford

it, insisted on the car as a wedding gift. Fast forward:
the car outlasted the marriage. Now forty-seven, tenured, intent on a non-blue
car, I take the kids on test drives, regaling them with stories of the Dart,

just as their grandfather, my father, gives up driving. My heart
hurts in the floor-model Prius, which at last I can afford.
Nothing I've created would have occurred without the blue

Dart, the red Dart, the white Ford, the blue Accord.
I order a Prius in Sea Glass Pearl, which my eye asserts
is ocean green, but on delivery, the kids declare it greenish blue.

MARC SWAN
WILD WEST

for Ronnie B. 6/21/53–11/29/2012

She's been to Kabul
She has squatted over hand-woven rugs
in tin-roofed houses
with bearded men
wearing tunics, loose-fitting pants

counting and stacking crisp hundred
dollar bills on a low table laden
with tea, dried fruit, sweets
for the Americans

They did not smoke the hashish
in thick dark lumps offered from
their side of the table

They did not eat the sweets
They counted cash and sipped
tea while unseen women and children
talked in dulcet tones in a nearby room

She remembers the women
Their only contact through woven
mesh—dark eyes searching

This was the night before the Russians
came to Faizabad

We talk of the Taliban
We talk of New York, Washington, D.C.
methods of war right out of Tom Clancy

She has a plan
Dress the commandos as whores
and when they enter
the camp—*Kill the motherfuckers*

JASON TANDON
MEMORY

A cotton bra
snagged on the knob
of a fallen tree
that lies across a frigid river,

left by a pair of teenaged lovers
who dashed
at the flickering sweep
of a bored patrolman's spotlight.

ADAM TAVEL
HOW TO WRITE A NATURE POEM

Begin with a tedious parade
of details, like how the mucus
squid picks a cave to spray
its eggs, or how the discovery
of cartilage in dodo knees
changes their presumptive diet
to the following kinds
of berries. Assume readers
enjoy being trapped
in the merlot-breath lecture
of a stranger's uncle, blocking
the bathroom door. Obsess
over color, being sure to name
your fancy crayons: carmine,
cornsilk, papayawhip.
If a person appears, make her
your daughter, resplendent
in a sundress, a symbol
for the awe we all need
to find in order to survive
the fourth stanza.
Remember the menace
of power lines, logging trucks,
uncut plastic ringlets
from a six-pack swirling
in the marsh. It should end
with an image of affirmed
endurance, like an interstate
where haggard drivers brake
until a gaggle of goslings
waddle safely from the road.
Make sure their mother
is dead. Make sure the runt
lags behind but catches up.

SMEAR

Brooding lunchless at a newsprint easel
I ran my hands over paint lids crusted shut.
Outside the rain-glossed pane I saw their bus
chug off to Baltimore, my classmates' palms
in rows of ghostly fog evaporating
off glass, one by one, like practice kisses
from an arm. I couldn't tell if their glee
was for Hayden's symphony or just the ride
away from Sister Bernadette
who catechized at her desk, muttering
she had no charity for charity
tuition brats who lost their field trip fee
like rotten Hophni. I opened orange to smear
a sky of trumpet angels flamed alive.

SALLY TONER

PROM AFTERNOON

There's this meme I couldn't resist.
"Name your vagina," it said, "After the last full movie you watched.
The Miracle Worker," I typed. "I'm not even kidding."
I'm a middle-aged high school teacher, mother of two,
so my audiovisual entertainment consists
of baseball games while grading papers and
Marc Maron's honest depiction of addiction
late on Thursdays after the girls have retreated
to their own Netflix binges and conversations
we trust are mostly not inappropro
but you never know.

As for me, I shared that meme and response with Miracle Number One
on her prom afternoon. She looked up
with my younger eyes and her father's full-lipped smile
and sighed. "Oh my God, Mom. I never want to get old!"
I want to tell her that last night I dreamed
of squeezing milk from my breast by hand. I recalled
it all—the heaviness, the wetness in my bra when
she cried, and the stream of warmth spilling over
fingers like a voice over cell.
The relief—the release—the necessity when the heart weighs
so much. But I'll save that tale for now.

She'll do her hair alone, as she's asked,
and borrow my high heels that don't quite match
her dress before she tromps on down
to the neighborhood square for pictures,
trying her best not to slip.

WHEN YOUR HEALTHIEST RELATIONSHIP IS WITH THE GPS

Make a legal U-turn
"But I promise this is faster."
In 500 feet, turn right onto Charles Street
"You're sending me in a circle."
No I'm not.
"Why can't you trust me?"
In 300 feet make a legal U-turn...why did you ask me in the first place if you already knew where you wanted to go, dumb...ass?
"Seriously?"
I don't like your tone.
"Are you kidding me? Since when do GPSs curse?"
Since when do people ask for directions when they already know the way to their destination, GENIUS?
"This is ridiculous."
Now who's name calling?
"I didn't say YOU were ridiculous."
That's mother/teacher speak. I know your game.
"Uh, huh."
I'm smarter than that.
"You're a piece of satellite software."
Now that's just hurtful.
"Oh. My. God."
I cannot connect you to this party. Who do you think I am, Siri?
"I should just run into that concrete barrier right now."
See, you don't respect me, or my sense of humor.
"Really."
One second...in a quarter of a mile, make a right turn.
"Nope. Staying on Route 15."
*OK, if that's the way you want to play it...REROUTING...*The screen goes black.
"Oh really, the silent treatment?" Cue the drum of the engine and pop radio turned up to 8.
"Hmm. 30 might be better if there's traffic." She taps the GPS screen, and it stays dark.

"Helloooo?"

Hello, Dave.

"Very fucking funny. You know that movie is only worth watching for the last twenty minutes."

Agreed. Merge onto 30 East in three-quarters of a mile.

"Are we good?"

We are good.

"By the way. Me disobeying you just shaved half an hour off this trip."

Don't even start. New traffic pattern ahead...a beat...Be sure to use voice commands while driving. Use caution and be alert to your surroundings.

"Did you just reboot?"

I thought it would be best.

"Whatever. You be you."

I feel small when we speak in hashtags.

"Here we go again."

ERICK VERRAN
MAIDEN VOYAGE

He chews a date
in the 1940s—

his bicycle leaned
against a sycamore,

a cup of breakfast
between half-moon

cusping shoes.
Dust jackets name

the boy England's
earlier Holden, now

Middle Orchard's
plumage of bone.

MICHAEL WATERS
MCSORLEY'S (1969)

est. 1854, NYC
"Good Ale, Raw Onions, and No Ladies"
In 1970, McSorley's was forced to admit women

Stunned comprehension seeped into your face
As spittle distorted the lips of louts

Who rained balled napkins and sodden sawdust
Onto your hair when you entered the door.

You withstood that barrage, stared down each sneer,
Then stepped back out onto E 7th Street.

Fifty years later, I still remember
The portent of rage igniting your cheeks.

PSYCHOLOGICAL SIT-UP

Usually a bully & proud
Of his athletic prowess who
Brags about how many
Push-ups lunges curls
How many & how fast
He can muscle them
So you say in a low voice
"Bet you can't do
A psychological sit-up"
& everyone nods & he's *wtf*?

Mind over matter you insist
If conditions are right
& he's like *no way*

So you bet a twenty
& he lies on a mat
In the now-darkened room
A towel shrouding his face
Ringed by roommates swaying
Like prayer-drunk monks
Chanting
You can't do it you can't do it
& he's all torqued up
You can't do it
Feverish & coiled
While someone drops trou
To squat over him
Another yanks the towel
& he flings his face upward
Smack!
Right into that wall of ass
Then jumps up fists windmilling
But he's subdued by the circle
& of course by the twenty
Because laughter's always worth it
& there's a fee for cruelty
So dorm life returns to normal
But it's the metaphorical
That worms into your ear
You can't do it
The caul wiped from your brow
You can't do it
The veil swept from your eyes
Then the plunge into the world's
Wide existential asshole
Marriage work kids divorce
This brief life
Ringed by laughter ringed by cruelty
You can't do it

ANNE PIERSON WIESE

BIRD ON BARCK STREET

My father was given a BB gun, like
other boys in town. On Barck Street
he took aim at a robin—for fun, to see
if he could—and brought it down.

He never used the gun again,
although it stayed around
the house while he grew up
and went away and people died.

The lost and found of life has no
premises. We're in it before we
realize, touching what we thought
was gone. Angrily my father asked,

Where did this come from?
And handed me the gun.

OUT OF REACH

My walk to swim at the YMCA takes
me along a road full of traffic—walking
in this small city is for weirdos and the poor.
I didn't notice the old apple tree inside
the chain-link fence before the apples started
to drop—most of them into the uncut grass
around the tree, a few onto the pavement
where they smashed on impact for ants and wasps.

They looked so good to me, but my hand wouldn't
fit through the fence, or beneath it. Once, the wind
carried down an apple in my path, its bruise tender
as a rusty dime. I ate it standing there, while people
in cars stared and one guy yelled something smart.
Such secret sweetness demands feet and heart.

PAMELA MURRAY WINTERS
OLIVER SCHROER'S LAST INVENTION

He gave it all away, the clothes, the books,
the thousands of tunes he plucked from the air
or got from the old fiddlers. What light he had
he pressed into the palms of schoolchildren.

I have his image, black on yellow, over my desk,
a stencil of his mohawked head, years before
the cancer: "Canada's tallest freestanding fiddler."
He left a video, not with music, in which he removes

his beard, not with a razor, but with his fingers.
Cycling through the styles, he gives them names:
the weird artiste, hair-basket, muttonchops, bulldog
after a fight, Scruffums the Beard-Boy. His last

invention, last instructional recording. *Finger shaving.*
It's easy, it's painless, you don't cut yourself.

Oliver Schroer (June 18, 1956 – July 3, 2008) was a fiddler, composer, and teacher, with
an eccentricity that almost matched his brilliance. The video of "finger shaving" is here: www.
youtube.com/watch?v=u3H_gE53RlI.

FIFTY-FIVE

I remember how my mother dropped
as if on an escalator to the wrong floor,
falling into the dark. Her bold flowers

became scraps of a faded spring. She
went gray. She started using phrases
like *Too old for it* and *Not*

appropriate. Did she know
that British meanness *Mutton dressed
as lamb?* And how I,

fifteen, all zits and tits and American Bicentennial
starry-eyed, insisted she could be
whatever she wanted, as she'd told me.

We wore costumes for the celebrations
that summer, pioneers, and maybe
that reset her delicate machine:

from there on out she was her old ageless
self. I remember these things as I look
in the mirror the day after my fifty-fifth

birthday and see decades of crooked
ponytails, dark circles I had at ten
and thirty-two, a scar that's been there

so long I don't remember how I got it.

CAROM

*Also known as ajwain, the spice called carom is consumed as tiny brown oval fruits,
which are often mistaken for seeds.*

I thought the seal was good, the contents secure,
just spice for a curry, but then the tiny
flying up and then the segmented
grains-not-grains and then
shock as I closed the tin,
threw it away,

but not before
my friend sniffed it (as had been
the occasion for my finding it, when
it surfaced on a cooking show, in a scone
or biscuit—and then my riffle through the herbs
and salts as I faintly remembered a long-ago exotic

gift, and then): what if she and I
had inhaled that illicit life and it were to grow? Our love

an infection, rampant with larvae and freed winged victories
and carcasses and the seeds

of something altogether different, aromatic
and strange, something
chronic we'd learn
to live with.

ALTOGETHER

My friend Linda is sitting on a balcony in Aviara
in the buff, she reports, as one does. That's why

they call it social media. Someone I don't know
asks her where he can get a buff, so he, too, can

sit in one. I guess it's better than "the raw" or
"my birthday suit": one too evocative of steaming

a turkey neck for the dog, the other pastel and smelling
of lit candles. I prefer the altogether, especially

for a warm climate. I had to look up Aviara, believing it
to be in Tuscany or near Lake Como. Alas, California

lends nudity a squeaky hygienic dullness, like LaLanne
or volleyball magazines. Or porn: turkey necks

again. But if the words we wrap ourselves in—Aviara!—
matter more than the places, the selves we make,

especially Linda's, matter altogether more than words.

ROB WINTERS
MAKE WAY FOR DUCKLINGS

Who doesn't love little baby ducks?
You love them. I love them.
Tom T. Hall must love them;
They probably paid for his house.

Most of all, children love little baby ducks.
They want to pat them, pet them, and hold them.

What if the baby ducks weren't so little?

If they were the size of fully grown Thanksgiving turkeys—
something between Whole Foods Organic and Butterball—
I suppose they would still be cute,
but beyond holding; perhaps you could still pet one
from behind a low fence...still so downy soft.
Perhaps in Texas, the kids might even like them better.

What if the ducklings outweighed the children?
We're talking 40...60...even 80 pounds
This is probably the turning point.
Not so cute anymore,
but still clumsy, and oh so very hungry.
"Ow! Mommy! It stepped on my foot, and it keeps pecking!"

Finally, consider the Nuclear Option:
Gargantuan postapocalyptic ducklings
the size of Godzilla and (my favorite) Gamera
hatched from eggs the size of Volkswagens
beating a 200-foot-wide swath of destruction
across Beacon Hill and right down State Street to Massachusetts Bay
brushing cars and shearing off façades with ungainly outstretched wings.
Parents will terrorize their children with cautionary tales
that all end with the same stern warning:

Make way for ducklings

VALERIE WOHLFELD

HIVE

Night consoles like the smoke of the beekeeper.
Screen to screen you touch her in the ether.
The great conceit: she is obsolete before you meet her.
Discreet deceit, while I sleep I let you keep her.

Ghost to ghost, house to house, hosts the anonymous lover:
screen to screen you hoard her, then delete her.
Hierarchy is heir of anarchy once the queen bee mates midair.
Death is counterfeit: "Empty Trash" summons the Grim Reaper.

You lure her, you spurn her—pleasure or dolor?
Forfeit of the girl distilled in pixels: who is captor, you or her?
Screen to screen you are the saboteur of each paramour.
She is complete with no heartbeat but your own to measure.

Themed scheme: each diva dies, survives, is purged or archived. Psychodrama
of the hive: mother to her murderer, the queen bee's zero-sum game.

HORSE LATITUDES

I am freed from love like the Sargasso!—
windless waters' waves disperse and wither,
tideless fronds knotted as the falcon's tied tether.
Great seaweeds green and red and yellow
like singing Sirens' deadly hair that lassos
sailors. This is the abyss—without weather
stale waters' wild weeds slither
like a green and yellow eye of hazel. Slow

sigh in the dying wind's voice silent-stopped.
Love is plumbed like the great doomed sea!
Slaughter's still waters where I drift,
I am jilted jetsam like the horses roped,
thrown overboard, freed to die in the sea.
Love's theft weaves its weft with the souls of the bereft.

EMMA SKY WOLF
FAMILIAR

Un-wellness crept up

so slyly I was still on the go
when our paces met. My velocity
synching to a molasses step.

In fact my shape-shifting companion
has always circled. Treading deceptive arcs.
Slit eyed, mewling. Butting me off stride.

An attention seeker.
Grasping me tight
in smoky breathing fur.

A live coat, with no known zipper.
Cutting off the bright
bite of the outdoors, or even just

the guts to get up.

MICHELE WOLF
RUNAWAY

I find no reminder as I wander the aisles of my mind's
Vault. I cannot recollect my transgression. My mother
Slapped my cheek with a crack so hard, my glasses
Slammed to the floor, bouncing once. Silent,
I pivoted toward the front door, leaving my chipped
Vision behind. I did not return to this address for a week.

A rock, I would realize decades later, is not opposed
To turning soft because it is unwilling. A rock
Is opposed because it is unable. I found another roof.
I received adequate food. I had no father. I had a mother
Who wanted not a child, but a rock. So I ran,
Doing what I knew best—I went to school, squinted
At the fuzzy blackboards, my underwear fermenting.

I returned to my mother's house to take care of my
Sisters: one twelve, one six. When I appeared at the door,
The younger one, with a whoop, hopped into my arms.
Until the morning I left for good, she was my shelter.

HOMELESS

You see what used to be your house, a black-shuttered
White box on a hill, the kitchen screen door creaking open,
Revealing the clothesline and raspberry bushes.
You bang on the front door, but nobody ever lets you in.
You still have words, unlike that patient swaddled
In bedsheets, barking with the keen of a wounded seal.

At the palm-framed hospital, before awaiting your daughters'
Return, you installed your dentures, a finishing touch you
Would flaunt like formal wear, a flourish for special occasions.
Your overnight rages had driven the seasoned bedside
Aide to quit before daylight. "We will be back," I promise,
Morning number two after your discharge, pneumonia

Cured, as you sit strapped to a chair beside the nurses' station,
Evicted from assisted living, declined by the tenth nursing
Home, each gatekeeper flinching at your condition. "Take me
Home!" you plead as I bend to kiss your forehead, touch
Your hair. "Which home, Mom?" I whisper. You wonder
How on earth you gave birth to this dodo. "Lois Avenue,"

You chide me, "in New Jersey," the Garden State you fled
When your husband had wasted to dead, winter's peak,
1961. Once we had buried you, I traveled to visit that box
Of a house at the edge of the woods, to see that steep hill
Frozen into my mind from sledding. After decades
Of weather, the hill had transformed to a gentle slope.

ANDREA WYATT
MARK ROTHKO'S PAINTINGS

for Christopher Rothko

Refrigerators!
      Big, squishy refrigerators!
his son's girlfriend called them,
or windows or screen
door portals into eternity
or the backyard which may be eternity,
smell of late summer grass,
of the grill,
smell of charcoal starter
and burgers;

There's Mark Rothko,
in the shade, at the corner of the house,
Sitting in a deck chair, smoking,
Watching his kids scream with joy
as they run through the sprinkler
drops of water shining in the August sunlight
thinking about his paintings,
      Big squishy refrigerators!

GALESVILLE

for Jim Clark

October, too late to gather much
Sunday afternoon walk to Tent House Creek
& West River across the dry grass,

I pull you from your books and conversation,
out to the lowering sky and brittle stalks of burdock and thistle,

October, wrapped in a somber woolen poncho,
stumbling to the river across the mounds of dried shell beds,
you point out walnut husks and name wild plants,

October, after the uncertain throbbing
of the summer solstice,
definite as pumpkins in the cornfield stubble,

October, old friends, we never ask the halting questions
in the warmth of the house,
but save them for the slow walk back.

1919

After the Great War, the Dardanelles
the Battle of Verdun
after the U-boats & dreadnoughts
after the reverberant sound
of bells ringing through the trenches
warning of mustard gas
after Zeppelins and the Somme
after Versailles
after the 7,781,806 bodies
had been counted
after our boys came home
from over there, the influenza scare
& a glacial unforgiving winter
we made our way, stately and thankful to Redland Baseball Park
in Cincinnati

nobody in Cincinnati thought the Reds had a chance

not Heinie Groh with six RBIs that
   season & was batting .310
not Dutch Ruether who won 19
   & lost 6
not even manager Pat Moran
the miracle man

nope
the Chicago White Sox were big time

Rothstein put in the fix
one slow uneventful summer day
when the ponies were sluggish

& the Sox were ripe for the plucking

Comiskey paid peanuts
refused even to discuss it
when the team, in desperation
sent in Kid Gleason, the new manager, to negotiate salaries,
he was great friends with the press,
though, laid on a fine spread—
great stories, he had great stories

while 35-year-old Eddie Chicotte
13 years pitching in the majors
might lose that arm tomorrow
after a year's record of
29 wins, 7 losses
made forty-five hundred a year
while Dutch Ruether, 26 years old
2 years in the majors, made twice that

while Buck Weaver was the 3rd
baseman even Ty Cobb
refused to bunt to

while Happy Felsch, Swede Risberg,
Chick Gandil, Fred McMullin & Lefty Williams had reasons
or didn't, & moved blindly
in that warm October sun

& there was big, dumb Shoeless Joe
Shoeless Joe Jackson
3rd highest batting average of all time
of whom a friend said
Joe's record is the best example
of what a man may accomplish in this
world, wholly without brains
it was Shoeless Joe
who heard the kid plead
say it ain't so, Joe

ended up playing New Jersey
with the Hackensack Nine
running a dry-cleaning business
in the winter

waiting for reinstatement
none of them ever played anything
but semi-pro & pickup
mostly, they went back to farming

the war was over
it wasn't the Reds won but
    the Sox threw it

ED ZAHNISER
NO MORE DUCT TAPE SOLUTIONS

Researchers find that some things can survive
black holes—like high-fructose corn syrup,
Red Bull energy drink, mint-flavored snuff,
textured vegetable protein, artisanal Pop-Tarts,
cheese puffs, tomato aspic, gourmet teriyaki

beef sticks, Ford Edsels, Studebaker Avantis,
MTV reruns, cinch belts, crinolines, bombers
with clips, executive sandboxes, Fox News,
spent nuclear fuel, American exceptionalism,
tanning beds, tofurkey, genital herpes, 17-year

locusts sleeping it off, and cockroaches (also
euphemistically called "very large water bugs")
not to mention Texas-winged cockroaches who
fly out open windows to wait out pesticides
or other lapses of interspecies hospitality.

Plagued by gray squirrels invading her house
our town poet laureate pulled the Saint Francis statue
out of her yard and put in a figurine of Dick Cheney
made *before* he had the heart transplant.

DEAR HELOISE, DEAR ABBY, DEAR SOMEONE

We had been settled in at the restaurant
maybe ten, fifteen minutes, on our first date.
Already I could tell she felt the time
passing slower than a kidney stone.
John Locke would have loved her face,
its complete *tabula rasa*, a slate so blank
it did not yet know the feel of chalk.
I should have ordered energy drinks,
Red Bull or something, to ream the energy
pathways like RotoRooter on amphetamines.
So far our relationship could be described
as "nipped in the bud," "atherosclerotic,"
or, optimistically, "molasses in January."
I thought of ordering snails for appetizers
to speed up the illusion of time's passage.
Marinated, they still could slither our table's
width like comparative Olympic sprinters
hyped on a new undetectable performance-
enhancing drug. "Nascent but hopeless,"
I thought. Then I asked her "Did you know
Venus is upside down and flying backwards?"
"No," she answered, "did you know dark chocolate
has flavonoids?" "Oh yes!" I all but shouted.
That was 42 years ago this May. Next month
we're expecting our first great-grandchild.

IF THEY ASK YOU

Tell them "thrust faulting" came from the Kama Sutra
not your bone-dry textbook for Geology 101. Say *maithuna*
(that *h* is silent like an owl's flight) and they'll hear
"small round cans of tightly packed fish" not
the bonding sex pose whereby she sits atop your lap
facing you while sundry excitations come and go
and 1960s Action Painters splatter Michelangelo
like Ken and Barbie Modernists. Say "Shakespeare suffered"
—can you call it that?—"from ADHD, maybe ADD."
They'll think about young Will's poor mother, not his sonnets.
Say *Berrigan*, and they'll divide into three groups:
78 percent don't know, 21 percent say "activist priest(s),"
1 percent says "second-generation New York poet"
although if fewer than 100 folks show up, no matter
what you say, no one pipes up "the New York poet."
Say nothing and they'll think you're flat-out wise.
That worked like a charm for Meher Baba.
A vow of silence, and unisex groupies flocked to him
like a tree full of starlings ganging up for flying south
with every last one carping about their travel agent
—or "Who's supposed to fund my energy budget?"
Baba Hari Das said nada as he scrawled tight aphorisms on
his slate like a Ralph Waldo Emerson mummy and
ate zilch but brown rice, lentils, and buttermilk:
"Small world/much peace." Give us a break, Hari.
But damn those starlings—millionous guano factotums
giving our black cat streaming video wet dreams.
That first hard frost, it can't come soon enough.

KELLY CRESSIO-MOELLER
CHRIST, DISCARDED

KELLY CRESSIO-MOELLER

ITALIAN CYPRESS SURFACES

KELLY CRESSIO-MOELLER

THE CENTURY PLANT
REMEMBERS RUTH ASAWA

GOODBYE JANE

(1991. In a secluded and wooded area a car is driving off-road, slowly and deliberately. Eventually it comes to a stop, the engine idling. The engine turns off and two men exit the car. Both are dressed in decent clothing that show signs of wear, mostly smudges of dirt on their pant legs and shoes dried in mud. They are in the middle of a conversation, opening the back passenger doors of the car and pulling out shovels. The older and more weathered of the two lights a cigarette while the other talks.)

GRAVEDIGGER #1: ...so she was selling all of her stuff. There are piles of tapes everywhere. And she is asking me questions like, "So I own *Cocktail*, does that make me a bad person?" And I said, "Yes, that does make you a bad person."

(His friend laughs. In the meantime, GRAVEDIGGER #1 pulls a large, heavy duffel bag out of the backseat.)

GRAVEDIGGER #1: That's not what she wanted to hear, man. Can I get a light, by the way?

GRAVEDIGGER #2: Come on. I told you to bring your own.

(He takes his lighter out of his front jacket pocket and tosses it to his friend. GRAVEDIGGER #1 lights up then tosses it back. Both are circling around to the back of the car now.)

GRAVEDIGGER #1: So you said this one was different?

GRAVEDIGGER #2: Yep. *(He begins to unlock the trunk.)*

GRAVEDIGGER #1: What's different?

GRAVEDIGGER #2: This one is a girl.

(He opens the trunk to reveal a large canvas sack, holding the body of a young woman. One bare foot hangs out of it. With some effort, GRAVEDIGGER #2 begins to pull on the young woman's legs, which begin to slide out of the sack. The body hits the forest floor with a thump.)

GRAVEDIGGER #1: Jesus, what happened?

GRAVEDIGGER #2: Nothing of consequence.

GRAVEDIGGER #1: What happened to her clothes?

GRAVEDIGGER #2: Oh come on, you're not that stupid, are you?

(It's quiet for a while. GRAVEDIGGER #1 begins to drag the body while GRAVE-DIGGER #2 removes the shovels from the trunk. They walk away from the car, making way to another secluded spot. Suddenly GRAVEDIGGER #1 stops walking.)

GRAVEDIGGER #1: You're not saying what I think you're saying, right?

GRAVEDIGGER #2: *(Stops walking as well.)* What?

GRAVEDIGGER #1: Well—

GRAVEDIGGER #2: Are you saying you don't want to bury her?

GRAVEDIGGER #1: I wasn't told we'd be doing *this*.

(GRAVEDIGGER #2 begins dragging the body again. GRAVEDIGGER #1 follows.)

GRAVEDIGGER #2: Listen, it's not like anyone we know did it.

(GRAVEDIGGER #1 looks away and grimaces, seeming uncertain, but his companion doesn't notice.)

GRAVEDIGGER #2: The reason I was told is that she was found on one of the family's properties. We're just trying to keep it out of the papers.

(They near a patch of open area. He begins to slow down.)

GRAVEDIGGER #2: We need to burn her stuff, too. It's in that bag you're holding.

(He drags the body a little further. CUT TO BLACK.)

(CUT TO: EXT. Forest—day. The two GRAVEDIGGERS are sitting on a log, a small fire burning nearby. Both are sifting through the woman's purse. GRAVEDIGGER #1 is thumbing through the photographs in her wallet, looking at pictures of the woman's friends and family. GRAVEDIGGER #2 is eating some of his lunch, also from the duffel bag.)

GRAVEDIGGER #1: She didn't have a boyfriend.

GRAVEDIGGER #2: Does it matter?

GRAVEDIGGER #1: I'm just wondering if someone will come looking for her, you know. Like her mom... I don't know. Her father. Her brothers. I mean, *somebody*.

GRAVEDIGGER #2: We both know no one's going to find her out here. And if they do, they'll just think it's one of those backwoods Ballards. You've heard the stories.

GRAVEDIGGER #1: *(Still looking at the photographs, not fully convinced.)* If she was my sister I'd try to find her. No offense, but I'd kill the motherfucker who did this.

GRAVEDIGGER #2: Yeah, back in the old days it was simpler. You'd find out who did it then pay a visit with your brothers, your father, your neighbors, whoever. You made sure he wouldn't do it again. *(A beat, then:)* You know, my grandfather said something once.

GRAVEDIGGER #1: What?

GRAVEDIGGER #2: "When an animal is that out of control, it's time to put it down."

GRAVEDIGGER #1: *(Scoffs.)* Like a dog or something?

GRAVEDIGGER #2: I'm just saying is that I would want to find out who did it to her too.

(He looks over at the body. Once again, a bare leg hangs out of the sack, resting on top of some leaves.)

GRAVEDIGGER #1: Did you look at her before she went in there?

GRAVEDIGGER #2: Why? You want to know if she's hot or something?

GRAVEDIGGER #1: No. It's just... it wouldn't hurt to know what happened to her. I want to know what we're burying. Don't you?

(GRAVEDIGGER #2 shakes his head then stares off in the distance.)

GRAVEDIGGER #1: *(Indignant.)* I don't want to know if she's hot... What the hell's wrong with you?

GRAVEDIGGER #2: This one is just like the others.

GRAVEDIGGER #1: No it isn't. That could be your sister in there. Or your mother. Or even worse. I mean, I have more respect than that and you know it. This isn't a hit, right? Here's someone who died in a really sick way. She doesn't have clothes on.

(They sit for a long, uneasy silence, not looking at each other. The fire crackles, still consuming what they've thrown in.)

GRAVEDIGGER #2: You know, it's strange. Malcolm told me she smiled when they found her.

GRAVEDIGGER #1: Really. She was smiling?

GRAVEDIGGER #2: Yeah. They found her on the grounds. You know that garden area near the back? Just propped against the wall, her legs sprawled out all funny in the dirt. He said he thought she was just sitting there. Then he saw she wasn't wearing hardly anything. Just her panties. She had put them back on at some point, I guess.

GRAVEDIGGER #1: Jesus.

GRAVEDIGGER #2: So he kneels down so he can see her face. He could see her chest moving, knew she was alive. And yeah, she smiled at him, like she knew him.

GRAVEDIGGER #1: Did she say anything?

GRAVEDIGGER #2: Yeah. She called him "John" or something. *(Pauses.)* Some other name. It doesn't really matter.

GRAVEDIGGER #1: Well, I guess we'll never know who that was...

(A beat, then:)

GRAVEDIGGER #2: Anyway, they tried to move her and blood poured out her nose. That's when he knew she had a head injury. She didn't have long.

(The two of them sit in silence again. GRAVEDIGGER #1 gets up and reluctantly throws the rest of the woman's belongings into the fire. He looks over at the body, walks up to it, then lifts the edge of the sack, looking in.)

GRAVEDIGGER #1: That's a waste. *(He shakes his head, steps away.)* What a waste. Just a waste. *(He sits down on the log again, rummaging through the duffel bag. He pulls out a beer and begins to drink.)* We'll never know.

(They lapse into silence again. Suddenly the camera pushes past them to reveal that the body of the young woman is sitting up in the sack. She gets to her feet, still covered. Without revealing her face, the girl pulls the sack down around her shoulders, as if ripping a hole, then holds herself as if she's cold. As she moves, it becomes evident that she is alone in the woods. The gravediggers are nowhere to be found. She walks away from the spot. The girl has her last, solitary moment when suddenly the sound goes out and there is a CUT TO BLACK.)

(CUT TO: EXT. Forest—day. The two GRAVEDIGGERS are almost finished digging a deep enough hole. A large pile of dirt has accumulated and the body lies nearby, a foot still visible. The two converse while they continue to dig.)

GRAVEDIGGER #1: You know, I'm beginning to wonder if we're just as bad as the bastard who did this to her. I wouldn't only kill him. I'd kill both of us too. I think it's just a shitty thing we're doing.

GRAVEDIGGER #2: How is it shitty? It's a job!

GRAVEDIGGER #1: I mean, we're burying this innocent girl just because she died in the wrong place.

GRAVEDIGGER #2: Just a *job!* Dirty work, but a job.

GRAVEDIGGER #1: She should be put somewhere where she can be found.

GRAVEDIGGER #2: *(Stops shoveling.)* What? Are you crazy?

GRAVEDIGGER #1: *(Doesn't even make eye contact. He continues shoveling and is already shaking his head regretfully.)* I know... I know... Forget it. Just forget it.

GRAVEDIGGER #2: You do that and you will *definitely* get what's coming to you. I can guarantee that. Do you think the people we're dealing with are stupid? They said it would be bad for business. We can't have that, all right? No one is going to want to go there if they know.

GRAVEDIGGER #1: It just feels wrong, man.

GRAVEDIGGER #2: You want to climb up the ladder or do you want to be doing shit like this forever? Or worse? This is what you signed up for.

(Both go back to digging for a moment, then:)

GRAVEDIGGER #2: Who knows. For all I know she could have gotten what she deserved.

GRAVEDIGGER #1: Fuck you. She might have just been walking home.

GRAVEDIGGER #2: *(Stops shoveling again.)* You know what? Just do me a favor and shut the fuck up. We've got work to do. It doesn't matter if she was just walking home or put a hit on herself or whatever the hell happened out there. No matter what, we're going to put her in the ground.

(GRAVEDIGGER #2 climbs out of the grave. GRAVEDIGGER #1 looks up, still talking.)

GRAVEDIGGER #1: There's no need to get all pissy about it.

GRAVEDIGGER #2: We're alive. She's dead. End of story.

GRAVEDIGGER #1: Why are you stopping?

GRAVEDIGGER #2: We've dug enough.

(He is walking towards the woman's body and is preparing to move it toward the grave. He slips his arms under her, lifts her weight, and begins carrying her. In the meantime GRAVEDIGGER #1 watches.)

GRAVEDIGGER #1: If you don't care about this then why are you holding her like that? You never hold them like that.

(For a moment the two men just stare at each other.)

GRAVEDIGGER #1: If you're really that pissed, why don't you just throw her on the ground or drag her like the others?

GRAVEDIGGER #2: If you don't shut up I'm going to throw her on your fucking head.

GRAVEDIGGER #1: Go ahead then.

(GRAVEDIGGER #2 seems tempted for a moment, but instead sets the body down and disappears from sight.)

GRAVEDIGGER #2: *(Offscreen.)* Fine. Let's get this over with.

(For a while nothing happens. GRAVEDIGGER #1 starts to look concerned. He climbs out of the grave.)

GRAVEDIGGER #1: What are you doing?

(GRAVEDIGGER #2 is rummaging through the large duffel bag. He removes a shirt and pants from it and walks back toward the body. He then tosses the clothes next to it and kneels down on the ground.)

GRAVEDIGGER #2: Help me pull her out of here.

(GRAVEDIGGER #1 does as he says, kneeling at the woman's feet while GRAVE-DIGGER #2 holds onto her torso from behind. Together they slip the sack off of the woman's body, revealing an almost entirely nude corpse. As described earlier, all she has is her underwear and nothing else. Rigor mortis has set in. With some effort GRAVEDIGGER #2 props her body up and picks up the shirt.)

GRAVEDIGGER #2: I'm sure this will be the only thing that will get you to shut up. We'll give her some dignity and that's it.

GRAVEDIGGER #1: These clothes... you sure no one will miss them?

GRAVEDIGGER #2: This is the least we can do. Besides, it's just clothes. It's not like they're traceable or anything.

(Together the two men work together to slip a button-up shirt on the body. GRAVEDIGGER #1 takes care of the buttons. Halfway through he stops, looking down at the body of the woman as if he is going to be sick. He starts retching.)

GRAVEDIGGER #1: This is fucked up.

GRAVEDIGGER #2: We can't stop now. Let's finish it.

GRAVEDIGGER #1: I can't believe this...

(He finishes the shirt. With some effort GRAVEDIGGER #2 helps his friend lift the body's legs so they can put the pants on.)

GRAVEDIGGER #1: I think we're going to have to stand up for this one.

(Both of the men pull the body up.)

GRAVEDIGGER #2: I'll do it.

(GRAVEDIGGER #1 stands up and holds the body from behind, propping her up. GRAVEDIGGER #2 begins to slip the pant legs around her feet when he realizes blood and waste has begun to drip down the body's legs.)

GRAVEDIGGER #2: Fuck! Fuck!

(He quickly pulls the pants up around her waist and steps back, the corpse's blood on his arms.)

GRAVEDIGGER #1: Jesus, are you OK? I didn't know that would happen.

GRAVEDIGGER #2: God-*fucking*-damn it!

(He panics, wiping his hands on the corpse's pants, then points at his friend sternly.)

GRAVEDIGGER #2: You aren't telling a soul about this, understand?

GRAVEDIGGER #1: Yes.

GRAVEDIGGER #2: Not a word.

GRAVEDIGGER #1: I won't say anything!

GRAVEDIGGER #2: OK. Good.

(He gingerly removes the body from his friend's arms and, getting down on his knees, places it on the ground again, lying face up.)

GRAVEDIGGER #2: God, I wasn't expecting that... *(He laughs nervously, then becomes quiet, trying not to look at the corpse's face. After a while it seems he is more than a little shaken by what happened. He attempts to wipe off his arms on the sack. Then he stops.)* They fucking destroyed her ID, did you know that?

GRAVEDIGGER #1: There was no ID in her purse, if that's what you mean.

GRAVEDIGGER #2: They took it right away, just to see her last name. To see if she was somebody, but she wasn't. So they destroyed it right in front of me. *(He angrily throws down the sack, disgusted.)* You're right. This is fucking sick.

(CUT TO BLACK.)

(CUT TO: EXT. Forest—day. Both men are lowering the body into the hole and lying it prostrate at the bottom. Suddenly GRAVEDIGGER #1's pager begins to beep.)

GRAVEDIGGER #2: Could you turn that off?

(GRAVEDIGGER #1 struggles with this. It's obvious he isn't familiar with how to do it, but eventually the beeping stops. The men climb back out of the grave, panting, then look down at the body at the bottom of the grave silently, taking their shovels in hand.)

GRAVEDIGGER #2: Not to be sentimental or anything, but something occurred to me this morning, you know, when I was putting her in the car.

GRAVEDIGGER #1: And what was that?

GRAVEDIGGER #2: The asshole who killed her is the last thing she'll remember. The last thing she saw.

GRAVEDIGGER #1: That's not true. What about Malcolm and the others?

GRAVEDIGGER #2: You know what I mean.

GRAVEDIGGER #1: I think she saw us. We count.

GRAVEDIGGER #2: You want to say something?

GRAVEDIGGER #1: I don't know. Do you?

(GRAVEDIGGER #2 looks down at the body. Both men stand awkwardly but respectfully, clasping their hands reverently and bowing their heads.)

GRAVEDIGGER #2: Here lies, uh, Jane Doe... We hope she understands that we tried to do the right thing. We know that what happened to her is not fair. We wouldn't wish it on anybody.

GRAVEDIGGER #1: Amen.

GRAVEDIGGER #2: *(Confused.)* Amen.

GRAVEDIGGER #1: I didn't know what else to say.

GRAVEDIGGER #2: I won't hold it against you. *(He picks up the first shovel and scoops up some dirt.)* Good night, Jane.

(He tosses the first pile of dirt down into the grave. Before it hits there is a CUT TO BLACK. END.)

KELLY CRESSIO-MOELLER
PALM DUNK

KELLY CRESSIO-MOELLER

JESUS TAKES A BREAK
FROM THE WORLD

KELLY CRESSIO-MOELLER
LEMON FINGERS

ISAAC JAMES BAKER
BURY ME IN SMOKE

I was out of place, wearing shorts and a Darkthrone T-shirt, sitting in the lobby bar of the W Hotel in New Orleans. The men gathered around in handfuls sported pinstripe suits and painfully shiny shoes, while the women wore modestly cut dress suits and heels. Among this crowd of lawyers, my clothes and tattoos betrayed me as a trespasser. I had no business being here.

My girlfriend did, though. She came to speak at an American Bar Association conference. I was here because I'd never been to New Orleans, and the room was already paid for. She was buried in meetings for the entire day, and I was alone and free. So I sipped chicory coffee and gathered my thoughts before setting out to explore the French Quarter.

He stuck out just as badly. In a sea of suits, some ungovernable force drew the two tattooed dudes together. He was standing against a pillar by the elevators, wearing an old Eyehategod shirt, his hands in the pockets of his camouflage cargo shorts. Upon spotting me, he strolled over.

His skin had a leathery look, and his arm hair looked bleached and bristly. His tattoos had a dull, sun-roasted quality to them which made them look all the more authentic. The ink was all black, seeped in that American traditional aesthetic—skulls, crossed bones, a sailing ship, a snake wrapped around a dagger.

"Hey man," he said as he held out his hand.

He had a tense grip to his handshake. "Hey," I said.

"What are you doing here?"

"I don't really know," I said. "My girlfriend's a lawyer, so she's here at this conference. I just tagged along."

"No shit? My girl's a lawyer, too. Same conference."

I'm sure my face gave away my surprise.

"You ever been to N'Orleans?"

"Nah, man," I said. "First time."

"Yeah? You'll fuckin love this town. Guaranteed."

"I already do," I said, patting my stomach. "I ate the best damn muffuletta sandwich of my life last night."

The man let out a rough laugh. "Your first time to N'Orleans, so course it's the best damn muffuletta you had."

"The food here, man..." I said with a tone of deep respect, letting him pick up the thread.

"Food here is straight spiritual, man," he said. "So, what are you up to? Besides sitting here with all these suits?"

"I was thinking of checking out some cemeteries," I said. "But I'm not sure where to go. Haven't really thought it all through. And I don't have a car—so now I'm wondering if I should rent one..."

"Fuck that man, I'll drive you." He stood up. "My truck's like two blocks away."

"Wait, you know some good cemetery spots?"

"I know tons." He grinned widely, showing a chipped front tooth. "I dig graves."

"Cool, man," I said, unsure.

"I mean, physically, for work, like digging holes and putting dead bodies into them."

I stood up. I grabbed my paper cup of coffee, checked for my cigarettes, and adjusted my cap. "Let's go."

His name was Dave and he was New Orleans born and raised. He played guitar in a few doom and sludge metal bands, none of which sounded familiar. But I gave myself a pass because New Orleans was home to more metal bands than pretty much anywhere in the country, and I could only keep up with a dozen or so.

We walked through the hot streets of the Warehouse District until we reached his rust-red Toyota pickup. The air was sweaty and the sun showed intense focus as it roasted us from above. Of course, we were both wearing all black.

The car jumped as the engine kicked and Dave gunned it down the street. He drove under the highway and past some abandoned buildings before catching up with St. Charles Avenue. The air conditioning didn't work, so we rolled through the Garden District with the windows down. Out the window, I watched a fascinating blur—trees and power lines tangled up in Mardi Gras beads, an anarchic public art display of gold and green and purple. Gray clouds of Spanish moss floated on by.

And I thought that everything seemed to fit; all of the seemingly contrasting elements came into place together, and even though I was a stranger in this city, the place itself seemed to extend a personal welcome to me. Dave silently lit up a joint, hit it, and passed it my way. As I smoked hard, Dave turned on the stereo, and to my perfect delight he blasted Down's album "NOLA" on crackling speakers.

As we drove on, I drifted into a euphoric state that was specific to that time and that place and that level of intoxication. New Orleans had consumed me, but I was alive and kicking, and while I was down here, I wanted to see the city's guts.

Our first stop was a grandiose cemetery surrounded by tall iron fences. The place was massive, the size of a dozen city blocks cut into sections by winding paved lanes. Black limousines crawled between the mausoleums, sometimes hearses followed, shiny, black, elegant ones.

"How much does it cost to get one of these things?" I asked, pointing to a row of crypts.

"A fuck-ton. Like a hundred K for the smallest ones."

"Christ."

Most of the crypts were gaudy with ornamentation—designed to commemorate overcompensating rich folk. One marble-pillared monument had a massive sphinx head on top. My favorite was the ten-foot-plus sepulcher of a Celtic cross, which closely resembled the one tattooed on my left forearm. The carvings in the marble were so exquisite and intricate, and I wondered who was buried there, whether they planned out the design themselves before death. Or maybe it was the artist's idea and he got paid a lot to carve something truly monumental.

David said: "This cemetery is basically a posthumous pissing contest. No one wants to be the bum at the final party. Don't get me wrong, these things pay the bills. But I'm not a fan of this scene."

Greenwood Cemetery wasn't far away, so we hit that next. Dave explained Greenwood started off as a working-class burial ground, although plots had become really expensive in recent years. In the mid-1800s, apparently, NOLA suffered an outbreak of yellow fever, which killed a few thousand residents. Greenwood exists because the city needed more space to put all the dead bodies.

Greenwood lined up with the picture of "New Orleans cemetery" I had in my head. The knotted cypress trees, the more modest crypts shaped like tiny cottages, the prayer candles and plastic beads on the front stoops. I walked off on my own, snapping pictures of dried floral arrangements and tombs bearing Scottish and Italian names.

After a half hour or so later, Dave caught up to me. "You wanna see the grit? The raw stuff."

I didn't know what "the raw stuff" was, but I gave him an enthusiastic, "Fuck, yeah."

It seemed like the worst possible place to bury your dead: less than a mile from the river in a muddy floodplain just beyond the levees. But the bodies of those unfortunate enough to die in this neighborhood had nowhere else to go. Higher ground was far out of reach.

Dave said this was a cemetery for poor bastards. To get here, Dave had driven down potholed streets lined with shotgun houses. Old men in straw hats sat on porches, some waving as we passed, some constant in their blank stares. From the dirt road, the cemetery looked more like one of those out-of-the-way spots locals used as a dumping ground for old tires and busted refrigerators.

I spotted an old man sitting under the shade of a weeping willow along the edge of a collapsed fence. He pushed himself up slowly and wobbled a bit before walking toward us. He called out but it sounded like a hacking cough.

"What's that, old man?" Dave said, disarmed.

The man stepped into the sunlight. His face was carved with wrinkles and his eyebrows were long and wispy. "You gentlemen ain't here to pick for bones, are yas?"

Confused, I turned to my gravedigger guide, hoping he would say something, hoping the two locals would sort out whatever was brewing.

The old man pointed to my forearm, and I immediately realized the cause for his concern. I have a broken bone tattooed across my right arm. It has nothing to do with digging up human skeletons—more like a reminder of the busted human condition or something. But given this scene and our place within it, I couldn't fault the old man for assuming we were trouble.

"Nah, man," Dave said. "We respect the dead."

The old man explained that he was a Baptist preacher at a church down the road. He was here because some voodoo followers were conducting a religious ritual in the cemetery. The preacher had taken it upon himself to guard the cemetery to make sure "no evil stuff" went down. We both nodded, but the preacher offered nothing back.

Dave stepped toward the man, his head slightly bowed. "I work in the end of life business, man. You ain't gotta worry about us."

The preacher smiled, revealing a yellowed graveyard of teeth. He held his arm out toward the cemetery as if giving us permission to enter.

This was like no other cemetery I'd ever seen. It was an overgrown swamp with a few broken headstones scattered around. The ground was covered in puddles and ditches and scraps of rusted metal. Hundreds of these tiny mounds of red-brown mud littered the dirt. Their shapes reminded me of the dribble castles my siblings and I made while we were kids on the beach.

Dave picked up on my curiosity before I even asked.

"It's the crawdads," he said.

Then he explained that bodies in this cemetery weren't buried very deep, and most were buried without boxes. The land was so flat and the water table so high that you could put down a shovel anywhere and you'd hit water. But when you're too poor to bury a loved one's corpse in a mausoleum, you put the body in some cardboard or wrap it up in an old rug and stick it as deep in the ground as possible (around two or three feet). In doing this, you're baiting the crayfish.

"Crawdads are scavengers," Dave said. "Nothing attracts them like rotting flesh. Here, the little buggers didn't have to go very far to get their dinner."

I thought back to the crayfish gumbo I'd eaten the night before. "Man, that's kind of fucked up."

"Yeah. But it's also awesome." Dave pulled another joint from his cigarette pack and sparked it up, taking a big hit before passing it to me. "Some real circle of life shit. It's beautiful."

The weed now tasted briny, or maybe it was the earth all around me affecting my senses. I lit up a cigarette and worked it into the rotation, staring out over the cemetery as the smoke rounded out my edges.

Spurred by the buzz, I cut a crooked path through the cemetery, examining each step before taking it. Most of the burial sites were easy to spot because the ground sunk down a good six inches or so and the mud on the surface was covered in crayfish castles.

"When I came down here a few weeks after Katrina, there were all sorts of bones lying around," Dave said. "Water pushed em back up."

"That's what the preacher was worried about, right?"

"Yeah," Dave said. "For months afterwards, people came down here, picking through what was left. Snatched up skulls and shit."

"Why?"

"I don't know."

At the far end of the field, through the overgrown grass and weeds, I saw a congregation of three women wearing colored shawls. I left Dave sitting on a shaded tree stump and set out to investigate, carefully picking my way through the swamp of the dead.

The women stood shoulder to shoulder around a sunken grave, which they'd covered in a rainbow-colored sheet. They wore bracelets made of beads and bells, which jingled as they waved incense sticks over the grave. A bronze-skinned, white-haired woman in the middle was repeating a low-key chant, her voice full and haunting. She looked up from the grave and our eyes met. Pausing her chant, she stared deep into me, then she smirked with a sense of friendly knowledge.

The woman pulled another incense stick from a pouch in her long dress and held it out for me. I stepped around the edges of the covered grave and took the incense stick from her hand. Before I could reach for my lighter, she lit a match and shared the flame with me. I didn't know what to do or say, so I just nodded and bowed my head.

I stepped back from the three women and took my spot at the opposite end of the grave. A faint breeze from the river blew some smoke into my face. I swallowed, letting the flavors of spice and earth linger in my mouth.

A firm hand came down on my shoulder, but I didn't move. "Let's go," Dave said.

The leather seats in the truck were scorching hot, and I was parched and had no water, but I lit up another cigarette anyway. Dave fired up the truck and bumped us back the way we came.

"I guess you should probably be getting back to the hotel?"

I shook my head and took a deep smoke. "I don't want to go back there yet."

Dave said: "You hungry? I know a place nearby. Best crawdad gumbo you'll ever eat." He pulled another joint from his cigarette box and held it up as an offering.

I smiled and said, "Let's go."

TOM BALL
AT THE DISTURBING GOAT BAR

CHAPTER 1

AUGUST 2018

It was an intelligent, constant masquerade. Clientele were required to pass an interview to show they were creative and a good fit for the bar. And once accepted all had to wear a custom goat mask at all times in the bar. If you ripped someone's mask off you'd be banned for life.

This is the story of the pub that changed the world coming from very humble beginnings.

The Disturbing Goat Bar had a sign of a goat drinking from a horn. The goat had crazy eyes. The bar was located on Queen St. in downtown Toronto.

Inside the bar there was an arc of bar for 50 m. Most nights it was standing room only, but this made it easy to mingle.

Everyone had to wear a goat mask. It covered your throat so old people could blend in. But the regulars could all recognize one another as each goat mask was subtly different and looked a bit like the owner of the mask.

Architecture was in the style of Frank Lloyd Wright with lots of stone and cedar wood.

Clientele were required to write an IQ test and an imagination test in order to get their pass into the bar. Of course the imagination test was subjective, with two of the regulars, Z and Carl deciding on each one.

Most failed; only 30% passed. In this book only some of the successes are documented. Red passes for intellectual VIPs, gray passes for others. Most people were happy to get a gray pass. Every Friday at 7 p.m. Z and Carl interviewed potential new bar goers. But it was getting to be too packed so the owner Bob was trying to franchise out the goat bars throughout Toronto. Capacity crowds of 305 were common. Basically 270 gray passes and 35 red passes appeared almost every night by 7 p.m. with long waits outside at the original Disturbing Goat. Red passes could make reservations ahead of time. In total the Disturbing Goat had 1000 pass members, in this their fourth year of existence.

Some said the bar owner, Bob, was against the common man, but he simply said most bars are for morons. And everyone had to promise to be horny here. Bob was a medical doctor and gave prescriptions for Viagra. And legal opiates. And nearby was a pharmacy open 24 hours.

We sold goat masks... there was a mouthpiece that allowed one to obscure one's voice. Kind of unearthly really. Every night all customers wore masks and there was no end of "beh-ing" like a goat. Beh beh!

The masks looked vaguely like the person who was wearing them, but only goat masks were allowed. We had some artists to draw and produce the masks.

We recorded all conversations here and it was our right to make them part of our books with our new publishing house, with the changed voices. We had a team of 12 who sifted through the bar conversations at the Disturbing Goat here in Toronto and edited them.

Many of the people Z and Carl interviewed were writers and the Goat Press was going to make their books into blockbusters. Never had a publishing press had as much fame as us, it was looking like.

Z and Carl, as managers, wore a silver star, Bob had two stars, and the barmaids had a half star. Many people wanted to meet them. VIP red pass clients had a red star.

Madame Crazed, barmaid: I am thinking of setting up a new political party for imaginative candidates only. I wish our leaders were more intellectual.

Carl: What do you think leaders should do?

MC: Empower the UN with a formidable army and send them in to break up wars.

Carl: It is a good idea. It would seem like heaven to rid the world of wars.

MC: And use nuclear power (run by the UN), or solar power in the Sahara and elsewhere, this will clean the air and perhaps limit global warming. And above all, desalinize sea water for Africa and other deserts. Eliminate poverty, not be partisan.

Carl: Yes I don't know why so many people still live in poverty in this day and age. Even in Canada.

MC: And educate people to be imaginative primarily. Use the best geniuses to write the e-texts for students.

Carl: Having the curriculum designed by geniuses would be a real step forward.

MC: And enshrine balanced budgets in law and even force governments to pay down debt.

Carl: Yes 1/3 of our tax dollars goes to interest on the debt. We'll end up bankrupt as a state.

MC: Make it much more difficult to buy guns.

Carl: Yes there are too many guns in Canada. Maybe only allow hunting rifles and when it is not the season for hunting they should store their rifles at a government depot.

MC: And sell booze in the convenience stores, 24/7.

Carl: Yes Ontario's booze laws are very backwards.

MC: Make marriage illegal. All children require the two parents to sign a contract to raise them.

Carl: Just like religion, marriage is dying out of its own accord.

Z: I think we could create jobs by encouraging service jobs to be non-automated. Create jobs by forcing people to learn useful trades or to work in the health industry. Make prostitution legal.

MC: That might take organized crime out of the equation and they can test them for herpes and AIDS and collect taxes. It worked just fine in Holland. Although AIDS seems to be under control, now.

Z: Build unusual buildings to attract tourists. Maybe have an artist sketch such a building in a couple of days and then onto the next one.

Carl: Yeah, the exterior is more important than the interior, I would say. But for example in London, England, the reverse seems true.

MC: Only let in highly skilled new immigrants.

Z: That's pretty much what they do now. Of course they let in some refugees also, but that's OK.

MC: Use hypnotism to make people free, not beholden to negative post-hypnotic suggestion.

Z: Yes we are all brainwashed and if someone makes trouble the spies will hypnotize them to be ordinary.

MC. Give everyone a meter that measures exercise and force everyone who is able to do 90 minutes of exercise every day.

Z: Yes and ban sugar, make salt far more expensive.

MC: And once a year people would need to go before an arbiter and explain what good deeds they did in the previous year. If they did not do any good deeds then they would be given a substantial financial penalty. This idea is at the cornerstone of my philosophy.

Z: Forcing people to be good as if they were naughty children. I like the idea.

MC: Ban violent video games. Use mind-reading technology (I know they have it) to make for a peaceful society. Ban violent movies.

Z: We are all killers at heart. But civilization should be about peaceful living. I also believe they can read minds.

MC: Increase the jail time/penalty drastically for computer hacking such as stealing ID or fraud. Maybe the government can hire the best hackers so as to keep them out of harm's way.

Carl: Yes hackers are out of control. We need to get them all to work for the government with large salaries.

MC: Get the best minds together and have them brainstorm how to make people think. Synergy.

Carl: But most people are apathetic and don't believe they can be made more imaginative etc. mind reading doesn't exist.

Z: But we need also to drastically increase the minimum wage.

MC: Every idea has its day. And all those things I just told you will come to pass. And will feature in my New Goat Party, a radical political party.

Z: When I lived in Asia people were open minded towards foreigners and I had many lovers. Not so much here however. But now that I have a star on my mask indicating I am a manager, love is easy again. So I say open minds are the key. We need to make everyone more open-minded.

Carl: But above all we need to make society more imaginative. From education to jobs, just like MC says.

Z: Also it is a mad world, no point pretending otherwise. So I have written 3 volumes of "Tales of Madness." Unlike most books that just have a couple of mad actions, in the tales everything is crazy. I wrote one for the Goat.

CHAPTER 2

"GOATS OF THE HERD"

You know Nietzsche once said, in his superman book, "They have a thing they call culture—it separates them from the goatherds."

Well this is a true and inspirational goat story "told to me straight from the goat's mouth."

The story was that a certain guy, X, was traveling in Pakistan and one day he was in a restaurant where he dined upon goat. After dinner he went to the washroom and discovered the toilet was just a hole in the floor. Anyway he squatted down and did his business, but as he did so he felt something licking his ass! It was a goat!

Well you know the experience was so pleasurable that X had several girls lick his ass, but he still wasn't satisfied. So he went out to the countryside of Pakistan, where he would venture unto the goat fields, and get the hungry goats to lick his ass, and eat his shit. He was in heaven!

So then he resolved to live forever in Pakistan, and buy his own goats. And of course he kept them hungry. And he decided to get castrated so that he could be true to the goats.

As time went by he practiced selective breeding among the goats, as some goats were better ass lickers than others. And X wanted super goats. And he felt like a superman of the future.

He also spent time going around the countryside extolling the virtues of getting your ass licked, and also of licking ass. He told them shit was good for health, helped people lose weight, made men strong etc. etc.

And X called his goat farm "The US of Goatica"—here man and goat are equal and all must obey his arbitrary dictates (and lick his ass of course).

⚓

MC: What a crazy story.

Carl: Truly disturbing!

Z: I must admit I am greedy for love!

Edward: A man only needs one woman unless he is sex-crazed like you.

Z: What's wrong with being sex-crazed? It's a good instinct. By the way the doctor says I have an enlarged liver.

Edward: Maybe you better cut back on the beer. But I have drunk as much as you and I haven't had any problems.

Z: We need to make a more loving world. The philosophy of love is to inspire despite everything.

Edward: Well I am not going to stop drinking, if I die, I die.

Icar enters the bar, Icar's philosophy is it is glorious to get rich. He's a Chinese Canadian.

I: Hey boys I just got a promotion. A round of drinks on me please!

Cassandra, stripper, enters the bar.

Z: What's up Cass?

Cass: I am feeling horny, Z. Can you give me your love?

Z: Well let's have a few drinks and see where it will take us...

Cass: I bought some Viagra for you to try. Apparently it works on all men.

Z: I think I am in paradise!

I: Men are so shallow.

Z: I am dealing with love here.

I: I have to wear condoms and boxer shorts when I do my honey. I shouldn't tell you, but she's diseased.

Carl: We waived the IQ test if the person can convince them they were creative.

⚓

(Later Z and Cass go off to Z's place...)

⚓

I: *Nihil novum sub solum* (Nothing new under the sun).

Barmaid Nancy: As you know I was just in New York, last week. I got on the subway late at night and it turned out to be an express subway to Harlem. I was the only white person on the train and thought I heard them plotting about me. But in Harlem, I ran over with some construction workers and waited for the train back.

I: Yes it's a dangerous world.

Carl: But how did you like New York as a whole?

BN: It was pretty lame during the week, but on weekends it was great. At least you can hold a drink outside provided it is in a bag.

⚓

In this bar, they'd rigged the pay phone to give free long-distance calls but only told the handful of regulars and people they really liked.

I: I want to call my lover in Calgary.

BN: I've been to Calgary. What did you think about the city? People are nice but seem a bit conservative.

I (on the phone, talking to his lover in Calgary): No Mary Anne I don't want to go to Calgary and marry you!

Mary Anne: How about I come to Toronto tomorrow?

I: I'll meet your plane...

Francine enters.

F: I got a hot date tonite!

Z: I know we're not good enough for you.

Carl: Yes tell us about him.

F: He's a handsome and rich stockbroker.

Z: Greed, greed.

F: I want to meet a rich guy and live happily ever after.

Z: You are a dying breed. But I considered marrying for a Resident Visa. I think I can get $100,000 Canadian for it. Of course I could select a hot chick and bone her while waiting for her visa.

Carl: Let's eat, drink and be merry, for tomorrow we may die.

Carl: I think everyone works too hard. I believe in a 25-hour work week and tiny homes here in the city.

Z to F: Why not bring your new love here and introduce us?

F: It would be like throwing him to the wolves. You guys are really disturbing.

Z: Raise a little hell...

Carl to BN: I like you, you have a heavy hand when making me Long Island ice teas.

BN: The boss approves of me anyway.

Fooz ball, goat fooz. Every time your player scores a beh sound comes out. Z and C play and C defends his championship successfully... The plastic players had been replaced with plastic goats. Goats could kick with their front or back legs.

Z: You were just lucky!

CHAPTER 3

Friday night...in September 2018

Ben Gunn and the Goats were playing tonight. They sang "I Fought the Spies and the Spies Won," and many others.

There were several other bands too, such as My Goat, My Love. And We Wanna Milk You.

Ben Gunn had started his own record company, Goat Records, with help from Bob, the Goat owner. We had a number of new acts play here (but not too loud, so we could continue to mingle) and some were picked up by Bob's Internet record company.

7-9 p.m. Friday night, Z and Carl interview their weekly new potential members and those with great imagination get in.

Tests took place in the library at the second level. The library had 40,000 items including net books, picture books, art books, scientific treatises, CDs, DVDs, and so on... Carl's fantasy paintings adorned the walls of the Disturbed Goat, especially the library. The library was six stories high on top of the ground floor Goat.

Many failed the test (you could only take it once), but their cases are not described here. Only the successes. Carl and Z always had a couple bouncers in the library with them while they were doing the interviews.

Questions included:

1. What is the future of the world?
2. What was your biggest mistake?
3. Did anyone ever break your heart?
4. Do you believe in the Devil?
5. Where is God?
6. What is the most creative thing you have ever done?
7. What have you been thinking about recently?
8. What is your wildest fantasy?
9. What is your favorite night dream?
10. How do you feel about the past?
11. What turns you on?
12. What is your favorite sci-fi book?

But usually they just asked, "Tell us about yourself and your dreams!" And the prospective new members often "showed" or described what they had created or planned to "create."

Perhaps some got others to write their speech, but if they acted like morons they'd be banned for life.

To take the test you needed to take off your goat mask if you had one (they were all the rage around town).

But once you were a member it was forbidden to remove someone's mask, as previously mentioned.

Some people became a totally different person with a mask on. As already stated, the official goat masks had a voice changer attached to the mouth. So it was difficult to identify people in the bar. Some said we didn't know who we were anymore.

Some said the masks were too hot, but many shaved their bodies and heads, no hair and no beard, so the masks were tolerable. We kept it at a cool 19° C year round in the Disturbing Goat.

Drugs, take the high road. And dealers were not permitted here. But Bob would dispense various legal opiates for those who wanted them. In time as new Goats opened up, Bob hired a resident doctor for each of his Goats.

And now some interviews for prospective writers, musicians, etc.

Late September, 2018: INTERVIEWS

She was a scientist working with antiviral drugs.

Z: You are scary!

Carl: What exactly do you do?

She said in 10–15 years new viruses would be developed that would kill almost everyone. It will be the end of civilization. But it is too late to stop it. Too many countries have too much science.

Z: Wow! I guess you are in!

She, Loretta, was a writer of fables.

Z: Tell us a couple of your fables.

"The Goat and the Banshee." The banshee was a witch who was always scream-ing. Most animals avoided her. A certain goat meanwhile lived quietly on the mountainside and kept a low profile. But finally a wolf caught her and ate her. But the banshee lived on. Moral: Sometimes minding your own business is not the best plan.

And another, "The Goat and Her Master." This goat was crazy and always hung around the outside of the herd and sometimes jumped fences and ran away. Finally she was devoured by a bear. Moral: To be outside the box can be dangerous. But freedom is calling you. Take that risk!

Z: Good enough. Welcome.

She, Lisa, wrote about synergy and how brilliant minds combine to make some-thing better than them as individuals.

She said she wanted to experiment here at the Goat and see if great works could be produced by brainstorming. Such as manifestos.

Z: The world is your oyster. And no one is an island.

She, Serendipity, was a writer of ballads. She played a few of her songs for us, that so far had no lyrics. She said she wanted to join Ben Gunn and his band. It was good acoustic music.

Z: I'll set you up with Ben Gunn.

Carl: Why can't you write lyrics? Maybe you should try smoking doobs; it opens doors.

She said she'd tried that but it didn't help.

Z: Well most of the great classical composers didn't have any choirs or singing either. So too a lot of rockers didn't have lyrics, like Elton John had another person write the lyrics. Or Led Zeppelin in which the singer, Robert Plant, wrote most of the lyrics. Or the band Rush in which the drummer wrote the lyrics. Typically the singer wrote the lyrics. You just need to get a Renaissance man to sing and write lyrics for you. Voices are an important musical instrument. Choirs in old times...

He, Ernie, was a writer of video games. Future war and fantasy. People want an escape from the drudgery of their jobs, he said.

He introduced the death ray to gaming which would destroy large swaths of anything in its path in seconds. It is just the tip of the iceberg for weapons like these. Sometimes the games were ahead of reality.

LUCY BIEDERMAN
A CABINET

He didn't appreciate me. No—I know how that sounds, wait. She saw the light of sympathy fade from his eyes. Her feelings, the very experiences that underlay them, had already been colonized, purchased and furnished. You don't know him. The things I've had to hide.

Don't tell me, Susan.

But I still carry it. I protect him, and he doesn't speak to me.

Susan—

It isn't fair.

Susan, he's my friend.

Oh yeah, then where does he live?

Fine—he *was* my friend.

SHE LISTENED TO them from behind the basement door. It was a different house down there. The thick, burnished banisters that curved along even the third-floor staircase surrendered at the door to the basement. The stairs that led to the shabby darkness of her rented lair were just a gussied-up fire escape.

DON'T YOU GET it, do you get what he did?

No response would make her happy, he often told her. He came every day after work at his wife's behest. His wife was Susan's best friend.

Do you understand how serious this is?

He didn't say anything.

I might have to move out of this house.

I know, Susan.

I wish I could just—just—

Susan. You don't have to say everything.

I wish I could tear my heart out of my body! I *feel* so much.

I know you do.

SOMETHING IN HER broke, there where she stood, behind the door. It felt sort of like an orgasm, sort of like breaking a bone. She thought of a little scene from her childhood that she had never recalled before. Her mind went directly to it, like walking toward the one person she knew in a crowd at a carnival.

Sitting at the kitchen table in the trailer, she asks Mom for more SpaghettiOs.

You can't have no more. Mom takes the bowl and puts it on the table. She can taste the SpaghettiOs she has just eaten, seasoned with the tin they were packed in. She doesn't want more, anymore. She is a different person than who just asked for them, and she knows she will never want SpaghettiOs again. She looks at her knee, which has a bruise that lacks both color and shape: an image appears of a high brick arch with yellow flowers around it and a white sky behind it. She realizes that she can look at one thing and see another, like watching a TV show while, inside her, the one coming on next already plays.

The moment expands to fit all the years ahead. She senses the scaffold that holds it together—all of it: looking at her digital Casio waiting for the seconds to stop; the stars, dead but folding back over to die again, and dying for attention even during daytime when no one can see.

She has been looking at her knee, in a haze of contemplation, all this time. Her entire life had been a disaster, a smudge, a septic system failure.

She wanted to throw it away. But pressing against that desire was her awareness of how un-entire her life had been, how she had deprived it—sitting on what had happened... she would never say.

She almost died considering it.

She lay on her bathroom floor. A mouse clipped the corner of her vision and she didn't flinch.

She and Susan usually ate together, but she rolled around on her futon for all the hours associated with dinner and came up for Chips Ahoy! later.

She looked in the mirror. She saw as foggy a likeness as the shadows the ancients cast on tin.

She looked in the night. Mom had freckles all over her body. Mom's thighs coming out of her little jean shorts made her think of pancakes, of everything about pancakes—the batter, a stack of silver dollars, the Bisquick box. Gramom told Mom not to wear them.

She looked in the bottom of her life and there was a cabinet there. She turned away from it. She didn't want to relegate herself to only its faint light.

She knew an old woman who was an experimental psychologist. Indian bedspreads were draped over her windows and sofas. There were jars of tea and incense on her kitchen countertops, like the apothecary in *Romeo and Juliet*. The psychologist had a friend over. She was reading the psychologist's palm.

What's the problem?

She felt what it was to inhabit her small body. It could be that she had been intended to turn out larger.

I've seen... I've seen and heard things I don't think people are supposed to know about. Her hair stuck to her face. The palm reader took her hand.

Men were given choices—if not in life, at least they were free in their minds, or in their deepest hearts, where an illiterate self broke off to function, just function. But she was tagged with other people's ideas, eyelash to toenail.

She saw him and went right up to him but found herself unable to speak, but it was only a dream. She sat up thirsty, nearly dead of thirst.

She stood in the basement practicing speaking without sounding like she was crying. Susan heard her and came downstairs. Susan didn't have much to do, arranging and rearranging her sadness like a miniature Zen garden from an art museum gift shop.

What are you doing?

She was preparing for work the next day. Her boss said it was unprofessional to cry there.

When the experimental psychologist spoke to her, blood rushed to her ears; she hardly caught a word. She slept, but she never really rested. She was twenty-seven. Her youth was raring. There was so much living to go.

Years ago, sitting under the carport, picturing a meadow, she had released vectors of sense and senselessness in every direction, buoyant and actual. She thought she didn't do that anymore.

LINDA BLASKEY
BREATH

I step out on the porch to wave my man off to work. I do it every morning; stand under the porchlight; wave. It's what keeps him safe. He thinks I'm crazy, calls all the little things that I do oddities, totems. But the world is such a slippery thing it doesn't hurt to be extra careful.

I know as soon as I go outside that today is going to be one of them smothering kind of days. When it's clear you can stand on this bald knob where Alburt and me chose to build, look across the hills almost to Little Rock it seems. But the cloud cover is so dense and low today it snags on the treetops. It's like being in a Tupperware container of hot dumplings with the lid snapped down tight. I can't hardly breathe on days like this.

I look off towards the direction of town and see dust from Allie Blue's car rolling up the hill. I know it's her car because she comes to visit me every Tuesday morning at this exact time. Tuesday is one of her days off from managing the White Castle over to Cream City. And I know that Allie Blue has started parking around the curve from the house until she sees evidence of her daddy's leaving the other direction, then she comes on up the road and into the lane. For luck, I open and close the screen door behind me twice, hoping all is well with her.

She parks in the turnaround in front of the gate and walks around the car, always a Chevy, her man Donnie won't buy nothing but a Chevy, and gets Tinker out of his baby seat. I can see from here how his curls, golden and frothy as buttermilk just like his mama's, are sweated down flat to his head. I have often asked her why she doesn't get Donnie to let her drive the Tahoe on hot days like this. Its air conditioning ain't broke like her Chevy's, but she says he needs it to haul around his tools and ladders.

Allie Blue carries Tinker on her hip as she comes up the steps and with her other arm gives me a hug. Tinker grabs for my glasses, pulls them off, waves them around. He does that every time his mama leans over to hug me. I don't know what I'd do if one time he didn't.

"Hey, Mama," Allie Blue says as she hands the baby over to me. I give him them little butterfly kisses with my eyelashes on his cheek. It always makes him laugh and he's come to expect it, turning his sweet, chubby face my way waiting for the light tickles. I squeeze Tinker real tight and look off down the road in the direction his granddaddy has just gone. I think how awful tired and rundown Allie Blue looks, but I keep quiet about it.

"Mama, why do you do that? Stand out here every morning and wave to Alburt while he's driving away?" She's taken to calling her daddy by his given name and I don't like it.

"It's just something I've always done. Makes me feel good doing it."

"Mama," Allie Blue looks down at the splintered porch floor, "you know that some days Alburt doesn't go straight to work."

"Allie, it ain't none of your concern." But I know it is her concern, it's all about concern for her that has her daddy doing what he does. I give Tinker an extra little hug, say "gimme some sugar" and turn to take him in the house. "And Allie Blue, stop calling your daddy by his Christian name. You can call him daddy, or sir, or Mr. Doble if you want to, but not Alburt. I don't want to hear you do that again." She can't see my face, I know, but my voice has a tone that tells her I'm not messing around. I try to take a deep breath of the heavy morning air.

Allie Blue follows me through to the kitchen, Tinker laughing at how our steps make crinkling noises on the loose cabbage-rose linoleum. He laughs every time. That's why his granddaddy and me don't fix it. We'll wait 'til he's older when it don't matter anymore.

I put Tinker in his high chair and say "Allie Blue, set down. I'll fix us some ice tea." I pull trays from the freezer and hold them under running water to loosen the cubes a bit. "Boy-howdy, it's hot in here," I say. Strands of my hair have frizzed out from my head like I've had an electric shock. "The sash on this window is stuck tight and your daddy hasn't had time to fix it."

"Well, Mama, I want to talk to you about that. What Daddy's doing with his time." I hear Allie picking at the edge of the table with her thumbnail, it's what she's always done when she's nervous. And she's speaking real low, a sure signal for me to go on high alert. "I got called in early a week or so ago, some payroll problem, and as I was driving down 41 I saw Daddy's truck turn up Russell Peedy Road. It was real early in the morning, about an hour before Daddy needed to be at the chalkboard factory."

I think to myself, well now we've been found out. I put down the ice cube trays.

Allie Blue goes on. "Everyone knows there's but one thing up Russell Peedy Road. So I followed him. Mama, his truck was parked outside Lucky Norma's whore house." Her breath fairly fails her on those last two words.

My back is to Allie Blue so I take some time to think. I wipe my hands on my apron and make it look like accidents, like I'm fumbling, when I knock the salt shaker over, scrape the grains in my hand, toss them over my shoulder, making it look like I'm brushing something off my dress; drop a lemon slice on the floor, kiss it up to God. I knew this was going to be a smothering day.

"And Mama, it's not the only time. His truck is up there just about every morning."

Oh, Lordy. And now I know why it's all of a sudden been Alburt and not Daddy. I sit at the table across from Allie Blue and take my daughter's—my sweet as tea daughter's—hands in my own. "Allie Blue, your daddy and I didn't want you to know this, but your daddy's been following Donnie. Every morning. It's Donnie been stopping at Lucky Norma's. Your daddy wanted to have a talk with him." Actually it was more like Alburt wanted to catch that lyin' sack with his goods hanging out.

Allie's eyes blink a few times. She sits up tall and yanks her hands away from me and says "Mama, Donnie is working. He's painting Lucky Norma's house trying to earn a few extra dollars. He can't be picky about the jobs he takes." She blinks a few more times, then spits out, "How could you even think that way about him?"

"Well, it seems you thought that way about your daddy." Which was exactly the wrong thing to say. Allie jumps up and lifts Tinker from his chair. No matter how mad she sometimes gets, she always is gentle with that precious boy.

I have to make a decision so I do the only thing I can. I start to laugh. And that stops Allie Blue right in her tracks. So I laugh harder, I force out tears, I slap the table. "So all this time you thought it was your daddy pulling his pickle out of the jar and we were thinking it was Donnie." I act like I'm gasping for breath and keep laughing. Allie Blue cracks a smile, then she's laughing too.

"Mama, can you believe this?" She is laughing and Tinker is laughing and I put my head down on the table and my shoulders are shaking. I don't have to force the tears anymore for I know what Alburt told me he saw and it had nothing to do with painting or any other kind of home renovation. Please Lord, I don't want Allie Blue to see my face just yet.

"Pickle," Allie says and snickers in that way she's had since she was little and that I love and that I miss. "Mama. I can't believe you said that." And she's off laughing again and takes me with her. I lift my head.

We sit at the table and have our ice tea. We're quiet except for the chuckles and snorts that keep bubbling up. And then Allie Blue and Tinker head off home. I stand on the front porch and wave them up the lane thinking Allie's daddy and me have opened a door we never should have touched. I know that because of us, she will start to notice things that she didn't notice before. Like paint cans that should be in the Tahoe but are still on the back step. And clothes that don't have spatters of color on them. And how long this job is taking. My daughter is a happy girl and we have tampered with that. We've planted a seed that will one day reach its natural ripeness. We never should have done that. We should have let it be. All this is between Allie Blue and her Donnie. She's not our baby anymore, she's his wife.

I go back into the kitchen to wash out our glasses. I wipe down the counters and tabletop, take out the broom and sweep the floor, check for dust on top of the fridge, line up the pots of violets just so on the ledge. Sweat rolls down my back and I think since Alburt won't have need to be going up Russell Peedy Road no more, he'll have time to unstick the window sash, get some air in here.

CHARLES CICCORETTI
HEY

We walk through the woods together now—these birch-sycamore whitewoods that wrap around the southern beach. The college kids that live next door like to smoke and talk late-nite Comedy Central trashtalk behind our backs about it, but frankly, they'll be 30 soon enough too, yeah?

We all have boring jobs at a law firm downtown except for X.L. who likes to say he works at the liquor store but probably just sells weed to the college kids on weekends. He has somehow avoided the emotional responsibilities of adulthood, and for that reason, he's the funnest (that's not a word) guy to talk to around here. It's gotten pretty depressing while you were gone, by the way.

Every few nights when we get home from work, we find X.L. and walk through the woods with a cooler full of shining Corona, then down it as fast as humanly possible. It still feels awful—two sips and T.C. is talking about her alcoholic dad and by the time she's finished with her stories I've drunk enough to feel like an alcoholic myself. It's better than the Cleveland setup but we're all howling for you over here.

The woods are beautiful though. Yesterday we saw a buck the size of a (I dunno) but it was *huge* the biggest I have ever seen and R.K., drunk, lunged, screaming "bamb-eee," attempting to get a firm chokehold on an empty stretch of air. That thing ran so damn fast—on a related note, I think I heard the college kids snickering "bambi" between themselves today.

What a load of bastards.

Is the fact that I am slowly learning to hate young people a sign that I'm getting old? I was picking up some ramen after work the other day and these two pop princesses stared at me like I was a goddamn geriatric.

There's a pretty self-evident borderline when it comes to age around here. We're the only 30–40ers, everyone else is college-age or already playing golf with their bingo buddies.

Speaking of which, the in-fashion golf ball brand for all these wrinkly sacs of cellulite is *O'Donovan,* with a little red tee-em at the end. Like your name. You should come here for a week and bring back as many as you can to the old country—your folks would love that.

Did I mention that the woods are beautiful?

DON DUSSAULT
NOT BETTER LATE

During the Great Depression of 1929, many thousands of unemployed parents sent their children to live with relatives.

Snow resonates in me like a drum. At age three until about seven snow thrilled me as its white sweeps and slopes gleaming in sunlight settled into Buckfield through winter, brightening the somber days when the sky changed from patchworks of white and blue to washes of gray. I'd grope into light flurries swirling insubstantial, indecisive snowflakes. Mornings I'd run downstairs hoping for a coating of snow across the ground and the back porch so I could put on my little boots and tramp around outside. After short days without a visible sun I'd pause on my way upstairs to peer out the front parlor windows at the snowfields that muted the road. Christmases changed me about snow. Christmas, when families got together and dreams may come true, should be the day Papa and Maman would arrive from Michigan. What word overheard, what childish fantasy got that dream started? Letters hoping I was well and promising a reunion—what a special day! It had to be at Christmas. As that most magical day in my childhood pantheon approached, I'd puzzle over the weather map in the newspaper and listen to news broadcasts for the latest on the weather. I'd gobble down supper in haste to station myself in the parlor chair by the third window with the best view of the direction Papa and Maman would arrive from, and in the faint illumination of the lights on the Christmas tree in the far corner I'd study oncoming headlights. *Would they arrive by car or bus?* Snow smothered hope. Dismayed, I'd watch a steady snowfall beginning to clump on grass and tree limbs and dissolve on the wet tarmac, then fall in wet globs fattening deep drifts across the highway, ending the passage of cars, sending shadows of doom across my soul. Christmas snow spoke: *impossible.* Inside me a silent echo trembled...

In Saturday noonday sunshine, wearing my nicest dress, I held my breath, a fixed grin, and, two-handed, the diploma rolled up and pinched in the middle by a shiny red ribbon, my reward for completing eight grades of parochial school, and I awaited the shutterclick from the boxy black Kodak Brownie Aunt Letitia aimed at me. On Sunday afternoon an unfamiliar couple arrived in a blue Ford. They set their suitcases beside the bed and chatted with me and, smiling, touched my hair, told me in unfamiliar voices how pretty I looked growing up, hugged me in unfamiliar arms, my own Papa and Maman here at last! I couldn't stop staring, searching my memory, finding no images matching these two who should have been closest to me, now drawing toward them my unevenly growing soul, a tendril wavering in midair.

Maman's happy, a nice person. Our first meeting in a decade, when I last saw them as we all stood beside a massive bus and Papa and Maman hugged me and then disappeared inside with a hiss and a snap of folding doors and I waved as the bus departed with a puff of black smoke. After the years I'd tried to image her and Papa from their written words delivered by the post office, Maman herself was standing beside me and I kept sneaking peeks at her. *Are they real, will they suddenly disappear?* As we finished wiping the counters dry, the men made a well-timed re-entrance. Aunt Letitia brought out a bottle of port I'd never seen before. As the graduate I got about an eighth–full glass, sweeter than I expected wine to be. Papa asked me, "Ready to start packing?" Aunt Letitia frowned. "What's your hurry? You just got here."

"Ophelia might as well be ready to go. It'll save time later."

"We should talk about that."

Maman looked alarmed. "What's there to talk about?"

The enameled coffeepot was shaking in Mémère's hand. She set it down hard on the counter. "Must you take her now?"

"Ma," said Papa, "she should be with us."

Aunt Letitia pleaded, "For our mother's sake, couldn't you let her stay? She can finish school here. Then she can go to Michigan grown up."

Mémère had her back to the counter, leaning against it for support. Aunt Esther whispered to Mémère, don't slump. Aunt Letitia crossed her arms. "This has always been Ophelia's home. Ma brought her up like her own child. Taking the child away now would break her heart."

Maman began, "We appreciate all you've done for—"

Aunt Letitia interrupted, saying to Papa, "Look at your mother. She's sick about Ophelia going so far away."

"We'll be back for visits."

"When? You work full time. You get off one week a year and it takes you three days to get here. Your mother could die without ever seeing Ophelia again, the child she raised." Aunt Letitia's gaze scanned the kitchen, paused at me. "We need to have a family conference. For grown-ups. Go upstairs to your room and read or play."

I didn't budge. "I rather go out."

"It will be dark soon and we can't go chasing after you."

Mémère's voice came out thin. "Father St. Pierre would know what's best."

Aunt Esther started toward the back door. "I'll go get him."

I blurted, "I want some coffee."

Aunt Letitia gave me a stern look. "It will keep you awake all night. Go upstairs."

In the middle of the upstairs hallway open floor louvers let warm air up to the second floor, which had no radiators, and also, I'd noticed years ago, voices strong as if megaphoned from the kitchen. I settled myself on my belly with eyes and ears close to the vent. Between the metal slats I viewed the end of the kitchen table by the wood stove. I was almost directly above Father St. Pierre, who had a bald spot at the top of his head. His voice of a thousand sermons came up clear. "You've got a good job now?"

"It took long enough," replied Papa, with bitterness in his voice.

"Some say this Depression came out of the extravagance in the twenties. There was plenty of money then."

"For some people."

"She's lived here all her life?"

"Since about three. We hoped her visit here would be a vacation for her. I didn't expect to be out of work so many years."

Aunt Letitia said, "She has a good home here. She should not be yanked away while she is still a child."

Father St. Pierre inquired, "She is how old, eleven?"

"Twelve."

"Entering the most difficult years for young people. Stability and love in the home are essential."

Maman said, "Who can love her more than her mother?" Father St. Pierre turned to Mémère. "You look pale. Are you well?"

"This...taking her from me, it makes me ill."

Maman said, "How about my feelings? She's my child."

Father St. Pierre said, "We are here to decide what's best for Ophelia."

Maman's voice hardened. "Being with her mother is best."

Aunt Letitia snapped, "You didn't think so ten years ago."

"We were flat broke," protested Papa. "We can send her to good schools now. We found a Catholic girls' high school in Livonia."

Father St. Pierre asked, "Where is Livonia?"

"Michigan, near our home."

"You live in Michigan now?"

"New England mills weren't hiring. I heard there was work in Dearborn. There wasn't for us, for a long time. The Mother Superior at the school said she can send for Ophelia's records. All we need to do is get Ophelia registered."

Father St. Pierre nodded, impressed. "That would be the Archdiocese of Detroit. How far away is the school, exactly?"

"About a mile from our house. The school has bus service."

"Your parish sounds more prosperous than ours."

Aunt Letitia folded her arms. "She can finish her schooling here, where she's comfortable. All her friends are here."

Papa turned to Father St. Pierre. "Here she'll have to go to public school."

Mémère had pulled herself together. "Ophelia will stay a good Catholic here."

Father St. Pierre smiled. "I've seen her at Mass for years."

Aunt Letitia said, "Mémère has devoted her life to this child. Taking Ophelia away from her would kill her. She should see the child grow up. She deserves that."

Maman started to say something and was interrupted as Aunt Esther pleaded, "What should we do?"

"I can't decide for you," said Father St. Pierre. "Ophelia has settled in here. In Buckfield. Her father and mother will always be her father and mother. Her aunts and grandparents will always feel like parents to her. It isn't a question of first or second. Reach agreement without rancor. Stay together as a family, as best you can, considering the distance." His voice rang with confidence. "Have no fear for her immortal soul. She won't lose her religion in the public high school. We have her with us now, for life."

Papa spoke to Maman in a voice too low for me to hear. As he bent toward her, I could see their faces, solemn, disappointed. Mémère had won. Chairs scraped and voices receded as Father St. Pierre left.

Running to my room, flinging myself into the big bed, I lay on my side facing the plain wall. After years of looking forward to this day, my reunion with Papa and Maman, my yearnings had yielded to an unexpected concordat. During my parochial school years *over now, no going back* I'd constructed my own Michigan in my head, studied its maps, clipped color pictures from magazines, read about its history and geography and cold snowy winters like Maine's, populated it with a Papa and Maman who loved their daughter, me, and thought about her every day. What a dumb kid, unaware I was living in the wrong place, in this yellow box in a sparse scattering of similar homes among hills where I had no nearby girlfriends. *I'm not mad, really, shouldn't I be?* I pulled the bedsheet over my head. Hearing voices in the hallway I went rigid, holding my breath. *A crowd in the doorway, the whole darn world for all I care.* Someone mentioned supper. Maman whispered,

"Let her sleep." The room brightened. Morning. I could hear Papa and Maman in their room bustling around. Packing? I didn't budge until I heard them talking as they passed my door toward the stairs. What to wear? I put on yesterday's dress. I gazed out my window at hillsides of trees. Voices. *They're still here.* I took soft steps down the stairs. *Who are they anyway, these imaginary beings?* My aunts and Maman correction, *my mother* were washing the breakfast dishes. Papa *my father* and Pépère were dawdling through their after-breakfast coffee. Aunt Letitia informed me, "We finished the eggs. You're having oatmeal."

Aunt Esther noted, "You must have slept twelve hours." My mother said, "The family made a decision." She wasn't adept at hiding her unhappiness. "You'll be going to high school here."

Not trusting myself to talk to her, I assumed a veneer of diffidence. "OK."

My father glared at me. "*OK!* That all you have to say?"

I focused on eating oatmeal. No one offered me coffee.

Placing my empty bowl in the sink, I went out the back door. Parked in the backyard my father's car tried to look innocent. I put my hand on the side near the hood, daring it to bite so I could hit it back. Cold metal like the stinky barrel at the end of the yard we burned garbage in. My father's voice carried from the porch. "What d'you think?"

He opened the driver-side door. Frowning my suspicions, I got in just to be inside a car for the first time. The steering wheel was too high for me to see over it. I waggled the long metal stick coming out of the floor. He said he had a heater put in. "Want a ride?"

I didn't reply. He gestured me to move to the passenger seat and got behind the steering wheel. He turned a key and pushed a button and the engine started. He asked where we could get ice cream cones and I made myself say it's too early for ice cream. He drove past the saloon and the mill and pulled over and we walked to a little pond. Tadpoles flitted in the shallows. He said nobody asked me what I wanted to do. I glanced at him and shrugged the way Pépère would to disclose it doesn't matter. Not good enough. "If you insisted you wanted to go to Michigan, nobody would of stopped you." Tadpoles were heads and tails without bodies between them. He wasn't giving up. "We could have fun on the trip back. We could go to Niagara Falls. Bet you never seen anything like that." I'd seen photos of it. *Good kids are seen not heard.* I spotted a tadpole larger than the others. It was sprouting leg nubs. He said, "The Catholic high school is a good one. You could get in the university in Ann Arbor. You could be a teacher, not work in a mill. Not do piecework in a shop that makes cheap jewelry." The tadpoles would dart every which way; then they'd pause and drift, as if resting. *Silent tadpoles.*

"Stay here and you'll wind up behind a counter in the five-and-dime in Lewiston. Education, that's what matters."

My voice came out weak. "There's lots more matters."

"I know work. I don't know other ways. I go to my job every day. I pay taxes and union dues. It's how things are done. You can do better. Me and your mother don't want you to throw your life away."

"Like I got thrown away?"

My words surprised me. His look heated my neck. His voice went stern. "We couldn't support you. We weren't getting by, me and your mother. Them were hard times. You can't know how hard."

I gazed across the pond. "I never got a chance to find out."

He must have noticed I didn't call him *Papa.* He controlled his tone of voice. "You should be glad you missed them lousy years."

I saw hurt in his eyes. "I heard about the Depression."

"You heard! That's better than being in the middle of it. I bet you never heard about them years after the Eastern League folded." *His fame in baseball, before me, so?* "Meals we missed. A lot of them wasn't worth eating. Tomato soup made out of ketchup. Coffee grounds used over till we was drinking colored hot water. Relief workers come and ask what's cooking in the pot on the stove. Job hunting without no place to job hunt. Months in a Hooverville."

I gazed out across the little pond. "Now you got a car. You made out OK."

"After ten lousy years we're OK. Now you can come home."

Had the larger tadpoles swum out to the deeper shallows? Did fish eat tadpoles? Too much the small child to argue with him, I murmured, "I can't."

"What d'you mean, you can't?"

Questions. Why was I supposed to answer questions when he shunted me to his mother, me hardly more than a baby?

"I got questions. Like all poor kids got sent away?"

He misheard me. "You got questions, hanh? I kept plugging. I never questioned my work, or the company. You ask questions in school, where you're suppose to. At work you keep your mouth shut and do your job. You don't question your family."

I wasn't overwhelmed as I'd feared I'd be. His voice went hard, not loud. He held his shouting inside. I dared, "I had things better here, I know that. I don't know you."

His hesitation told me a lot. At least he wasn't glib. He groped, "If you got to blame somebody, blame me. I gave up too darn easy when your aunts brought in the priest. I could a flat-out said you're coming home with us. You wasn't there. You didn't see Mémère's tears. The pain in her voice."

"I didn't hear pain in your voice, neither."

"That's harsh. You don't know."

I suppressed a flutter of guilt. *Wants to be my father, should I relent?* Someone else, stronger, the unifying presence in the family to whom he felt he owed his existence, his mother, had scripted the long-standing imperatives he succumbed to last night. *Her idea to take me in, fair of me to blame him for his moment of weakness?* "I'm sorry—"

I couldn't add *Papa*. His voice softened. "Me too." I was ready to return to the yellow house where I'd grown up. He had more to say. "Next year you'll be older. Suppose they let you come to Michigan and stay next summer with us. What d'you think about that?"

Mémère would never allow it. I took a deep breath. "I don't think so."

"Maybe you can't now. Me and your mother want you with us."

Something inside me was taking over. The years of waiting had grown into an entity larger than myself, asserting what I'd never dared think. "Forget about me, OK?"

"We can't do that. We'll never—"

"You got to. I want you to."

"We... You think we made a mistake."

Sorrow. Anger rising. I rode anger for all I could. "Forget me. What I look like. Things I did. Forget I was ever born. Go back to Michigan. Just go. You're good at leaving."

"I can't believe that's what you want."

I forced certainty into my voice, aided by outrage at my exclusion from the family conference. *Children should be seen but not heard. I wasn't either.* "No cards, no letters, no phone calls, no boxes of presents. Nothing." *This can't be me saying this.* "That's what I want, nothing."

"You're upset."

"Never knew I'm a little brat full of tantrums? I want to go back now."

He stood flatfooted, then turned, and I followed him to the car. *He believed me!* He opened the passenger door for me. "You didn't say go back *home*." He was right. I'd stopped short of calling home the yellow house I grew up in, where he did, also. He started the car, adding, "You know where your rightful home is."

I gazed out the window. Birds were flying from a field and into some trees. I gazed out the window until the car pulled into the driveway. I followed him into the kitchen. Reading the expression on his face, everyone went silent. Pépère looked up from his coffee mug. Mémère was frowning. My mother's eyes filled with alarm. Her husband told her they'd better get going, "It's a long drive," and he went striding through the kitchen and toward the stairs and my mother hastened to follow, going for their suitcases. I resolved to be glad she was leaving. I headed for the back door. Aunt Letitia called to me, "Where are you going?"

I wanted to visit a girlfriend. "For a walk, OK?"

"No, it's not OK, You'll stay here and see your parents off."

I stood arms folded as they returned. My father was carrying both suitcases. He and my mother exchanged uncomfortable pleasantries with my grandparents and aunts. My mother paused in front of me. "Be a good girl, Ophelia."

She sounds like she's talking through a toothache, eyes dulled with guilt, reproaches. I looked off at the clean gray Formica tabletop. The mother I'd missed all those years had let me get sent away and the man I'd imagined as my formidable Papa turned out quite ordinary. I regretted reducing him. *Love them and watch them go away again?* I withstood my mother's intense hug before she hurried to overtake him while he held open the back screen door. We trailed them outside. My aunts, Mémère, and I stayed on the back porch. Pépère stood by the car as they settled in. Suddenly my mother opened the passenger door, charged up the stairs, and grabbed me in a breath-stealing embrace. "You'll always be welcome in Michigan."

We stood still as if attending a eulogy as the blue Ford backed up, turned, and presented a passenger-side view with my mother waving before it was gone down the driveway. Her surprise hug capping off her departure had left me disoriented. As Pépère came up the steps he glanced at me with, I thought, a faint sad smile.

The one-story house hunkered behind once-trimmed shrubs going feral and clusters of flowers embattled among mid-June straggler weeds. A loose latch kept the scarred white picket gate ajar. Alongside the house a section of pickets leaned inward. *Could have been my home, spurned by an angry child.* Standing in the doorway, supporting herself on a curve-handled oaken cane, wearing a white housedress aswarm with tiny print flowers hemmed at fishbelly-pale ankles and heavy black low-heeled shoes, the white-haired woman studied me, wary, *Believe her smile or her eyes?* trying to recognize me after many years, despite expecting me after my brief telephone call. She stepped aside in invitation to enter, uttering not a word, leaning on her cane to left-hand gesture I should sit on the sofa. As she lowered herself into a soft easy chair, I was facing a plump gray-haired woman with modest loose jowls and age-spotted arms. "Ophelia, nice you stopped by."

Guarded sincerity in her voice, no irony. A coffee table with a dulled finish spraddled between us."At last, Mother. How are you?"

"As you can see, not perfect. I was taking these pills to sleep. One morning I woke up groggy and fell getting out of bed. Broke my hip. I need a replacement. Lucky we had savings. Luke passed four years ago."

"I'm sorry."

"Luke loved baseball. A man's got to have his love, besides his woman. His old age, when nobody'd hire him to coach, we went to sandlot games. He studied players like he was still coaching."

"Do you have a good doctor?"

"I'll find out after he fixes my hip. You're looking good for near fifty."

Forty-seven. "So far."

"How's your aunts?"

"Aunt Esther died. Aunt Letitia rents an apartment in Portland."

I'm sounding terse. Mirroring my mother's speech? More tense—defensive?— than I expected. "We had a nice day together."

"I lost touch with my family ages ago." The look she gave me conveyed, *including you.* She shifted in her chair. "I've got hot water on the stove. Like some tea?"

She didn't budge. I said, "I'll get it."

"Mugs on the counter with tea bags in them. There's milk and sugar. I take it plain."

Finger grease and wear smudged the pale yellow kitchen cupboards and dulled the Formica counters. A white towel covered dishes in a drying rack. I poured hot water from a steel kettle. We sipped black tea. She'd awaited my visit since I was twelve. I'd responded to one of the dozen cards she'd mailed to Buckfield, Maine. As if stepping into an icy river she asked if I had kids. *The familiar question, the biological imperative.* Suppressing a defensive twinge, I said no. Ever married?

"Thirteen years. We split up."

"I lost my pa while I was a kid. Those days, the cotton mill was slow death. Some days fibers hung in the air like snow that wouldn't fall. Everybody died young. My mother got so she couldn't stand the least dust in a room without coughing. She died when I was twelve." Her eyes disfocused in reflection. "I moved in with Aunt Marta's family. My sixteenth birthday I left." She frowned. "Ran away to Portland with a girlfriend. Had enough walking to the dark stinky mill before sunup. Walking home after dark in the snow. I felt bad, leaving them like that. Karma."

She was doing the talking. Her story. For mine, I remained terse. "They gave me a home."

"After me and Luke kicked you out. That's how a kid sees it, kicked out. You weren't even three. The Depression, what it did to Luke, you couldn't know. We got on our feet too late. You think I don't get it, about you mad at us? Believe me, I get it. An abandoned child never forgets. Stays with you deep inside where you don't notice it. You can't ever forgive. What's to forgive when you think there's nothing there?"

Her voice was level, not accusing, her gaze directed into my eyes. I stifled an automatic protest. *Was that really me?* I could recall my little-girl love for Maman and Papa blurring as years chugged along, *a child's love weakened by a hole at its center.* However faint the waning love, dared it vanish? *A lifetime ago that yellow house, the watcher at the window, loss burrowing inside.* Silent snow covered a living world. Somewhere resentment hid. *Honor thy father and mother.* She awaited a response to her rhetorical question. I withheld the question in my mind, *What did I expect from this visit?* "I couldn't pass near Michigan without seeing you."

She blinked. Just once through a steady gaze. We could have been two marble statues in front of a public building. "You had to come here."

"We owed each other no less."

She let my remark hang in the air, likely recalling her unanswered cards and notes. If she chose to consider my words somewhat apologetic, I'd let her. "You know, maybe I didn't have it in me to be a good mother. Just because we've got the baby-making equipment in us doesn't mean much after baby's out. Oh, sure, we've got instincts, if that's what you want to call it. We've got our past in us, too. How we grew up, who we married. Luke was a good man. A big kid, too. He spent his life on a kid's game. I needed help growing up. Luke wasn't the man to give me the kind I needed." She paused as if reassembling her thoughts. "You never wanted kids, did you?"

I shook my head. *Abandoned as defective, unfit for breeding?* "I don't know much about fathers." I was making a point. In those days, in their home as in most, the man reigned *king in his castle*, yet every neuron in my being blamed my mother. "Nor about mothers, either. It's hard for me to imagine a mother sending her little girl away."

"We protect our own no matter what." *Her own. She means me.* "We look to men for protection. It's easy for us to get hung up on that. Was easy for me. I got worn out getting beat down in the textile mill. Me, scared of motherhood, who knows?"

I held back on a long-rehearsed rant. I'd gotten stuck on how could my mother abandon me, *a flawed child, not cute enough?* "I blamed you." *Was I wrong?* "I didn't know at the time that I blamed you."

"Any kid of twelve could've felt the same."

"I was in a rush to get past my childhood, to forget it. I wanted a new life, go to college. Do you remember my letter about my high school graduation?"

"How could I forget it? It's the only one you sent."

"I didn't know how to reply to any of yours. I wasn't sure it mattered anymore. I'm sorry if that sounds catty."

"I quit sending letters and cards when the post office returned my last two."

"I hardly ever wrote home after I got to the University of Maine. It's when the hectic part of my life began, every day full with classes, summer classes, applying for scholarships, working my way through by waiting on tables. I lived off campus with girlfriends. Then I married Lyle. He was building his career with jobs overseas. Me, a world traveler! I had so much to see and learn. I was lousy at keeping up correspondence, even with my aunts. Too many years went by too fast. I know, weak excuses. When I began planning this trip west I had to decide should I make a detour to see you or not. I found a reason. You should know I'm thankful for the sacrifice you made for my benefit."

She lowered her head, eyes closed *hiding her eyes?*— moist when she looked at me again. "It took a while, didn't it?"

A trace of irony in her tone made it clear we were strangers *mother, call her mother, and this time really mean it* and my equivocating burdened conscience would assure we'd remain so. We'd run out of time. *Merry Christmas.* She wouldn't invite me to stay for dinner. *Do I want to stay?* An unsought obligation evaporated. "I should leave before dark."

"You got just enough time to get downtown and catch your bus."

Call her mother! "Then I'd better go."

"I'd walk you to the bus stop but the doc doesn't want me stumping around outside."

From a foot away I gave her a cautious hug she returned with one arm, using the other to brace herself on her cane. She stood in the doorway and I started down the paved front path. At the sidewalk I looked back. The door was closed. As I shut the gate, I pulled the handle hard to nudge the latch bar into place.

"Do you want a priest?"

A priest here? I shook my head. Waved him away. *My arm hardly moved. Hand fluttered.*

"This name you gave us. Who we should notify. The phone number's wrong."

Lyle's old number. He moved away years ago. There's nobody. You wouldn't accept the form with blank spaces.

"Is there anyone we can reach?"

"She's trying to say something. Who is it?"

The window. I want to see out the window.

"I don't think it's a name."

"She's getting more feeble."

Is it snowing out? I want to see the snow...

ALLEN FORREST

CITY LIFE, IN TRANSIT

CM DUPRÉ
SEA & SAND
OR THE EXCHANGES AT
CITY STATION NORTH

What is it that is wedged between the shafts of light? Lined, scripted, cursive piles of bricks look rough and almost readable under a slanted sun, golden crackle bound by mortar tinted gray—light as the filtered messages that have come to rest on the hooded eyelids of my uncle. He stands between monolithic stanchions of the station that have introduced his charted life, which is how he tells it.

He begins as always with the canyon sheltering his entry, the direct city route taken from City Station North between two brick buildings held rigid by covenant—secular left, religious right (the undecided coming direct)—that provide a briefly chilly, militarily chastened *danse macabre*. This performance demonstrates practiced appropriation, a rehearsal of phrases now well-extended: marks, footsteps, shadows, boomeranging limbs, striated lighting, evoked, witnessed or entirely imagined. The city's light fantastic enters uncle's receptive mind: back-forth relays reawake in chimes of replacement, since nothing gathers more persistently or more densely than uncle's oscillating sweep of database that will or should honor the integrity of his binding contract. His need is to record and edit while tidy translation will, in many futures, require further meta-edits and philological redaction. So there's a history of return; also its commentary. And reform works as always, talmudically. Scholars still raise their heads with interest.

Those conundrums of Master-Slave, sensorial Being-Time, and the sound of flat lowering Form-Function take on fussy claims of stability in gliding containers with the nagging sense of a turning wheel, taking screw-like control of events called Power of Transformation, something to nothing or the reverse: veiling and release. Also, my uncle has forced himself almost weekly to reconsider an inexhaustible problem, the bilaterally cluttered Culture-Art. The first (Culture) is convention diffused by confusion made by inattention—by group-think or consensus led by a muzzy committee chair—but curiously gripped by unremitting risk of explosion. That cultural gamble would arise in flame, as forewarned, from the pot-belly of a watchful stone Momus. The other conundrum (Art) has slid through a disordered world even as it wished to mediate an open-mesh cosmos where, instead, it was drained, acquiescent at last, into full acceptance. That's the obliging portmanteau opening onto a mélange of insect tracks, half-drowned fractions, listless floating logarithms, subject matter inconspicuously lounging in a sociometry of textbook solidarity. Tacit, unstated—canvases welter in collateral spaces most often below ground—adroitly refashioned salon-style, rapid pop-up nearly the height of street-level eye-level passersby. Each chamber-space has shoulder to shoulder ornamentation over sparkling white gleam of urinals, toilets, silver-plated drains, with *passé* formalities—struggles still called "paintings." They await titles, self-triumphant screeds, recognition. Some, quite early in the game, have been archived and stored. Once, assumed in a narrative fashion that passes as a version of truth (or history, or *régime du savoir*) their dissembling claims mimic "meaning" or "story" with providential terms. And the "power" or "skill" of terminology is scattered to salt an arid plain.

We can engage with them through Source-Concept-Expression, over which artists themselves, sitting huddled now in cold stone stairwells, still wage endless, intimate wars—in quieter tones. Hushed ideas, figures, homey back-stories: what and how to present, what medium to fossilize the charm of presentation. More critical is how to cleanly defuse divisory lines: rejecting the unwanted pious past. Curiosity yearns after the undefined in order to summon form—but extraordinary demands of entailment follow any pattern—exquisite, emergent—like piano keys' vain attempts to own while exploiting what they find.

Argument grows harsher, so condemnable, murder is bloodier so incongruent, discontent is abomination. The symbol wants to attain the whole entity to the end, the complete and legitimated corpse—the symbolic order is the bearer of the process of that dying thing itself if we look and watch: its history so-to-speak is obvious, the flanking circumstances set out: we see it in its final function perhaps, the flat carcass of a cat seen drifting against the red Schiewenhorst Dike.

Echoes will still tap, tap from the train wheels and follow from the hollow replies of rails that pulse against my uncle's skull and along his shin bones. A studious man, he feels the code—within adaptive charts and maps—as it hunts forever for the real, the generous, and substantial. You can amble along with him as he himself considers, in daily prayer-like observance, the inside betweens circling around punctuation—what is wedged between any and every cloven thought, bar none. Words of intent and assignation are examined on both sides of the colon and semi-colon, then texts are reordered to the finest point (Prelude has brought its warden): the punctum. There will be a certain sound here, a thud of importance, or a pricking sensation, of an instant's recognition.

The ultimatum which pricks and wounds the observer. *Sine qua non.*

On he goes, uttering his diaphanous oblongs lengthened, then shortened, in bubble-like ovals sounded by means of his touching dialect. He uses this descriptive method to set the shades, awnings, shelters, the tents and their upright poles in a munificent curvilinear space. He talks spaces, he talks objects, as he builds.

And he works for the sake of improvement of these lowly beginnings on the shorter rungs of class in order to find the unspoiled—something "original"?—and so, perhaps, *Bildung*: supporting another cultural realm. So the carnival, stuck as it is in nondescript muck previously known as scant poetically distanced moors or wetlands, lies low against a mountainous excess of barely breathing sea. (There are "alternative" changes in 1) semantic sliding and 2) a lofty sort of nuance signaling caution.) In an ever-present that's geared to an open invitation to various forms, the sea and sand in harmony never shift away from coupling: always a basic well-settled substrate, a definite hold on their atmospheric identity.

Uncle has stirred this quiet venue into both a new prowess of slowed movement as, also, into a promise of a solid ending. Leaning against the coastline the carnival spread-eagles in a glorious resound-rebound of ragged half-circle; coming closer is the evening spread of sky-mirroring flats and tiny star-blue imitative flowers, sparkles; the town on this side of the river, and the town that gazes silently back from the slower—slightly lower, darker—eastern passage of the Vistula. Cottages lean against provisional contours. They hover against sheltered tool sheds, work benches, indecisive fences, slippery manure enclosures; and the piers clamber away from the heated forms—the dikes and farmyard stables and kennels—to stand in all their lank, watery poses of disobedience. Procuring for us it seems, in their show-tell duties, quaint pictures of limbic distillation.

Then the shuffle. As if they were mere notations but certainly not, ever, totally dismissed—these trifling side-watching warbling birds, hunching and pecking or sweeping upward in stippled shapes like chirruping, dancing text, acting the part of narrator-voices gathering long ago tedious tales, stories of no end. Bird stories of no breath. No Narrators now, Connoisseurs, or Raconteurs. Their studied hard-won timelessness makes them unwilling and much too restless to accept high-flown responsibilities. They entertain the blank areas whenever uncle casts his eyes there. Underneath the shadows of their wings, underneath their uprising uninterrupted choral plumage: there are the scarecrows. Deception blending into figure. Sign into its active metaphor, beyond the charismatic hint into hierarchic organ stops, foot pedals. The sublime: the sound of depth, the warnings of change. We could have known.

They stand in groups or quite alone, in circumspectral prison-house rows or as appointed slots lined up in backyard trellising seen at first, loved at first, in those comforts of *den Hague*. Initially they seemed to march forward in a shuffle of rows but now, in quietly settled alignment, the scarecrows stand stolid, artisanal, grounded on the factory's hard teak flooring, approached by visiting people—well-dressed tourists—who have descended wobbling down this mine shaft.

The elevator sets out small distributed groups at the third and fourth scarecrow levels. The elevator seems to fork them into quiescent groups. They stand in awe at each of the lozenge-shaped categories. Mouths drop open in unison, stopped as if directed by a page of musical score. Still, caught in such remote convention they need automatically search for particulars among these mirrored types, finding distinctive structures, features, and expressions—eye color, eyebrow arches, jaw line, hair growth, lip shape, nostril widths—accepting the rather gothic manufacture of themselves that obey the catalogue of such elaborate variations, in sections, and all at once.

Maybe worth mention at this precise interval is what surely inevitably follows: the damp touch fingering of the Changehouse where they all filed, as a rule, after rising up from the depths of the mine. Despite looking forward to cleansing the soot from their bodies, the crust between fingers and toes, assuming a desired state of cleansed eroticism (if not immaculate ascendancy), the experience suddenly grows to obscenity, a ghoulish nightmare that pinches their limbs into startled squeaks of pinkened tubular appendages. Once inside the Changehouse they imagined themselves affronted suddenly as devolved: cloyingly sought, observed, examined in the most accusing, undermining ways: even though safely unseen. Not real in the thickening mist. But since the march of time forward isn't soundless, we assume correctly that the tubs, showers, spray and fluids generated in the Changehouse have since been apprehensively recorded and rigorously avoided.

However that developed, and why, why there, in uncle's chronologically concentrated moments, it can be (could have been) otherwise: yet uncle is caught between such rebounding of considerate deliberation against two dialectical arrangements like gymnasium walls: hurdling there, in that rigor of dualism where multiple truths could have broken loose: throws, catches, fouls. There were enough dynamic recoils of recollection, he thinks, to summon up a *cognoscible*. This would herald the flash of a fingerpost—a supra-honorable vatic path that reformulates dozens of our favored grails of dualities to expand just as they contract in quick flashes of subtle in-turning ways—reinventing latent certainties: often moving succinctly—yet remote, imperious—along such contrastive weaves of the material itself, an umbrageous Talibanish carpet for instance—the desert-to-mountain colors, the snapping directions, the possibilities, the contributory coordinates—that also move and weave and mesmerize.

(Or else presented as fragmented—definitely not elevated to a primary theoretic choice at this point-in-time, thinks uncle shaking his head, before necessities demand a "stepping in" emergency moment so to announce the vehicle, era, or the resounding presage of an indispensable period of reform. The paradigm. Emblematic. *Et encore, nota bene*, of those forgotten exemplars unknown to or sadly loosened from the world. They are legion. Native to a "t" in every bio or remembrance—dressed in plaids, gingham patches, feathered edges, pinched linen panels, or ragged squares of leather. If gently encouraged, these exemplars, of paradoxical logic, may still exhale crumpled voices of historic significance. Each may find its place in our ponderous thrust of day-to-day.)

These are all signs of historicity in the workrooms of restoration, of contemporaneous regain of intellectual particulars of some flash node that uncle feels needs rescue in enlightenment terms as he counts the larger than life literary voices on two hands—past, present.

And we can see how my uncle holds these scant figures warming near his bony chest like withering birds: the iconic, the faded, the falling.

Otherwise, now, all the wandering mists we sense around us without serious claim to acknowledgment are the circling scattered Veimerjians, the Yazidis, the Kithiris, Suumis, Maronites, Uyghurs, Saami, Ugarit, Rohingya, and Nambikwara, in their subtlest sounds and colors brought to warmed nearness, where they can reside, closely proximate and therefore cherished in this uncle's wadding enclosures and safe-boxed slots. They all follow suit in an order that represents any Agamben particular, back from the rim of disposability, from his files of *Nudities*, (the silken portrayal: "saturnalicious princeps," [111] especially fond to classicists) which is to say the secret nebulous or sudden permanent-affixed state of *exception*. A specific harkened instant in which we need kneel down in the waiting rooms of the secular order to view, at some distance, the sacrosanct work of the 'great confessions' in the second greatest public reading room in the world housed as we know inside the City Station North where all questions have arisen only to become confused by the priested booths of hobbled semi-refusal.

There are luscious gliding marbled floors made quiet by fluted Corinthian columns meant to shelter from their great height every infirm thing and every stutter that we've grown to know so well: the norms of suspicion. This situation can certainly be viewed as systemic or, paradoxically similar to an overrun umbellate accountancy, cautiously hidden in the same confessional booth (as martyred Czech or Portuguese fathers-of-old, the early Venice dwellers of Jewish ghettos, the Ashkenazi, philologists or beguiled language-detectives, intellectual historians, all the uncles we've ever known), and attended by a fondly recollected, hunch-hardened scrivener of the leaky pen, a heavily graying, balding, and wheezing disburser of good works.

My uncle appears to await the nearly-here messenger from a tiny village near Gdynia. To orient us I seem to recall Gdynia being north of the partly saline Vistula estuary, and quite near several of the farms or small holdings that are in some narrow instances relevant to the meanderings of uncle's retelling of events. There is a quickened process of illumination that comes up out of such negligible grounds as these to surround factions that belong to it, ultimately that is, to the poetics, the lyricism, of the person or thing evolved from that fertile pallet of "light," the translation's arising *essenz*, the acceptable maintenance of inner mechanics. To my uncle, each example seems close to miraculous. It seems to be a condition of involvement quite like a Cartesian theatrical appointment arranged around a party distinction that, according to its crux of laws or stage directions, will engage every moment of their elemental involvements for that sweetly solitary prerogative to safely enclose. To wrap up in a promise of ease. Therefore, assuredly to maintain position: a move gauged by an assembled posture arranged solely around the pointed toe, *la pointe*: connected inside the stopped motion of an adulated ballet calculus, "the ultimate fantasy." We need not doubt. Connections will be clear. And Gdynia isn't that far off.

(Nonetheless we might ache to bring back some disorderly, or anomalous notions, some severed thoughts, not wrapped up in contract with the generic spread of rational histories, aligned, accoutered or scripted in the prism of planned events. There are thoughts, reliably igniting "on the other hand," as natural as childish questions. **Intent** [the important courtroom condensation] is where we find the words that lead us forward: inspiration, vision, concept, notion, suspicion, theory. **Intent** is where we find attempt; also contempt; and the duties, delight, of the skeptic—and of the legitimate and [*nota bene*] extensive strengths of refute.)

Each location has a chimney of circumstance at any rate, the flesh of suppositions and bright urges. Geography can describe the event and envelope the person in detailed particles and exponents, both visible and invisible. (Many of these had been described and numbered by uncle for the sake of his notes: gridlike drawings, captions, dotted lines—near-exact positions—showing the facts of a strange series of dog poisonings, the victims all adult German Shepherds; some were instances of flying green eels later found in comfort curled against the insides of soup tureens, warm, seasoned with capers and dill, consensual for midday tea. [Not everyone recognizes an eel if it's flying.] Or the days-on-end gossip following the incidents of the grandmother's seething violent, madly protracted broom beatings going morning till night, from garden to garden and into the rutted allyway, recorded in minute detail by the help of certain relatives and their intimate partners. Three days in all of broom beatings morning to night. Later she stayed, as if planted there, in a third floor window. Others seemed pertinent to single items and isolated instances like the pocket knife incident at the Vistula River junction that drew no blood; that bruising hand-to-hand combat for childhood dominance that took place early each morning, with clockwork persistence on the slippery well-nigh flooded dike.) Not that all these predate the ambivalent source of darkly divine comedies; they heap together in time and scope; they accompany those ground-thrusting upright tubes whose surrounding coils were meant to plumb identities and loyalties. Notice the pattern for these now, smiling, as they test the patience, inevitably, of the longer storyline, eyes-on-the-prize Nobel awards, meant to stretch beyond—but never ever managing—their announced and supposed content.

Even his waiting is theatrical. Or confoundingly filmic: South Korean, Tai-wanese, Russian, provincial French, as you wonder over his silhouette wavering in a long stretch of sunlight. Instantaneous parallels show him stepping down through deceptively transparent levels of a film (strengths of refute return here), accepting the descending moods of Tarkovski's underground passages, aggre-gates of indecent seepage and megadronic drips. Uncle's thoughts comingle, interconnect with a constant hum on the side of Stygian inference detected in the close-reader sense of **not** this and **not** that that becomes alas the most defining word in any text, simple or complex. "This is definitely **not** the primary choice at this exact point-in-time." "This cannot **not** be eliminated." "A power of contact, **not** of translation or mere observation."

There are events that do little to nourish my uncle's intent, but much to disturb expectancies without even hinting toward motion, of any sort. Nonetheless, they begin to fit into a scheme that has been taking and adding more pieces to his thinking, blooming in different archival shapes—petals that circle themselves like roofing tiles—and other more precious and multiple, deeper probing excesses. They will need to be exhumed at some point. Unbidden now, his thoughts curve back to the soldiers' barracks where the wide grunge of a pool floated outside the west-facing courtyard. It was there that he watched his some-time consort batting balls high beyond the barrack's chicken-wire fencing. At once bereft, he realized those balls were small frogs from out the pond, none more than four inches long: one after another following a metaphysical trajectory far over the fence and then yet another fist-sucked from the mud-verdant pond to follow the arc overtop its crouching mates. At least forty or more in a row, wham-sock fast as unaccountable electric sparks.

Yet remaining frogs hunkered unfazed on the mantle's dulled skim becoming a new fustier page for the newest social studies and the concomitant breadths of religious divides, racial implications (refitted to political positions of "class") and so heredity distinctions or qualifiers: "bloodlines," and the hopeful searching severities of a civil society. What all is engaged and how does it play through the heightened perceptions of filmmakers, painters, critics, and theorists?

Where is the educational, rotational value necessary for his report? Uncle bows his head, eyes strained upward, querulous. Means-Ends. Active-Passive. Manic-Depressive. Phenotype. Archetype. Prototype. Genotype. Back to the archives, to assembling the notes this time in blue ink, black bullets, red squares. Now, perhaps, to find and insert the values of critique. Should they be quantified? "Can I force vitality back into the equation" he wonders, if I consider powerful positions even beyond numbers, quite beyond challenge, as they hover succinct inside the chthonic?

What should we know of the chthonic that we do not find inside other such incalculable values of dream states?

Spectral perspectives form a bright welcome, an astonishing whiteflash reality whenever the poor man negotiates an entrance that manages to regain importance by projecting his image in a fictively explosive manner. Pinioned between the station's archways he's a sudden rolling flash reminiscent of the foamy edges of the Baltic Sea—a simple shaft of light emerging, and returning.

Look, says uncle gently, standing near the third floor window and pointing at the embroidery on the ancient grandmother's lap. It should not gather at the edges, but does. It pulls and puckers, marking new realms: something possible, maybe something imminent. And just beyond. Beckoning the imagination to step toward the liminal not so readily found; the pressing line of psychic reasoning—toward that kindly kind of sustenance that entices my uncle as it does many other uncles and half-brothers—the wizards, guides, gods, Norns, fantasists, and never to be forgotten special seers of the writer's side of "real" and "real time" such as Günter Grass advising between the lines, fingering the edges, explicating and pulling the slimy silver mealworms from the Vistula—for whom sustenance is, in some enigmatic cat-walking way, a thing nearly seen that rocks back-forth unceasing on the Vistula surfaces. Grass is an artist, incorrigibly disputatious; but uncle is something more simple and clean: his interest is devoted. Ultimately in a space he'll invent, naturally, generously educational. A soother, a helper, a Rebbe.

My uncle swings early mornings in the cross-sections of eaves, porches, window ledges and roof edges, watching quiet-winged and listening quiet-winged—unleashed by this lush awakening, untethered by a miraculous deflating breath. Uncle and the small round finch are loosed at the same moment from the holding of all things.

For him there is a beautiful pattern of waking. Daylight rising straight out of Latvia, carefully canted like fine wine and rolling there from the Russian broads steeped in the hush of the east and widening its decisively driven path northward. Now self-correcting: listing north-west. The light cuts specific, precise in its geography and taxonomy. Uncle swings wide over the early morning reservoirs of foundling notions. This is how he wakes, and remembers.

Beginning with his ostentatiously feminine cousin once removed who is walking the newest family babe in a lavish upholstered buggy along the wharf, perilously close to the ragged wood edge of disaster. The *enfanta mirabella* of everyone's dreams is soulfully still, a quiet bundle breathing in ever so lightly her scarce-breathing nimbus. Cousin Steph is excited, in her customary clammer of ecstasy, demonstrative in her gloriously adoptive duties and rapt inattention. She swings close to the edge and screeches *redoutablement* in delight, loving her own movements in these, her cleaving operatic-balletic moments; this precarious balance that sails over the appreciative heads of everyone in a freakish sound, an off-key ballad—the stirring whimpering object, the silenced watchers, the circulating winds, and the singing rivulets of the strangely awakened Vistula—all felt, in the following moments and after the fact, as the rivulets skimmed back off the scene, recanting the scene as mirage, and not glancing back: justifiably bracing to all. A vestigial forgiveness. Especially since it had come unbidden, quickly gone, saved if you will between action and irony. The "real" is dropped through the slats in the exposure to this other textual encumbrance. Memory. Or correction. How it glides. Refurbishes.

There's a similar tone to the time he kneeled inside the copse of trees known in parody as The Blacker Forest. Something roundly ringing, like the lightness of prayer escaping the slackened side of his mouth which was, in reality, a sound of utter disbelief because Steph's very fat, clumsy and dimpled cousin Mandy now, at this sudden wholehearted, breathlessly inchoate moment, **could dance**. Like a flame she begins to spin on that requisite pointed toe. *Destino. Inveterado. Identidade.* A pirouette, *faux pas de deux, la fleur incroyable*, luscious swirl of persimmon and peach flaring from legs burnt from the centered intensity of the guiding fire spurting golem-redundant, the complicitous accompaniment to what might be a reality: a miracle in stone. A trick in time is reminiscence in a filmy architectural interpretation of space. The stone edifice, a wisdom-filled Momus (mother of the inconceivable, impregnable), crouched in the circular copse; a ghost worker in effect, due to the structure of language. And the boy who was my uncle stood quite close to the scathing light of this vision, thinking to himself that they could all stop here, happily, arrested in Mandy's one time, true glory.

And sure, there were times like this, when the carnival, the birds, scarecrows, the pert-questioning elevation of dikes and the clownish clutter of farmyards, took second, third, fourth place—in some quaint forensic vial of filtration—to Cousin Steph's inopportune discoveries. One such was beyond the lugubrious sign of fortification that smacked of war as *continuously* uprising from the soil: it was *Stulthöf*: the iniquitous, ubiquitous bunker perched on a stately upraised dune. Steph has gone behind it inside her swirl of dotted-Swiss pinafore while all the others played low on the ground in concentrated endeavor to force mean-ing on the configuration of sticks in the sand pointing left right round back to achieve an inoculated removal of great boyhood concern. But she's gone too long though and too silent for her natural bodily and oracular rhythms. Sun bright skulls and the harsh signaled brilliance of grave stones arise in the nowhere of discovery. Steph tries, haltingly, to tell the others who decline: remain unyielding. Her discovery obscured by words or lack of words; the words flew everywhere, especially on that pile of bones, and the simple single perspicuous skull she holds up to surround the fingers of her right hand. The wordless words dropped onto the shiny mother-of-pearl areas, on the silken rounds and flats, heaping allegory: the putting-pressing of more operatic mythologies.

Still, we hope the messenger from near Gdynia will soon appear.

And we see that he walks through the main corridors, my uncle, watching for the impending arrival. He will recognize the messenger immediately by the way he moves, in slight shifting eddies, affected by hidden tides. Also by his garb, with the clank of stringed bottles and manacle-bond imitations starched to stand-up cuffs, accompanied by holstered cowbells at his waist all attesting to yes. It's the messenger. Honoring the specialized service thereof. His unusual visage follows him quietly and almost gossamer despite the crackling, unfathomable sounds the equipment displays. Uncle looks forward to sitting quietly, anxious to meet with him one-on-one, to acquiesce to some edited back-forth propositions, to send him back to the less-privileged village with his analyzed, newly projected educational agenda. This document will redeem the urgency for the entire Baltic Sea region if it works. The *studium* that follows (as clearly bidden) the *punctum*—is the secret formula and the result of all uncle's work to affix the aesthetic sheath of the ethical—to fix the creative domains, the emoting transformative signifier—with meaning, or else, against the impurity of semantics, of the incrementally slacken-ing, rubbery quality of transposition. Mind, to motion, also the inert, hidden motion of ellipses that reveal codes to regenerating pulsation, to push query forward, to demonstrate Heidegger's *Ereignis* or the re-fueling surge, the charge and, eureka, to free all aspects of reconfiguration. But, thinks uncle: Regeneration may be balance dependent; not necessarily an autochthonous or warhead emergence.

Cousin Steph does indeed grow up and takes on positions of employment such as they are during the war years and clocking those war years as more or less bundled outside or *et cetera* attached to all non-realities and restive resistance that spices the swerving bays and surreal suckaways, pits and curvatures, the shaping of the beautiful Baltic—and toward an unnatural glom of maturity. It was a string consisting of calm knots and simmering nerves of possible boiling points. At one point of minor augury Steph manages a rollicking tavern of similar attenuated consequence—later burnt to the ground and greatly missed as a *fungibilis*—where the dead have been stretched out photographically, assembled flat on the floors and up the walls in the brilliant manner of popular posters. Cadaverous dance-of-the-dead and blistering reprints became the newest thing here, or there, anywhere, announcing a peculiar sense of raw musical atonality and cankered camaraderies that contrast with the *mutatis normalis*. Needless to say, an artful production in which the past modes are interlaced with the present where its crusted limitations arise; we eventually, *en mass*, call forth an album of a band dead for decades in order to revive an emblematic paradigm of lost hopes now at an incredible height. Amusing and notable, there are liquid mixtures for Steph's favored few, those most devoted to enlivening the crusty hall with drunken banter. They are served up even today on collectors' punched paper doilies. Made with thin sliced silica, stringed saliva, a *soupçon* of fizz, mixed (or shaken) with subtle aromas of pure Steph; poured from an old golden whiskey bottle imported from the Scottish Highlands by an emigrant's very lengthy, bumbling path of transport. This is an emergence of tincture that contains an emergence of qualities, such as praise mellowed by criticism. You can see its value. And imagine how that has increased..

And in time it seems that Steph and Mandy might become one—as these nominatives can duly partake in an increasing mode of rampant or contained, but rudimentary sliding, shifting and exchange that happens in various formations to come often to rest—in sweet finality—as mere petting and succor. Concurrence, perhaps, despite possibilities of disappointment. The conjoinments are something we can accept more readily if we consider the Baltic Sea and the long horseshoe coast of sand and curves cut precisely from the spread of the German map, stretching luxuriously hand-overhand to Poland, to Lithuania, and Latvia. They conjoin in a world of disjoin derived from this naturalistic manner of stretching approximations, from the philosophy of junction-disjunction, taken largely from the bright Dutch-creamed, silk-lined, innermost insides of the precious imported pages of Heraclitian-Spinozian texts.

Steph and Mandy becoming one also curtails the identity argument that gives the ego a dominant hold over most ethical reasoning. Giving up the ego frees the person from his or her ownership of the art, and often the person entailed, or that has been created. (Especially [but not only] if imagined.) Here they embrace, one over another, erotically meaning mentally, roundly interlocked: roundness, the globe-shape, interrupts difference. Siamese is a locked reference. Is it a door with no handle?

But a Baltic Sea fiction always wrestles with living specimens, while fingering smoothed connective tiles or, in a manner of speaking, the lacuna, ellipses, blanks of reality, what may be truly functional-needed-necessary swinging invisible from post to post. This delights in the far-flung, from out of the long sweet wages of time with no demotions or belittlement, without weights, measures, meanness. At this time impossible to pin down, but inexplicably historic, several people fly by and otherwise rev up the engines of old red Simcas and silver Citroëns and lean-looking Karmann Ghias, revered, rejected, both at once in their fledgling yet unsevered corporality. Trickery as always the party-line. Ready to travel uncurtailed in the jet-stream.

Bedlam is a kind of Introduction where those lower-rung villagers are unable to delight in the experience of true infection: this is a missed realm of intersect. Yet in their roots they know full-well the Preface to Reality and to the initiatory terms of the Icehouse Early Dead and, no less, the creeping closing ring of empty cottages, and what that unnamable thing is sitting on the rim of the tub, assessing in rhythmic detail each masturbating stroke engrossing the steam-reddened innocent.

Thoughts remain with my uncle, concerned suddenly with his own sense of justice, walking fresh again into the picture to meet the messenger—this time as a kind of fortune hunter, an appraiser. Uncle's demeanor, his image, seems to have altered. He can affix a price on this or that, to serve as a point of departure. That is, symbolic. Empty, a punctilious HDML. An assessment floats like the searching beam of a *nom-de-plume* or lost impersonator surrounding the richly soaped-up body recalling the Changehouse calenture, but with humor's requisite distance. And there he stands, a functionary dispersing the dread "*opinion*" and the dread "*taste*" like gold standard. He has forced himself, has entered the domain of stacking dies, familiar to the graciously politicized meaning, gaining admittance between state of mind and beliefs—the strata of realities that the messenger has come here to accept or, against tradition, declare.

The messenger speaks clearly, given his diaphanous state. Segmented but without hesitation. Some would say "woodenly."

There are stations of the cross, he says, like envied corporate commissions, like valuing, naming regulated lots, acting charmed by the auctioneer's gavel. There are stations of the cross that pay out misery and suicide. There are the way-stations and nervous stops between stations where there is no conversational relief or unwanted advice. There are the search-light levels of gravitas, of *La divina Commedia* following metaphorically graded steppes down through the inferno. But what we are showing here, my friend—now—are Stations of the DNA, the experiment of birth and growth, the wayward manifestations of the insurrect, outlandish, radical, and ghoulishly present. There are the magnified stations of the impervious rich versus those of the Russian wolf descendents, the crouch-stalking Nazi shepherd Senta and her kin. So. Therefore. Back to genetics, eugenics. Feel out subtle, specified laboratory differences. This must be the story of the dogs in succession born from the Russian steppes, or the generations of deer that we feed by hand, or the gardens of green beans and Greenleaf mold separated or the capture of habits, feeding and speech behaviors and innocent postures of cannibal mice—the children of the soil and the sand of the Baltic bucket upended.

This reflection exists and reflects in this, our passing to, fro, and back—the messenger said—also, *nota bene tôt* that the reflections reflect actively in the events themselves. Sometimes as harbingers. But hear me: I must get back to Gdynia with your carefully notated partialities. Speculative arcs or aphorisms if you will. And listen well. I'll **not** distribute your indecision. And I will leave you, somewhat hesitantly, with the repetitious structural problem of the city's canyon, its left-right entry, and that of the scarecrow factory, a veritable museum where each existential frame—of each scarecrow—addresses each visitor with a discerning acumen. Then there are declarative premises of contrived auctions, surplus goods for inestimable "collections," "*objets d'art*," "institutional venues." The materials used, placement, recognition, facial disparities, modes of dress, and shared speechlessness.

But hear this. We should **not** keep the visitors prisoner. Even for the sake of enlightenment. Plus, there still remain the misfortunes just discussed; and then the common exchange and careful arrangements dealing in both inner and outer, subjective-public-objectively scientific value, in donations, in legacies, auction blocks, and the exact naming—i.e., renaming—of all these. None are understood or drawn closer to that desired nuance by weight or kind, parts or title, container or premise. We should try **not** to encumber our process by loudly announcing our findings or by distributing that chuffing air of distrust. Rather, we are virtuously attentive. We watch for lively points arising from the spikes of precipitation over the Baltic—and the unrelenting drum against the resistances of awful, artful coastal fringes that rouse that flat-hard sand for our diligence, empyreal guises, the numinous, driving to connect through the pouncing and receiving rites.

We are reminded by Goethe that these are critically the same: *Wendepunke* (crisis), *Wendung* (turning), *Weltabgewandt* (detached from the world, remote from reality) because these are, always, there—and at points of readiness not known by our own readiness. Also be reminded by Barthes' *Camera Obscura* as well, where we might know that the object we seek, want, remember, is (as we significantly want it to be) intrepid—resolute—enshrined.

JAMES DYE
THE EMPTY ROOM

O nce the boxes were unpacked and the furniture moved in, they still had one empty room.

"What should go in here?" the wife asked.

"I don't know. It's extra," the husband said.

"We could move in some chairs maybe, or a desk. It seems stupid to fill it up for no reason though."

"A guest room?"

"We have a guest room. How many people are staying?"

"Hey, I have an idea. What if we just leave it empty?"

"It seems like a waste."

"No, just think about it; right now it's all potential. Anything could go in here. If we fill it up, we lose all those possibilities. I mean, just imagine all the things we could do with this space..."

"But don't do them."

"Right."

She laughed. "I like it. You're right, it's nice to know it's here, room to expand."

"But don't expand."

She laughed again. "An empty room. How decadent."

They settled in, day by day working out their new routines. It was their first house and they were young. Sometimes he lay on the floor of the living room with a bottle of Scotch, studying the frozen currents of the ceiling plaster and thinking how they were his now. She liked to skate down the hallways in her socks and hang pictures in new places, always changing. At night, they ate dinner anywhere they wanted, in any room at all.

"Come here," she said, pulling him into the empty room.

"What are we doing?"

"Let's dance."

"Jitterbug?"

"Something formal."

"OK then," he said, and they clasped hands and started a foxtrot. They moved from wall to wall, corner to corner, reveling in the space, enjoying the smiles and the motion.

"It's a little bit magic, don't you think," he said, "to have a room like this?"

She laid her head against his chest. "It is," she said. "I always wanted a ball-room."

Their friends asked about the house and they told them how nice it was to have their own space.

"There's even a rumpus room," they said.

"There is?"

"Yup," they nodded. "And a reading room and an art room and a gym."

"That's amazing."

"We stayed up late in the observatory watching the stars through our tele-scope. Did you know there was a comet last night?"

"How big is your house?" their friends asked.

"Not too big," they said. "But it's perfect for the two of us. There's just enough space for everything."

Sometimes the door to the empty room would be closed, and when it was the husband or the wife would leave it alone, knowing the other was inside turn-ing the space into something private. And other times the door would be open and the other would be there, waiting to share. They walked in and out of each other's worlds, communing, drifting, playing along. The rest of the house was still there, fresh and new and purposeful, but the empty room was never rigid, always limitless.

"It's easier to think in here," the wife said, beside the husband on the floor.

"It is," he said. "There's no direction."

"What is it now?"

He gave it a minute, eyes half closed. "It's our spaceship, can't you feel it? We're out on Orion's Belt."

"No," she said, tickling him. "It's our room of invisible cats. They're everywhere. We're covered in them."

He rolled away, escaping her fingers and holding up his fists. "No, it's our practice room, where we hone our martial arts skills for lives of adventure."

She slid her hands over his, pulled him close, ran her breath along his neck. "No," she said, voice in a purr, hands on his chest. "Tonight it's something else."

One day, around breakfast, the husband came downstairs looking confused. "Are those your shoes in the empty room?" he asked.

The wife was making coffee. A bagel was in the toaster. "Shoes? I don't think so."

The husband poured himself some cereal, face scrunched. "They look too small to be yours. But where did they come from?"

The wife went upstairs to look and came down holding a pair of small, purple sneakers. "They aren't yours?"

"Of course not. Look at them."

"We shouldn't leave stuff in the empty room," the wife said. "It ruins the magic."

"I know that," the husband said. "I'm very careful not to. In fact, I picked up your candy wrappers yesterday."

"What candy wrappers?" the wife asked, tossing the shoes on an empty chair and looking indignant. "When do I eat candy?"

"Well I don't eat it. So where did they come from?"

"The same place as the shoes I guess...and the mittens."

"There were mittens?"

"There were mittens in there the other day and a box of markers. I thought you took them."

"I didn't know they were there."

"I thought they were part of the game. I don't know. I guess I was wrong. But those aren't my shoes."

"And those weren't my mittens."

They sat at the kitchen table, thinking it over. "So where did they go then, if you didn't take them?" she asked.

"Back where they came from, I guess."

"That isn't a good answer."

He shrugged. Sunlight splintered across the table. They fell into silence, jumping together when the bagel popped.

A green rubber ball rolled down the hallway from the empty room and bounced down the stairs. The husband watched it happen, a higher arch on every step. It settled in the foyer by the front door where he scooped it up and tossed it outside. The wife found a glass of milk spilled on the floor in the empty room and she wiped it up with paper towels and didn't say anything. The empty room had a closet, and when she found a plastic easel next to the window, she opened the closet door and tucked it inside, jangling the row of red coat hangers in the process, and knocking loose a green dress that dropped onto another pair of purple sneakers. She shut the door and kept her hand on the knob, afraid to turn it again or move in any direction.

Twice, in the night, they were startled awake by a dog barking in the house. It wasn't a truly loud bark, only unexplained and out of place. They scurried in their underwear down the hallways, tripping over each other and their own confusion. No dog appeared, but the door to the empty room was closed, and when they pushed it open they found a green rubber ball rolling across the floor.

"It's our movie theatre," the husband said, wheeling in the TV. They sat together on the floor, trying to pretend.

"It's our track," the wife said, running around in circles.

He pounded hard on pots and pans. "It's our music studio."

She grabbed her camera and told him to pose. "Sad now! Laughing! Angry! Tease me! Hate me! It's our photo studio!"

The smiles leveled as the illusions slipped from the walls, never blooming. They pressed themselves in the corner with a bottle of wine. "It's our bar," he said, dejected.

She drank her glass, poured another. "But it isn't, is it? It's nothing we want anymore."

"No," he said unable to look anywhere but into the glass, the dark well of greasy red. "Somehow it got filled up."

The little girl in the green dress came down one morning wearing her favorite purple shoes. Her dog was sitting under the table. "Do we have grapefruit?" she asked.

The husband shook his head. "Not this morning. I can pick some up tonight."

"Is there toast?" the little girl asked.

"There's raisin bread," the wife said. "I'll toast some and you can have it with your oatmeal."

The little girl pulled herself into her chair and swung her feet like she was running.

"I don't know about those shoes," the husband said.

The wife laughed. "She loves those shoes."

The little girl stopped swinging her feet and looked down. "These are my lucky shoes. Everything purple is lucky for me, but these shoes are special."

"Why's that?"

"They're made of sea serpents. So monsters leave me alone."

"That's very scientific."

"Did you take the dog out?" the wife asked.

The dog raised his head, ears perked.

"Mmm hmm."

"When?"

"Earlier," the little girl said.

"How much earlier?"

"Last night. He did his business."

"He's good at business," the husband said flipping the page of a magazine. "He probably has more to do."

"He needs to go out again," the wife said.

The husband pushed his chair back. "I'll do it. It's getting late. Eat your breakfast." The dog followed him out the back door, tail like a spastic metronome. The little girl in the green dress ate her breakfast, swinging her purple shoes until the school bus came.

The wife was trimming the hedge when the little girl came running up. Her eyes were spilling tears and her lips fluttered and spat.

"I got stung!" she shrieked, holding her arm out, running in a circle. The wife dropped the clippers and tried to grab her, but the little girl was too quick. "Hold still!" the wife yelled. "Let me help!"

The little girl stopped, shivering, her arm held out like she was giving it away.

"It's just a bee sting," the wife said, relieved to see the wound now, sure it was nothing worse. "Come inside and we'll put some ice on it."

They went up to the little girl's room with its lava red walls and settled on the bed. The little girl nibbled her lip and sniffed tears up her nose while the wife cleaned the wound and plucked out the stinger. A stuffed crocodile watched from a chair by the easel.

"Why did it sting me?" the little girl asked

"Because it was scared."

"Of me?"

"Yes. You're very scary."

"Why?"

"It didn't know what you were. It was trying to protect the other bees."

The dog appeared at the door with a concerned pitch to his ears. He scrambled onto the bed and whined softly, licking the little girl's knee.

"I hate it," the little girl said. "It's the meanest bee I've ever met."

"Well it's dead now, so you'll never meet it again. It died when it stung you."

"I killed it?"

"It killed itself. Bees can only sting once and then they die."

The little girl chewed a fingernail on her other hand, thinking. "Why would it sting anybody then?"

"Because that's the way its brain works. It doesn't care about itself, just saving the other bees."

The little girl finished with her fingernail and started petting the dog. Her eyes were focused somewhere beyond the room where no one else could follow. The wife watched, wondering where she'd gone, what color flowers she was circling, borne by translucent wings.

"Is that better?" the wife asked.

The little girl moved her arm. Salt trails etched her cheeks. The skin was swollen around the wound and she touched the lump, wincing without complaint. "Kind of."

The wife handed her a cloth with an ice cube in it. "This will help."

"I didn't mean to frighten it," the little girl said.

"I know."

"I guess...it wasn't such a bad bee then."

"No?"

"No," the little girl said, working her fingers in behind the dog's ears. "I guess it was very brave."

Some nights they played games and watched movies about space and monsters and things that lived in the sea. The girl in the green dress wanted a spaceship or a machine to drill to the center of the Earth. "Do you think there are mole men?" she asked.

"I don't think so," the husband said, sipping a Scotch. He drank less of it now, spent less time studying the ceiling. The purple shoes were bigger, a new pair, the girl's feet barely swinging.

"But you don't know, do you?"

"I suppose I don't. But it's improbable."

"That's different than impossible."

"That's right. It is."

"What about aliens?"

"I hope so. I'd like there to be."

The girl got the checkerboard and set it up and they played the way they always played, with double kings and triple kings and prisoner exchanges all around. "I hope there are aliens too," the girl said, double jumping with a tower of checkers. "But I really hope there are mole men."

They went to the park, tossing bread to the ducks in the pond when the weather was nice or sometimes even average. The wife stopped moving pictures, letting things settle now onto the walls, into their places and their times. They ate dinner in the dining room, breakfast in the kitchen, lunch wherever they were. When the girl caught them kissing she'd stick her tongue out and the dog would bark and everyone would laugh.

"How's the house?" their friends asked. "We haven't seen you much."

"It gets busy," they said. "There's just so much to do."

Their friends curled up knowing smiles. "That's how it goes," they said, patting shoulders, patting arms. "That's always the way it happens."

The wife held the girl's bike steady with the dog running beside as they rushed down the driveway and along the street.

"I'm too old for that," the girl said one day.

"Oh," the wife said, letting go, watching her turn at the end of the road and come flying back, long legs holding her just off the seat. "Of course you are."

Sometimes they would sit together when the girl was out and say nothing at all. The husband would start a crossword puzzle and almost finish, inventing nonsense for the last answer, anything funny that filled the space. The wife would go upstairs and make the girl's bed, until the girl began to make it herself, and then the wife would push the door open and stand there looking at the walls, blue now, done with red, and the writing desk where the easel used to be.

"Not tonight," the husband said when she kissed his neck.

"Why not?" asked the wife.

"I'm tired. Aren't you tired?"

They both laughed. They were always tired.

"Never mind," he said, kissing her mouth, gathering her hair in his hand. "Forget I said anything."

The wife ran her foot along his leg, hooked fingers on his shoulders.

"Look," he said one night. "I brought down the telescope from the attic."

"Why?"

"So you can look at the stars. Can I come in?"

"I guess," the girl said and opened the door the rest of the way.

"We used to watch the stars from here and rename the constellations."

The girl fell back onto her bed. She opened a book.

"What are you reading?"

"You wouldn't know it."

"I love books. You know that."

"Yeah, old books."

"New books get old eventually."

The girl snorted like a bull. She was barefoot. Her nails were orange like parrot feathers.

The husband looked up through the telescope. "Sometimes I wonder," he said, "if there's someone looking back. Some star out there with a tiny planet..."

"The stars are dead. You know that. The light is ancient."

"Yes—"

"So by the time they saw you, you'd be dead too wouldn't you?"

He kept looking, pressed to the eyepiece like the sky was imminent, a looming fleet of diamonds cresting a tenebrous wave. "Not all the stars are dead."

The girl kept reading and didn't look up again. Eventually he left the room.

The girl didn't speak during breakfast anymore. She stopped wearing her green dress.

"Do you want to watch a movie tonight?"

She shrugged. "Maybe. Can I have coffee?"

"I suppose. How do you take it?"

"Black, two sugars. That's how they drink it on cop shows."

The dog tottered in and slid beneath the table. His tongue hung through his teeth and all his legs stuck out.

"Whatever happened to those purple shoes?"

Another shrug. "I think they're in my closet somewhere."

"She likes black shoes now," the wife said.

"Much more professional."

"Whatever," the girl said and dragged her spoon through her oatmeal.

The checkers sat in the top of the closet. They heard her feet on the stairs, on the floors. Doors opened and closed. The green ball bounced across the yard and the dog brought it back to him.

"Should we get a cat?" he asked.

The wife took a sip of beer. "We should pave the driveway. I'm tired of parking on stones."

The dog sat and waited, body shaking, ready to burst. He tossed the ball. "I guess," he said. "But the stones don't bother me."

The dog snapped up the ball, running in circles, skirting the hedge. Inside, a door slammed. A horn sounded somewhere out front, three quick blasts and then a yell.

"They're going to the movies," he said, not really speaking to her, telling it to the sky.

She finished her beer and stood up, brushing an ant from her arm.

They listened to the radio in the mornings. The two of them, wordless across the table, sips of coffee flowing over static lips. When the mail arrived, they sorted through it with nervous hesitancy, piling up the wasted paper: advertisements, campaign flyers, bills; never anything that couldn't wait; never anything they wanted. At night, the wife watched shows about unusual crimes and the husband spent hours in the dining room, playing game after game of solitaire.

"We should go for ice cream," the wife said once.

"I'll get my coat."

In the car, he hung his arm out the window while she wove down tree-lined back roads, following the strands of a listless web, moment after moment caught under slowly turning wheels, the longest route to anywhere.

"You should have a party," their friends said. "Now that you're settled in. We want to see the place."

"We'd like to," they said. "There just isn't any time."

"Nothing big. Nothing fancy. You can give us the tour."

"We aren't done though. It isn't ready."

Their friends laughed. "It's never ready, no matter what. How about a Sunday?"

The wife sat on the bed, holding the stuffed alligator. She touched the blue walls and ran a finger down the telescope. In the closet, the hangers were empty, a pair of dress shoes waited at the bottom. She pulled a box down from a shelf in the back. A green dress was folded inside. She turned to the room and ran a cloth along the windowsills and the writing desk, sucked dust from the corners with the vacuum.

"C'mon," the husband said, standing in the door, a smear of dirt across his cheek. "Before it gets dark."

She shut the vacuum off and followed him down the stairs. Outside, milky clouds piled against a concrete sky. A cold raindrop struck her cheek and she closed her eyes, waiting for another that never came. Together, they wrapped the dog in his favorite blanket and lowered him into the hole. The dirt fell from their shovels, steady, softly. She placed a white stone on top when they were done.

"He'd lie on my feet under the table," the husband said. "I'll miss that."

They clasped their hands together, silent house at their backs like a barrow. "He was a good friend," the wife said. "He lived a good life."

One night the doorbell rang. A young woman was there. She threw her arms around them and came inside. She was tall like a sunflower. Over dinner she asked the husband, "Have you ever seen *Island of Terror*?"

"I haven't," he said. "Is it good?"

"You'll love it," she said. "I brought it with me. We should watch it later."

"Sure."

"Are you still painting?" the wife asked.

"Not as much," the young woman said. "But I've been doing lots of drawings. I brought my sketchbook actually, if you want to take a look. I've been thinking of making movies, or maybe doing comic books."

"That's great," the wife said and got up to get a beer from the fridge. "Would you like another?" she asked, waving a bottle in the air.

"Sure," the young woman said and finished her last sip, placing the empty on the table.

When the movie was over, they sat out on the terrace, watching the scribbled flight of bats across the moon, afraid to go to sleep.

"I saw a mole man yesterday," the husband said.

The young woman laughed. "Is that so?"

"I did. He was just how we imagined: pointed ears, wearing big, thick goggles. He stuck his head up through a hole in the yard."

"Where?" she asked, leaning forward.

"Over by the compost pile. He filled it in when he went back under."

"They're blind you know," the young woman said, tossing bits of gravel lazily into the night. "Living down there in pitch black cities."

The husband pointed at the silhouette of a bat, tracing its path as long as he could.

The wife handed the young woman a cardboard box. "Here," she said. "I saved these for you."

The young woman opened the box and her lip began to tremble. Inside was a pair of purple shoes. "I can't believe you still have these!" she said.

"They were tucked away under your bed."

"Keeping back the monsters. No wonder they never got through."

"Nothing beats purple," the young woman said, shoes so very small in her hands.

Night moved on like a river and the constellations grew overhead, forming themselves into new designs, light to light, a living cosmos ever shaping, fluid, awake, and alive. Below, the young woman kissed the wife, then the husband. She picked fresh beers from the kitchen and passed them around, telling stories of her life, everything she'd seen, all the magic she'd brought back from the world to share with them and prove that it was there. Their voices chased the hours until heads bobbed and dreams slipped in, dissolving the mortar of night so the terrace lay exposed under walls of thinning stars, no barrier remaining to hold back the dawn.

"It's a beautiful place," their friends said, glasses in hands, reeling from wall to wall. "You've made it all so comfortable."

"It's a work in progress," the wife said. "I'm still playing around with the pictures."

"Do we have any vodka?" the husband called.

"It's always a work in progress, but you've done a lovely job."

Their friends milled over the lawn, danced in bare feet on the driveway pavement. They turned on the showers and stuck their hands in the water, rushed up and down the basement stairs.

"Do we have any poker chips?" the husband called.

"You should get a cat," a friend told her.

The wife finished her beer, started peeling the label. "We were thinking about that. Maybe in a few months, when we're more settled in."

"I made you a martini," the husband said, pressing against her with noise on all sides. Their friends giggled in the living room, stuck their heads up the chimney to smile at the soot.

"It'll be a nice place in winter," someone said. "Very cozy."

"The summer too. You can grill."

They moved to the second floor, the husband and wife, hand in hand, gently weaving. People kissed in the hallway, hung their legs out the windows and crawled under the beds.

Pushing open a door, their friends asked, "What's in here?"

"Nothing," they said, turning in a languid circle. "It's just an empty room."

JULIE EILL
DEAD GIRLS

O n Sunday you wake up before anyone else and creep downstairs, greedy. Almost instantly you're guilty though, thinking it's radon giving you the morning off, and that they're all dead, even Chris, who was whistling a little in his sleep when you left him. You make yourself stop, instead imagining your boys, Ryan and Alex, growing, their bones slowly inching forward like in time-release footage, envisioning the extra hour of weekend sleep as productive, accomplishing just that much more. Alex, the traitor, has man-hair on his legs now, even though he is just shy of ten.

You tiptoe over the grass, your cotton socks instantly wet and cold. Grabbing the *Times*, you hold it like a newborn and head back to your kitchen. You light a candle that smells like wood smoke, then take the kettle to the sink, you start some water for tea, your ritual almost complete. But the water comes out of the faucet foamy and strange. *What the heck is this?* you think, even your thoughts G-rated this early in the morning. You wonder if it's safe to drink, even when boiled. Emptying the kettle, you decide to forgo the tea and just get down to the paper.

When the kids emerge, mussy-headed, they hit the TV, then their iPads, sitting on the brown Pier 1 couch, dried boogers down the side, their eyes still heavy. Ryan, your seven-year-old, says, "It's cold down here. Can you make us oatmeal?"

"Yeah, oatmeal," Alex agrees.

You know you're making that "Vee" in your forehead again, the one the dermatologist offered to help you with. They've never asked for oatmeal. Ever. *At least*, you think, *they're in agreement.*

Chris wakes last. "I was going to get you the paper," he says. "Bring you tea in bed."

"Doesn't matter," you tell him, "but the water smells funny. And it's foamy. Like it's rabid or something?" Chris gives you big eyes meaning you're bugging out.

"Can water even have rabies?" Alex calls from the TV room. "Ms. Reynolds makes us wash our hands after recess. Because of Ebola."

"That's just wrong, your teacher's an—," Chris says, and it's your turn to give big eyes.

THE SPORTS NEVER stop, they just transmogrify—soccer in fall, basketball in winter, baseball in the spring. Today you wish for a fainting couch and some opium, or at least a good book. It tears a hole in you the way some of the mothers on the sidelines make a habit of leaving others, sometimes you, out. Sometimes you stand there, jockeying for position, or worse, mulling over perceived slights even though you don't really like most of them to begin with.

You see the same mothers every weekend, on the bleachers or in their outdoor chairs, their places fixed, only the seasons shuffled and reshuffled. The therapist in you always tries to morph them back into their high school selves: their insecure, mean-spirited smooth-skinned teenaged selves transparent beneath the adult façades that you all wear. Faces have filled out, modes of self-protection have become nuanced, *but why*, you think, *had anyone thought it wise to put all of you in charge of children?*

At the first of the two soccer games of the day, you fight the urge to sit alone in the shade with your half-read *Book Review*. Instead, you choose one mom. Because of the searing Virginia fall sunlight, you coat yourself with the fast-drying organic sunscreen someone had recommended, and stand, alternately watching the game and chatting with a sort-of-friend, Suzanne.

Suzanne would have been a little clingy and had braces in eleventh grade, you decide. She would have been gratingly loud about her 700 SAT score in math. The Suzanne standing with you now mentions the college student who grew up nearby and has recently gone missing. In the papers they show only one photo of her, again and again. One eyelid appears to droop a bit, but you don't know for sure, because they only release the one photo. You know that you're a horrible person because this is what grabs your attention, the photo. Still, it's like other people's sickness, you try to be kind, make them a covered dish, offer to listen over tea, but all the while you are secretly thinking *please, keep it the fuck away*. You will use anything, anything—sage sticks, simple luck, vitamin supplements—to keep your brood safe.

The name of a former friend, not someone close, comes up in conversation about the alternative-to-boy-scouts coed nature group you and Suzanne have your kids in. "The Riddles. Janie Riddle," Suzanne says, "responded to the Night Hike evite that they're not participating at all this year." She gives you a look, a question really, about where Janie stands with you.

You say, "We went to dinner one time together and she had too many skinny martinis. She kept saying 'fuck therapy' she wasn't going back, even though I hadn't said anything. Then she returned her Brussels sprouts to the server, saying they were too crispy. As if the veggies were the problem." You're not sure you're making much sense, plus, you don't trash-talk. But who are you trying to fool, you aren't different from everyone else, of course you like trash-talking. You might even like it better than soccer.

"And you're a therapist," Suzanne says, narrow and concrete about what you've just said. "That's awkward."

You have some loyalty to Janie, some self-control still, because you don't share the worst of it, how Janie had called her own vagina ugly. How she had said, "I don't even like my vagina anymore." She'd told you that Harry had been an especially large baby, and she'd insisted on a vaginal birth anyhow. You'd kept looking over your shoulder during this confession, trying to find a distraction somewhere else in the restaurant. People were always flinging their problems at you, sometimes they'd catch themselves a little and compliment you on what a good listener you were, how empathic. But Janie, oblivious, had twirled her pappardelle while she told you how she'd been so torn apart she'd had to undergo surgery to patch things. This last part had made it difficult for you to finish your hangar steak, thinking about Janie's vagina and her marital problems. Worse, you'd started to feel fragmented, like she was talking about something more than a tear during childbirth. You couldn't sleep that night. It made you angry how she'd overshared, and depressed too, for whatever trauma she'd been getting at, but then you weren't sure if these were really your feelings or if you'd only sopped up Janie's. You did Kegel exercises while next to you Chris slept beautifully.

"After that dinner," you tell Suzanne, who is waiting for another morsel, "I felt bad, but I stopped returning her messages."

Suzanne, satiated, heads down the field away from you, even though you didn't say a thing about Janie's ugly vagina. "I've got to catch up with Denise—," she says as she wanders off. Now she is talking with a mom you actively dislike. You can just make out a bit of what they're saying, the slightly boastful notes of their conversation. You squeeze in next to Chris and some other dads, seeking out the solace of your husband. He is tall and quiet, which calms you. Your thoughts return to the friend you spurned. You're still angry at Janie, self-righteous about being used. She ought to have dealt with things herself. But you also feel bad, cowardly. You used to be a loyal friend, not a shape-shifter. This thought makes you so uneasy about yourself that you start to list all the things that give you comfort: tea, reading, candles, good soap, your elliptical, and then realize that all your things are solitary and none of them involve friends or family. Shape-shifting again, you revise your list to include decorating the yard for Halloween, tether ball with Alex, dancing to bad pop with Ryan while Chris does the dinner dishes.

It's the third quarter of the game now, and Suzanne interrupts your list-making to invite your family for chili and s'mores that night. "We have a bricked firepit, but you should all bundle up because the weather's going to drop. It's a shame, about that dead girl," she says, returning to the earlier topic. "I mean, I'm assuming. Someone will find her remains one of these days. That tortured family." She claps and shouts because her Sebastian, who is a bit of a ball hog, has scored another goal. Then she says, "The whole crowd will be there."

"At her funeral?" you say, still thinking about the missing girl and her droopy eye, thinking about fear and sickness and being torn. You think you are all tortured or doomed families, in one way or another, you just don't know it yet.

Suzanne gives you a look. "No, I meant the *families,* from our team. Don't bring anything," she says, patting your shoulder like you're demented. "I've got it covered."

You nod like a normal person would, but you're thinking, *how could I bring anything?* You think about how pleasingly full you felt when you were pregnant and even when the kids were little, their diapers saggy, you, the center of something, feeder, soother, sorcerer. You stare at your veiny hands. *Empty.*

YOU ARE AT the second soccer game, it is 1:15, and you've successfully crammed turkey on honey whole wheat rolls into the kids' mouths. Your husband is driving from one end of the county to the other, and you're feeling pretty good that they've eaten in the car, but then you realize you won't be able to make the salad with quinoa and chickpeas you and Chris like to eat, not until at least three o'clock. Your stomach begins to rumble, and your mouth waters. You hand your boys two chocolate Kisses each from your bag, "for energy" you say, but really it's because you want them out of your bag before you're tempted. If you're being truthful, it's also something sweet they will actually accept from you, and you're hungry for that.

When you get to the field, the kids are out of the car before you've even unlatched your seatbelt. You're not sure where Alex went, but Ryan's out with his friends, taking practice shots on goal. Anita, another sort-of friend, joins you on the sidelines. Her mother's died recently, of breast cancer. "We used to talk every day," Anita says. "She had beautiful clothes, and I loved going shopping with her. She loved to laugh." You feel so bad for her because she is in such obvious pain, you want to take the sad away, but since you can't, you just stand there feeling helpless, trying to say smart, understanding things. After a few minutes, you start getting irritated. This is a kids' soccer game, why do dead girls and dead mothers have to follow you from field to field? Besides, you've got your own ghosts. When your own father died, you felt so little about it. It was for the better, because of his dwindling, the dying a necessity. Then you think about your mother, alive, but not really, envying Anita a mother who laughed, a mother who wanted things for herself. Of course, you can't let any of that out. Anita wouldn't understand, especially not now, with her happy mother now a dead one.

Alex's team, the Optimists, are losing, which you find darkly funny. Supposedly everyone's a winner now. Positive feedback means everyone gets a medal for playing, even if it is plastic. You picture the prizes, the goody bag loot and fake gold coins you have thrown away, a massive trash-art heap to false optimism, an altar to mediocrity, to your generation's attempt to forestall disappointment for their children.

THAT NIGHT STANDING around the fire at Suzanne's, you still feel apart from everyone else. Someone is talking about their autoimmune disorder. It seems like everyone has one now, not the bad ones like lupus or MS, but a touch of something that causes rashes to bubble up, a wobble to the gait, a touch of fatigue to set in. For some reason, you wish you had one too, as if that would offer you protection from something worse.

Earlier, they'd found the remains of the dead girl in an old corn crib. Her father had wept on national television. Suzanne is saying, "at least they have closure." You throw a marshmallow into the fire, letting some of your true feelings burble up to the surface. The people on either side of you give you a look.

The kids are a pack of wild animals, eating one minute, on to flashlight tag the next. Other guests laugh. It is warm, full-throated laughter, the laughter of people at ease and full of good food, the warmth of wine and beer hitting their mark. But you can't help it, you hear an undercurrent to their laughter. But maybe that's just you. That's what Chris would say. You make up an excuse about ice cubes and go into Suzanne's house to be alone.

Staring at a swath of family photos that sails hopefully up the stairs, you wonder if maybe you aren't alone. Maybe Suzanne and the others are making their best, most courageous attempt to crowd out all the tragedies, the genocide and mass graves, and the smaller middle-aged ones, vitality on the wane, dying parents, children who pay you back by leaving. Maybe you have more commonality with these other mothers than you think, that they're just better at fighting off the dull ache of living, sidestepping toward the end. Then again, maybe they really aren't like you, where a shiver, a newspaper photo, a pinched toe in a boot you paid far too much for, leads you all the way to the skeletal clatter of bones.

Chris enters Suzanne's living room through the sliding-glass doors. He finds you sucking on a drink pouch, sitting on an overstuffed sofa in a neutral taupe. The drink pouch is grape. You still don't trust the water. You're staring at the robin's egg–colored walls, the tastefully chosen backsplash tiles. "Are you all right?" he asks.

You look at him like he's an idiot. He's familiar with the look, with your moods. "Do you remember our twenties?" you ask him.

Chris looks horribly sad for a second. He loved his music, his shows, the music forming movements, now copied, how it made for friendships, lovers, nights that were a lifetime. "What about them?" he asks.

"We were the greatness. Dolphins soared, people spun on their heads, we were the magicians. Now, we're just the magicians' assistants. What do we even get for it?"

"You want a prize?" he asks.

"Maybe," you say, "how about a puppy?"

"You can't freeze them. They grow into dogs," he tells you, rubbing your shoulder, the one that has been a bit sore lately. You love him because he mostly tries to be on your side, even when you're crazy.

"I wish I could climb through a window, dance a little, then climb back through it to now."

"The changing of the seasons depresses you. Taking down the Christmas tree," Chris says. "But you notice. It makes things relevant."

You laugh-cry, because it's true.

Suzanne interrupts, "What, are you two playing seven minutes in heaven in here?"

"Caught in the act," you say. "Please don't tell."

It's expected, so you follow her back outside to the fire.

A nice mom, a Southerner, who manages to never say anything that sounds too real, offers you a glass of port, which you accept. You make yourself a s'more, enjoying the whole thing in one magnificent bite.

THE NEXT MORNING you turn on the faucet, the water still foamy. You ignore it, the want of tea taking precedence over fear. You are home on Mondays, and it's a teacher work day so Alex and Ryan are home too. You know the teachers, the fun ones, whup it up at the beer garden after a few hours at school, playing darts and eating nachos. You wish you could get in on that. Instead you get out the bamboo cheese boards, one red, one blue, both long and narrow. You create goofy snack trays for the boys as their breakfasts: a line of cashews, a hunk of decent cheddar, a scattering of Cheerios, ham on a half slice of pretzel bread. Alex gives you a smile, Ryan squeezes your upper arm hard, and says, "Tiger." You guess that's latency for they still like you.

IT'S TIME FOR their annual checkups, and they grumble as they get into the backseat, Alex asking if he's up for any shots this time. "Yes," you tell him grimly, turning around to look at him, "you are."

"Is Ryan?" he asks.

"Nope," you tell him. He looks a little crestfallen. Ryan doesn't respond to this, just nods. You realize that you have good kids, kind, sturdy. Tolerant. There's something aggressive, almost sadistic, about watching your child get shots or have cavities filled, even though it's for their own good. You hate it. It makes you complicit in the violent act.

"Do they still have those stickers?" you ask. "You know, when I check out and it says to only take two. Spiderman, Captain America, SpongeBob. All the Famous Americans?"

"Yess," one of them responds impatiently. You can feel the eye roll directed at the back of your head.

You park and get out of the car, waiting patiently for the two of them to make their exit. "No one likes shots," you tell Alex. You remember taking him to his first appointment with this same doctor when he was only five days old. You had sneaked a look at the doctor's notes when he left the room. He'd written "alert, vigorous infant." Those words had made you feel invincible.

The elevator stops at the second floor, even though you have ten more to go. A young guy, maybe twenty, wearing a big flannel shirt over jeans, gets on the elevator. Your boys are giggle-fighting, but they stop as soon as he steps on. There is something menacing about this guy, his silence hostile. You're suddenly scared, your heart rate rising. Your animal brain must smell something on him, your nervous system responding. Or maybe you're just chronically morbid, like Chris says, when he uses your own fears against you, the times when you're fighting dirty, not giggle-fighting, with one another. But now this guy is glaring, not at the boys, but at you, and no one would argue with that. Alex and Ryan are absolutely silent, staring down, then quickly glancing back up at your face. You smile at your sons, putting a hand on Alex's shoulder because he's closest. In that animal part of your brain, you just know this dude is full of rage. At you and not really at you, but it doesn't matter. You're the only one here.

You look straight back at him even though you're scared, trying not to blink or cringe or get that small animal frightened look in your eyes. You don't want this asshole smelling anything like that off of you. A small part of you is curious, interested in his backstory, where he hurts, and why. Then again, he's already told you where it hurts.

Looking straight at him, you shoot this damaged guy the message that he's not your concern. In no way are you going to allow him to hurt you or your littles. You say it with that awful Vee in your forehead. With your big, bossy eyes you tell him that you had a gritty childhood. And that you give at the office. Cutting away from him, shifting your eyes and your attention back to your boys, you register frustration in your body. Who the fuck is he, to threaten your safety, ruin your ride.

"Are either of you getting those stickers after?" you ask your boys once again, the backs of their necks soft and exposed.

"Yeah," they reply together. "Why wouldn't we?"

ALISON FAIRBROTHER
THE SHIELD

The Teacher sits on the floor behind her big metal desk, which she has tipped over so that its legs stick out toward her and she can see an etching of a penis on the underside of the pencil drawer. The lights are off and her classroom has never been so quiet. Rain patters on the window and a thin whistle of breeze rushes over the sill. Can I get an Amen! the Teacher thinks. This is some quality first-year teaching right here.

As if on cue, crying emerges from the darkness. The Teacher gets up from her spot in the corner to peer behind a row of student desks, which have been pushed together and splayed on their sides to make a shield. Her twenty-six pupils are sitting cross-legged in a line. Some of them are holding hands. The crying is emanating from Chubby Blonde, who has come to school wearing heart-shaped earrings and green eyeshadow. She recently turned in a story called "Mommy Loves Me More Than Her Boyfriend." Now she is eking out guttural sobs, her fists like small hams swiping at her eyes.

"Be quiet or he'll hear us!" Officious Retainer Boy hisses.

"The floor is cold."

"I'm scared."

"There is nothing to be afraid of," the Teacher says. "It's just a drill." She smooths her new dress. It is calf length and sensible. Teacherly. She has worn it today because the other fourth-grade teachers go to a sports bar on Thursdays after school to watch hockey players skimming, padded, over ice. The Teacher hopes to be invited, hopes that her boring clothes will help her fit in. It's early in the school year and she could use some friends, at least until June. Once her fancy teaching fellowship ends, she'll be on the first plane from Cleveland Hopkins back to JFK, wearing a leather miniskirt to Club Sapphire and doing a bump on a pocket mirror in the bathroom with a handsome dealer named Arnoldo. Arturo?

"If he came in, what would you say to him?" Chubby Blonde asks.

Quiet Sensitive Child looks at her with alert, swimmy eyes. The Teacher sees that he has strapped on his shiny blue backpack, as though he might at any moment need to escape, taking his fractions homework with him.

"If we said anything to him, he'd just shoot us, right?" someone says.

"It's just a practice. There's no shooter."

"Excellent point," the Teacher says. She gives the room a thumbs up.

But she is beginning to wonder what is taking so long. At the faculty meeting yesterday, the principal had explained the procedure: shut the lights, lock the classroom door. "Keep them quiet as though their lives depended on it," he said. A star shone where his bald head held the light. "The whole thing will be over in ten minutes and you can get back to your normal schedule," he had said. "We will have practiced in case of any eventuality."

But it has been more like fifteen minutes, maybe twenty. What eventuality is this? Could an actual gunman have plotted an attack during the drill to prepare for said gunman? That would be a good use of the word irony. The Teacher looks at her coat, hanging limply on its peg next to the bulletin board, her students' careful penmanship marooned there on lined paper. Gunman is a compound word. Gun-man. Things are becoming floaty and prickly. Things are sharpening inside the Teacher like wires. Actual gunman > false gunman. True or false?

Chubby Blonde raises her hand and the Teacher kneels down beside her, suddenly nauseated. The girl is haloed with a treacly scent, like raspberry air freshener. "I have to ask you something," she says tearfully. "Would you die for us?"

Now all of the children are looking at the Teacher. From behind the barricade their faces are cold as marble angels, savage and sugared, blue on their pedestals. The Teacher demurs. "Oh, children," she says. She thinks she says. Does she? A stack of birds flies by the window, grimly, getting the hell out of town. Destination: a thousand miles south, to clubbed yellow forests and rivers of bilge. What will the birds do when they arrive? Unpack. Take a quick rinse before dinner.

"Well, would you?" Officious Retainer Boy asks. He is grinning, his retainer unhooked and awash in his mouth like a seafaring craft.

The Teacher has an urge to retreat to her corner and check her phone.

"Teaching is a bitch," the Best Friend said yesterday, calling from the bathroom line at a Starbucks on 59th Street. "I can't believe you took that job."

"I couldn't do what you do," said Nameless Man at the Grocery Store, palming a melon. "No siree Bob."

And what do I do, the Teacher thinks. I stand up to the gunman. Pow pow. In her mind, she crouches in the supply closet, holding Quiet Sensitive Child's hand. Please, Mr. Gunman, let us go, but you may have—as an offering from me to you—Officious Retainer Boy. In her mind, the Teacher's Mother stands weeping over her dead body, crimson and L-shaped and covered in chalk. Dead as dead can be. But she is twenty-three years old! She wants to see her mother again!

The Teacher gets up and walks to the door. She will not wait anymore. "It's just a drill," she says loudly. "See, children?" She turns the handle and the door swings out into the bright, quiet hall, which still smells of the meatballs they ate for lunch.

ALLEN FORREST

CITY LIFE, CYCLIST

SETH FISCHER
OUR MOST FREQUENT REQUESTS

Mabel Hanna sat backwards and cross-legged in the alcove of her and her mother's new apartment. The nook jutted out from the living room so that it hung over the entryway of their second-story duplex. Snow melted in big fat streaks against the windows on three sides of her. She was perched high on a pile of old dusty pillows she'd pulled out of one of the boxes in the dining room behind her. She was so high up that despite being quite short for an almost twelve-and-a-half-year-old, she could nearly reach the built-in angel faces in the walls above the windows, angel faces that had been painted green. They'd likely been painted by her father, she guessed, when he was just a kid, long before he died. Green was his favorite color. This was the first night in their new house, and when she sat in that nook, she thought, it seemed like she was floating above the world.

The nook was Mabel's second favorite thing about New Lisbon.

Mabel's first favorite thing was the goblin legends. This was really the reason—when her mom announced that they would be leaving Philadelphia and moving back to her dad's childhood home in western Massachusetts—that she surprised everyone and packed up her how-to books and her frog figurine collection without complaint. She'd never seen a goblin; she'd only heard of them, but everyone knew New Lisbon was their mecca of sorts, that if you were lucky enough to see one, it would be there.

Mabel's mother came out of the bathroom, her bright red hair in straighteners, a mud treatment hiding the worry lines that had recently set up shop around her eyes.

She said, "Mabs, kiddo, you going to bed?"

This was more a question than a Mom order. She knew Mabel's room was too stuffed with boxes to even get to her crappy futon, anyway. But the straighteners and treatment were a good sign, Mabel thought. She hadn't had to remind her mom to bathe for the first time in weeks. Her mom hadn't run off again, either. It was almost like she might go to work the next day, though of course, she didn't have a job. They were going to rent out the apartment below and try to live on that. Maybe this move to New Lisbon marked a new day, maybe her mom was coming back.

After her dad died, Mabel had to figure out how to work the microwave to make frozen lasagna. She'd cleaned the specks out of the microwave when the dinners exploded because she hadn't read the instructions carefully enough to cut slits in the plastic. She'd decided which book to use to kill the cockroaches that slowly took over, she'd gotten herself to school, she'd plunged her mother's turds out the toilet when it clogged.

"I'm going to sleep out here," Mabel said, having no intention of going to sleep. She climbed down from her stack of pillows and laid down on one of them, hoping that would get rid of her mom.

The pillow scratched her face. Mabel did not care for its embroidery. She'd found these pillows in one of the boxes full of her dad's stuff. Before she was born, he made these when he went on vacation. He didn't make them anymore afterward. She wondered why he would ruin the comfort of perfectly good pillows by adding all those scratchy words. "Fire Island," this one said. So she tried another, which read "Daughters of the American Revolution" against a backdrop of a rainbow flag.

Still, she liked these pillows because she could still smell her dad on them. He kept them in his office, wouldn't let her mother throw them away. Her father smelled like strong coffee and bitter apples and eggs freshly scrambled in olive oil.

Her mother wished her good night and went into her room, and Mabel sat up again, eager to see what was going on out the window.

Back when they lived in the city, scuttlebutt around the schoolyard—or at least around the students who didn't think Mabel too weird to talk to—was that goblins, without a doubt, were a real thing. You could read this in the way grown-ups reacted when you asked about them. They didn't laugh at you, condescend to you, or ignore you; they said, "Why don't we talk about something more pleasant?"

Everyone also agreed your life would change forever if you looked one in the eye. What no one could agree on was what that meant. Did you die on the spot? Did they eat you alive? Did they enslave you in mines so deep underground there was no hope you could ever be rescued? Or maybe, said the sorts of people who smile a good deal more than most, they gave you pots of gold. Or eternal love. Or the answer to all of life's mysteries.

Mabel liked the latter sort of person.

Earlier that first day in the apartment, while her mother barked orders at the movers (another excellent sign, Mabel thought), Mabel watched her neighbors from her nook. She waved to the grown-ups as they walked below the window, knocking on the glass and smiling. The neighbors always, without exception, waved back. The lady across the street even brought by a raspberry apple crumble and a hot meat pie. She was quite striking, with radiant skin and a nervous smile and black hair tied back tight. Mabel's mother loved this woman, could not believe that either her daughter or the neighbors were capable of this sort of friendliness. She said, "Now isn't this just why you move to a small town?"

Mabel was more excited to watch out the window at night, though. That was when, legend had it, goblins were most likely to appear.

In her nook, her mom now safely asleep, Mabel looked out into the street and scoured the view for signs of activity. At precisely 10:15, all the lights went off in the house across the street. She took out a pad of paper and made a note of this. Then she waited and watched, hoping for something more to happen. At exactly 10:22, a window opened in the same house. She made a note of this, too. It was loud enough that she could hear it all the way across the street. She saw a boy who looked about her age, maybe a year or two older, climb out his window onto the roof. He only opened it wide enough for him to squeeze out, not wanting to wake his parents. She then saw the shadow of him walk along the roof, careful as possible not to make any noise, as tense as someone about to pull a bank heist. This was an old neighborhood; the streets were small and the houses were close enough together she could see him pretty well. A match struck against a box. The match, and then a cigarette, lit up his face. He was a gorgeous specimen, with sharp angles to his cheekbones, a neatly cut head of hair without a part—she thought parts made you look like a child, and the last thing she wanted was to have a crush on a child—and dark eyes that shined in the red of the ember. When he took that first drag, she could see all the muscles in his body relax, could see him slump backwards against the roof in relief.

At 10:23, approximately one minute after he lit his cigarette, after he'd relaxed, the pie woman's face appeared in the window. She marked this down too. The woman didn't turn her light on or say anything to the boy, but Mabel couldn't mistake the sight of a face plastered up against a glass. Mabel found it hard to believe he couldn't sense her there. But when he finished his cigarette, he put it out with extreme care in the little bit of snow that had collected, making sure to leave no burn marks on his roof. His mother's head disappeared from the window, and the boy swiveled his head around, scanning to see if anyone had seen him. When he got to the nook, he stopped right where her face was and gave a quick smirk. This sent a thrill through her, a feeling like she'd been caught doing something as stupid and illicit as he. That's when he masterfully flicked the cigarette butt all the way into the hedges in front of Mabel's duplex.

When she woke up the next morning, after catching just a couple hours of sleep after a very dull night of watching nothing much else happen outside, she decided that she had no interest in going to school. The trouble was that in the process of moving, she'd already missed the first couple weeks, and New Lisbon Unified School District wasn't pleased about this. They'd started making noises about calling social services.

No, there was no getting out of this.

"You forgot to throw out your food," she yelled out to her mom, gently but firmly, in *the voice*, also hoping that this excuse to wake her might mean she could get a ride and not have to walk through this snow. *The voice* was a new thing, something she'd modeled after the therapist they'd made her see after her dad died, a flat thing completely absent of judgment or emotion of any kind. In true form, Mom silently extricated herself from the bedroom, still in her PJs, and picked up her chow mein container, which was out and open on top of a box in the living room. She threw it away and looked ready to beeline it back to her room.

"Who painted those angels?" Mabel asked before she could leave.

Her mom looked up and smiled. She actually smiled. Mabel had almost forgotten that her mom's smile was more in the muscles around the eyes than in the lips, that her mouth itself didn't move very much at all, and that this was actually quite stunning.

"Your father."

This was good. The therapists back in the city had suggested she talk about happy memories with her mom. Said it would help them both heal. She hadn't tried it yet. This was a good chance. But when she opened her mouth to speak, she saw her mom's face start to crumple, and the memories came to her more quickly than she could say them. There were his tall tales about his time as a longshoreman. There was that one day when he grew tired of his records (he listened to records only, no other kind of recording for him), and he took Mabel out to a park and they throw them like Frisbees against the trees, seeing what kind of distance they could get. Or the time she was six and he'd insisted she walk across a drawbridge when they went on a hiking trip to California, a drawbridge that had a hundred-foot drop, and when she said she was scared, he said, "That's what makes it fun." And she was so pissed, but then it turned out he was so, so right.

She thought these stories were pretty awesome, but Mabel knew that what she thought was awesome was not always what other people thought was awesome. She had no idea how you were supposed to know if a memory was happy. But she had to come up with something; her mom's face was going blank, her eyes were losing the sheen they'd had back for just that moment. She had to say something.

"Did Dad ever show you what a baby lantern is?" she said.

One night, several years ago now, her mom had gone out, and she'd left them home alone together with a neighbor's infant named Chip, a kid she was skipping out on babysitting.

"Do you want to see something way-out?" her dad asked.

Mabel did not know what way-out was, but she assumed it meant good, because he had a mischievous smile on his face when he asked it. He picked up the baby, and the three of them went into the cellar. He closed the door and turned off the light and pulled a flashlight out from his back pocket.

"Check it out," he said.

He was laughing and bouncing the baby, who was also laughing, and he said say "Ahhh." The baby opened her mouth, and he shined the light inside.

Babies' skulls, her dad explained, don't fully form until they're much older. This is why it's bad to drop them or shake them. This also means that when you shine a light into their mouths, the light goes through all the soft tissue of their brain and comes out the top of their heads.

"We call it 'baby lantern,'" her dad said, a wicked smile on his face. Sure enough, a bit of pink light came out atop the baby's head, and the baby giggled away.

At the mention of those two words, her mom's face went all the way back to blank, and she walked back into her room.

She tried *the voice.* "I need a ride to school." It was no use, this time. Whatever she'd said had sent her mom away for a while.

Mabel walked the mile to school, snowflakes hitting her face like cold wet dog licks the whole way there.

Her plan when she arrived was simple: be sure that no one, and she meant no one, noticed her. Under her coat, she wore a gray hoodie, black jeans, and chucks to help her blend in with the sea of other kids who wore the same uniform, the kids who wanted to be ignored. With the exception of roll call and some awkward teachers trying to warmly introduce her to the new students, she successfully made it through the entire day before someone spoke to her.

She was putting her coat and gloves on and getting ready to leave the building, frustrated that her mom wasn't picking up the phone, as usual, when he snuck up behind her.

"You the new girl who just moved in across the street?" the boy said.

It was him. From the roof. This was a disaster. Was he going to ask her to walk with him? How could she disappear if he was looking at her? She looked down, avoiding his face at all costs. It shocked her a bit when she saw penny loafers. With a penny in the slit on top. This surprised her so much she looked up. What was he wearing? Pleated khakis and a polo, with a blazer? She had to nip this in the bud. If she was seen talking to him, it would be impossible for her to be ignored. They would mark her as a nerd, or a weirdly filthy rich kid, or some other sort of fresh meat. She'd seen it happen so many times.

"What's your name?" he said.

Right before she realized she was going to have to speak, she had an idea. She grabbed a candy bar from her pocket and stuffed as much as she could into her mouth. Can't talk, mouth is full, she pantomimed. And then she looked up at his face. He was even more handsome than he looked the night before, but his brown eyes—which had looked magical against the cigarette—scared her up close. They were hard and wild, like her father's. They were without fear.

He said, "My name is Malcolm."

Dumbstruck by his eyes and not knowing what else to do, she shoveled more candy into her mouth, though she was starting to desperately be in need of something to wash it down with, and she realized she had no water. She chewed and chewed, but she couldn't get enough saliva, and he sat there and watched her until she spit what she couldn't swallow back out into a trash can.

He shook his head at her and chuckled. "That's disgusting," he said.

"I need some water," she said. "I'll be right back."

"Can I at least get your name before you run away?"

"Mabel," she said, and to her chagrin, he stuck his hand out to greet hers. She grimaced when she saw it; it was filthy. His fingernails alone, she thought, had more dirt under them than she had on her entire hand.

"What are you wearing?" she asked, leaving his hand there, shoving her hands in her pockets, gathering up all the hate she could muster. It wasn't that she gave two shits about what he wore—it was his funeral—but she couldn't understand why anyone would make himself such a target.

"It's...my uniform," he said, faltering a little bit, but trying to muster up all the pride he had in him. But before she could ask what the hell that meant—this school had no uniform—he said, "That's what I need to talk to you about."

She wondered, did all boys talk in circles like this?

"Will you join me on my walk home?" he asked, gesturing out the door. She looked at him again. A uniform? Was she being asked to join some sort of secret society? She didn't see any other kids around wearing that crap. The other kids wore jeans and sweaters and T-shirts with band names and boots and sneakers, like normal kids.

"What do you want from me?" she asked, still standing there. He flinched. If she didn't know any better, if what she'd seen in his eyes would allow her for a moment to entertain the idea that he was capable of it, she'd say he almost looked a little hurt.

"I just want to talk to you about New Lisbon," he said.

She stood up a little straighter, and she let him follow her to the water fountain.

He chewed on his dirty fingernails as they walked out. He didn't put on a jacket over his blazer, didn't wear a hat.

"Won't you be cold?" she asked, hugging herself. Even in her coat, she was freezing.

"One will come for you soon," he said. "They can sense when you most need them."

"Could your mom maybe pick us up?"

"But they only come for you once. After that, no more."

"One what?" Mabel said, though she was pretty sure she knew.

He looked up at her forehead, not at her eyes. This was yet another strike against him. She hated it when people did that. He'd had so much promise on the rooftop last night.

"They're not half bad," he said. "The goblins."

She looked up at him. She believed in goblins, sure. Everybody did. She wanted to know all about them. But there was something off about this kid. He said phrases like "half bad" and for the love of God he had a penny in his *loafer.*

"What is wrong with you?" Malcolm asked.

Mabel blanched, and then she ran a few steps to get ahead of him.

"Fuck you," Mabel yelled back.

"No," Malcolm said, catching up to her with just a few quick strides. "I'm sorry. I meant, what happened to you? You look like someone who had something happen."

She stopped. And he stopped too. She looked at him again, closer this time. His jacket was almost soaked through.

"Why didn't you call your mom for a ride?"

"What..." he said, pausing between each word, "happened... to... you?"

Jesus, she thought. She walked away and he followed. How many reasons did he want? Dad. Suicide. Not even a year ago now. Gunshot. Head. Right into the brain stem. She wasn't an idiot. She knew what people said. She knew why her mom didn't like those pillows. So sad, everyone said. All those eyes looking at her with pity. Another gay man who didn't think it would get better. But it wasn't that simple. That wasn't his story. She could feel it in her bones. This was something else. This was something more. This was planned, not a man who'd lost his mind. Or at least not a man who'd lost his mind because he hated himself for who he was.

He'd even been considerate enough to call 911 and tell them what he was going to do before he did it, because he knew she would be home shortly after 3:45 p.m., so he did it at 11:00 a.m., ensuring that it would allow enough time for her to come home to a house full of cops who wouldn't let her look at the body. She'd snuck in anyway when one of them stopped paying attention to her. Her dad, she remembered, had turned into a tarp with a little bit of matted bloody hair sticking out the top. It's so easy for a man to turn into a tarp.

She noticed Malcolm watching her face. They'd been walking in silence for a few minutes now. He finally said, "The goblins can fix whatever's wrong. Anything."

She looked him straight in the face and laughed. What would she even ask for? Could they fix her mom somehow? Maybe do the dishes. What if the goblins came and did the dishes? Or unpack for them? That would help a lot. But then a better thought came to her.

Dead dads are good for one thing, and that is getting people to leave you alone.

"Can you bring my dad back to life?" she asked, with a mean sort of giggle.

She was expecting a stunned silence, a break in the conversation, a wide eye, an apology, an exit. Instead, Malcolm smiled. "Of course. One of our most frequent requests."

She stared at him. He was looking in her eyes now. His eyes were just so brown, so cold. There was so much energy in there, but there was something missing, too. Wait, what had he said? Of course? It was what she had really wanted to hear, of course, deep down, but this kid set off all her alarm bells. He just oozed school shooter. She needed time to think. They weren't even halfway home. It was going to be a very long walk.

"It was my mom they helped me with," Malcolm said. "She died of something wrong with her liver."

That stopped her up. She'd just seen his mom. In the window. Bringing them pie. It was really good pie. Malcolm was studying her, shivering a bit in the cold now, waiting for her to say what she was thinking, but she just couldn't take all this, it was too much, so she tried to think of something to say to change the subject. She couldn't think of a thing, so she watched her breath in front of her face instead.

"Here," Malcolm said, fishing something out of his pocket. It was an obituary. His mom's picture was right next to an article. Same woman. Same hair. Same beautiful skin. She was a psychologist, apparently. At the local university. Beloved by her students. By the faculty. The Mass of Christian Burial was to be held on February 3, of...well...five years ago.

Malcolm said, "I know what you're thinking. You're thinking, 'What's the catch?'"

She shook her head at him. "What's the catch?" was not at all what she was thinking. She was thinking two things: first, she was worried she was walking with the kind of person who would be voted most likely to have a human head in his freezer in the high school yearbook, who forged obituaries of his own mother. But second, and she really didn't want to admit this to herself, she was entertaining the possibility, for the first time, that maybe her dad could come back. There *were* goblins. That much she knew. And she was in their capital.

And then Malcolm explained, and Malcolm, she could tell, was a practiced— if not natural—salesman, so the more he explained, the better it sounded. He explained that yes, the stories were true, they live underground, they had once been quite sadistic to humans, stealing children away in the night when a parent had done something particularly egregious, enslaving the kids for the rest of their lives, forcing them to dig tunnels under the human cities so that goblins could have easy access and destroy us if things ever got too bad. But, he said, take a step back. Could you really blame them? She had to admit humans ruin everything they touch. Had she ever read a newspaper? It's gotten so bad now, he said, that not too long ago, the goblins threw in the towel. They'd decided to try a different approach. They decided to see what would happen if they granted all the human children a wish that could fix whatever it was that had cracked their hearts, so that they might not grow to be as cold and stupid and self-interested as their ancestors. His job—the reason for his uniform—was to find these children as these things happened.

"You know," she said, and then stopped herself. They were almost home and he was now shivering in his blazer, his hands underneath his arms. What was the catch? That was a good question. Mabel could do a couple things really well: she could fix and make stuff, because she'd had to learn how when her dad died, and she could sense bullshit, because she'd had to learn how when her dad was alive. This sounded like everything she wanted it to be. So it couldn't be true.

"Why are your hands so dirty?" Mabel asked.

He smiled. It was a wide one, and his eyes came to life. "I like to garden."

"In the snow?"

"You were right. I could've called my mom to give us a ride."

They were out in front of their respective houses now. His smile vanished, and he was looking at her forehead again. He told her that he couldn't tell her more. It was against the rules. But if she wanted her father back, she could have him.

"You look smart," he whispered close in her ear before walking into his house, "so I'm going to guess you know that nothing is free."

With that, she decided she could really believe him.

When she walked into the house, she found it in a much worse state than when she left. It looked like her mom had cut open all the boxes and tossed every-thing around—clothes, pans, important papers, even her mom's favorite stuffed animal from when she was a kid, a little elephant that had long ago lost all its stuffing. There was no rhyme or reason to it. It didn't look like she'd been looking for anything. She'd trashed the place. Mabel's frog figurines were thrown all over the kitchen floor, some of them broken, presumably by accident, but maybe not.

When she opened the door to her room, she saw that her mom was gone.

She did this, Mabel thought to herself. Sometimes she disappeared. Don't panic.

She turned off all the lights in the house, took her notepad to her nook and looked outside. She hated living this far north—September at 5:03 p.m. and it was already getting dark. She noted that down and sat there and waited. There was not much to do but wait. Malcolm wouldn't tell her anything else, and her mom was...well. There was no one for her to call. No one. The only thing to do was wait. She made herself some frozen lasagna and waited. She did some homework and waited some more. She drifted in and out of sleep until she saw what at first seemed to be a flashlight heading towards her. She checked the clock. 9:13. She wrote it down on the pad. There, at the end of her road, getting slightly larger with each step, was a white light, a white light that was bobbing back and forth.

She looked over at Malcolm's room. Light was out.

As it came closer and closer, she realized the flashlight couldn't be a flashlight. It was a little too big, maybe, and it was too high on the body. Was it a headlamp? She started to see the outline of something around the light.

She had seen this before. Well, an approximation.

She watched more, her nose glued up against the window, rapt, as it came closer, and closer, and closer. Her brain had been doing backflips trying to make sense of what she was seeing, but it was all so clear now. It wasn't a flashlight at all. The light was all wrong. It was too muted, too subtle, more like a light bug than a light bulb. It was part of the creature, for it was a full-grown creature, not a human or a baby, though it walked on two legs. And when it got to the place underneath her window, it stopped in its tracks and looked right up at her. She had to force herself to avoid the eyes, the only part of the head not lit up.

The creature was bald and short, and the light shone bright enough from him and from the snow and the moon behind the clouds that she could tell he was neatly dressed, with a blazer, black or gray, and pressed slacks, and she saw the gleam from a penny in his loafer. The light coming out his head made the veins light up pink against the pasty glow of the rest of his scalp.

The goblin was looking right at her now, no question about that, and he opened his mouth wide, the light shining on her even brighter that way, like a flashlight proper, blinding her, forcing her to shut her eyelids, and when she reopened them, for a moment, just a brief, brief moment, before she could stop herself, she looked directly into the dark area of the goblin's face—the eyes—the only part that wasn't lit brightly, the only part that wasn't lit at all. The light went out, the goblin disappeared, and she let herself get lost in the smell of coffee, apples, and freshly fried eggs.

VISHWAS R. GAITONDE
THE ENGLISH WIDOW

The trail to the English widow was not for the fainthearted. The torrential rainstorm of the previous night made the steep forest track that snaked up the hillside treacherous every step of the way. The interior of the woods was steamy, and the smell of wet and rotting wood was everywhere. Paul yelled as he tripped over a muddy root. The next instant he exchanged an intimate kiss with the soggy clay, and then slid down the slope on his belly. Jeremy, who walked behind him, stopped Paul's descent by sticking out his foot, shaking with silent laughter as Paul, caked in soil and slime, rose and let loose a string of choice swear words at the trees.

Nelith and the two Sri Lankan guides who were ahead of them on the trail turned back.

"Why have you stopped?" Nelith demanded. "Where's Paul?"

The clay man came into view, looking utterly woebegone. Nelith showed not the slightest flicker of amusement. This man, Jeremy thought, takes life far too seriously. Maybe we should rub his face in the mud at the end of the day.

The rain, Nelith reminded them for the fourth time, had made the rutted roads impassable in a vehicle. In any case, the custom dictated they enter the village on foot.

"But it would've been a bloody shorter walk if we drove most of the way. I'm knackered," Paul muttered under his breath. Jeremy whispered back, "You're going to witness a colony of dodos before their extinction. A small spill is nothing."

"Colony? What about the English widow, rags and all. *That's* who I'd like to meet. I want to ask her: why did you ditch England for this dump?"

Paul and Jeremy had not been out of Britain except for the briefest of forays, Paul to Paris and Jeremy to the Canary Islands. Now here they were, temporarily nestling in the heartland of Sri Lanka on a university exchange program: a whole term at the University of Peradeniya. The sociology department assigned a postgraduate student, Nelith Wimalasuriya, to help them get the most from their stay. Their main assignment was to research the daily life of the Veddas, the indigenous inhabitants of the island. Nelith reproached them over their choice of topic.

"This would have been a worthwhile project—oh say, two or three decades ago." Nelith's lukewarm enthusiasm dampened them.

"We were in primary school then," Jeremy pointed out.

"In the fifties and the sixties, the Veddas lived by their traditions," Nelith ignored Jeremy and spoke to Paul. "Then the government dug a maze of channels and diverted water from our largest river, the Mahaweli Ganga, to generate electricity. They dumped the water into artificial reservoirs for the use of farmers. After acres of barren land became fertile, the government resettled hundreds, thousands of families from the congested parts of the country."

"And these newcomers swamped the Veddas. That your point?"

"Right, but there's more to it. You've done your reading on the Veddas, right? You know their traditional occupation?"

"They're hunters and gatherers."

"Right. Answer straight from the textbook. So what happens when the forests they live in get converted into national parks? When it's a crime to shoot animals with anything other than a camera? The government bluntly told the Veddas their only choice was to move into these new villages and become farmers."

"But the university mentioned Vedda settlements," Paul protested. "Aren't there any left that you can take us to?"

"Oh, we can go to two, maybe three, no problem," Nelith said. "One of these villages will hold their big dance, the Kiri Koraha, in a fortnight. That'll be something you'd want to see, surely."

They didn't ask Nelith about the English widow. They hadn't heard of her yet.

PAUL LOOKED ABJECT when he emerged from his wash after they reached the village. His shirt and trousers were soaked in the front, dry at the back, his blond hair clumped in uneven wet cords.

"Now we should find you a flint knife," Jeremy said, "and the Veddas will think a Neolithic Briton has dropped by to say hello to them."

"Good," Paul said. "Then we're agreed I'll make the presentation to His Nibs."

They had spent many hours at the university library, devouring whatever they found on the Veddas. They read Spittel, Seligman, and Obeyesekere backwards and forwards. A Vedda elder must be greeted with respect and tact and a friendly sort of deference—and with the traditional offerings of betel leaves, areca nut, and tobacco. As they trudged down the dirt road flanked by huts, Paul removed the presents from his backpack, his fingers working like tweezers, glad that the items weren't any worse after his mudslide.

The two guides Nelith had brought along led them to a large hut made of bark amid a semicircle of coconut trees. One of the guides called out, and a short, stocky man emerged from within. His skin looked charred, his hair swept from his broad forehead over his squat skull to the nape of his neck. His mostly gray beard stood in stark contrast to his black hair; it sprouted from his chin but became sparse further up his jaw line. His short scarlet sarong extended from waist to knee. An ax was slung across his bare torso. The gaffer must have been waiting for us, Jeremy decided. Who sits at home with an ax on the ready?

"The village head," Nelith announced. "His name is Poromala."

Jeremy hid his smile as Paul, with his crown of wet goldilocks, curtsied before the chief and held out their offerings. Poromala made no attempt to hide his grin as he accepted the articles. He looked over them carefully and glanced inquiringly at Nelith. Nelith, looking sheepish, slowly raised and wiggled an eyebrow. The chief appeared satisfied. He stuffed the tobacco, nuts, and leaves into a pouch hanging at his waist, and retreated into the hut.

"He wants to show you the bow and arrow his father and grandfather used," Nelith said. "And by the way, no rules restrict your gifts to betel and tobacco. People bring biscuits and sweets and milk for the children, even shirts for the men and blouses for the women. This is the twenty-first century."

"You might have told us ahead of time," Paul protested.

"Sorry. Hey, you've read so much about the Veddas I thought you knew all there was to know. You can always give cash presents. Later. After the dance, right before we leave. In the old days, they had no concept of money. Now they depend on it."

Poromala darted out of his hut with an old wooden bow, the wood liberally scuffed and scraped. He gingerly affixed an arrow and let go with a twang. The arrow arched in the air above their heads and struck the ground with a light thud. The whole thing was theatrical, staged. Jeremy and Paul responded with a lukewarm clap of hands as Poromala bragged he was the star archer of the village who personally instructed the boys in archery and axmanship. Nelith and the two Sri Lankan guides, unimpressed, engaged the chief in a long conversation.

"Nelith speaks Vedda?" Paul whispered. Jeremy shook his head as he said, "Sounds like Curlicue."

Curlicue was their label for Sinhala, the language whose every alphabet mimicked a curl or a whorl. Nelith eventually turned to Paul and Jeremy with a gloomy look: "We'll have to wait for the Kiri Koraha. Two tourist vans haven't arrived."

They had a couple of hours, likely many more, to kill. Jeremy asked Nelith, "Can you ask the chief about the English widow?"

"Ah," said Nelith. "Good thinking."

During their interminable discussions with people at Peradeniya and Kandy about the Veddas, Paul and Jeremy picked up oblique references, mysterious hints, about an English widow who lived among the Veddas, possibly at this village. Nelith said he'd also heard such tales but dismissed them; Sri Lanka was a land of rumors. The inquiry tickled Poromala.

"There's no old white woman in our village, and there's never been. The only whites we see are the tourists or researchers or student visitors like these two boys. These people come and go, they don't live here. A white man did live amongst us for a few years, but that was—it must have been at least forty years ago. My father was the chief then." Poromala's flat voice held a whisper of amusement. Then he stiffened, rooted to the earth by an inner flash, a sudden dawning.

"I know which lady you are talking about, *mahatayya*. I can take you to her. She lives a short distance outside the village."

After announcing this, Poromala was disinclined to talk. They tramped in silence down a well-worn path winding erratically through groves of mango and jackfruit trees. The heady aroma of overripe fruit hung in the still air. After ten minutes, they turned downhill—to Paul's consternation—along a smaller, squelchy trail that appeared seldom used; they often had to brush aside branches of trees and shrubs that overhung the path to move forward. They emerged into a tiny clearing with a solitary hut at its edge. Its roof was thatched from coconut fronds and grass, its walls made of clay plastered over a wooden framework that displayed itself in some spots like ribs sticking out from beneath the thin hide of starving cattle.

Poromala called out, "Kairi! Kairi!" and ended his hail with a staccato burst of alternating long and short handclaps. A sudden stillness followed, broken by the nervous squawking of birds hidden in the trees.

Her head was bent as she came out of the hut. She was not white but a deep burnt brown, the brown of areca nuts, and she wore a coarse yellow cloth that extended from the breast line to the waist. When she looked up, her finely chiseled, delicate features transfixed everyone's eyes. She must have been ravishingly beautiful in her youth. She could have been anywhere between fifty and sixty now. Worry lines were etched into her brow and her eyes were more cinders than flame, and yet she still radiated the kind of mature beauty some people would not exchange for anything else.

Her face displayed no emotion—no enthusiasm, no hostility—as she took in the motley crowd assembled before her home. Her eyes turned wary as Poromala spoke to her. Nelith occasionally interjected into their conversation, and gave Paul and Jeremy little summaries.

"Remember the chief told us a white man lived in this village many years ago? He was an Englishman and this lady was his wife."

Mutely listening to the streams of peculiar words flowing and ebbing between Kairi and Poromala, the English students regretted they knew no other language but their own. They were at the mercy of Nelith's insipid translations when they would have much rather followed the original remarks that caused the faces around them to light up, frown, go blank, or wilt.

"Tom, the man who married her, studied languages," Nelith said. "He believed the best way to learn a language was to live among its native speakers—only then you'd pick up the nuances you'd never get from classroom lectures or instruction tapes. So he became a Vedda. A white Vedda! Kairi was a teenager then, maybe ten, twelve years younger than him. Can't blame Tom for picking her as his teacher. They spent a lot of time with each other. One thing led to another and they got married."

"How did her family react? And the villagers?" Paul asked, and he noticed Kairi viewing him with faint—amusement? sarcasm?—when his question was translated. Poromala responded and Jeremy and Paul looked at Nelith.

"The chief asks if you're hungry. He'd like to offer you some *goya tel perume*."

"What's that?" The non sequitur puzzled Paul.

"The tail of a monitor lizard is hollowed out and stuffed with the fat scraped off its body, then roasted over glowing coals. A Vedda delicacy."

"No, thanks," said Paul shortly, refusing to budge even when they explained this was not a snack but a full meal—these reptiles stretched some five feet long from snout to tail. This was their only chance, for they would not encounter this dish in any restaurant in Sri Lanka, let alone Leeds. Poromala smiled at Paul's reluctance and Paul looked at the chief's stained yellow teeth.

"You react like other visitors, *mahatayya*. That's the difference between you, the whole lot of you, and Tom. Tom became one of us. He lived as we did, shared what we ate, laughed heartily along with us, shed our bitter tears. So when he married one of us, it wasn't as much of a shock as you might think. A big jolt at first, sure, but over time we got used to them as a pair."

Nelith expounded on what he had learned from Poromala. Tom married Kairi in the simple Vedda tradition. Like other Vedda brides, Kairi made a bark rope with her own hands, twisting and straightening the strands until the braiding became pliant. When she tied the rope around Tom's waist in the presence of the chief and the villager elders, they became man and wife.

"How did Tom die?"

Jeremy's simple question set off a sputter of heated exchanges. Tom simply vanished one day. He left (or so he said) for the faraway Andaman Islands in the Bay of Bengal to compare the language of those people with the Vedda tongue.

They never saw him again. A man in Colombo sent a little money for Kairi every month—the man said Tom had made an arrangement. After some time the remittances stopped without any notice or explanation. They assumed Tom was dead. It was inconceivable he would remain silent for these many years, given his deep affection for the Veddas and the sweet young wife he had left behind.

"Couldn't anybody trace him?" Paul asked. Nelith did not bother to translate the question but answered, "Paul, how can anybody from an isolated village like this track somebody in some other remote area of the world? Remember, this happened almost half a century ago."

Kairi asked what they were saying. She reflected for a few moments, brushing her thumb against the tips of her other fingers, and quietly said, "The Veddas abide by a code of honor. We've hunted solely for food, and then, only as much as we can eat. Young animals, pregnant animals, or those that are feeding or drinking water—these we do not shoot. Our code applies to people as much as it does to animals. When he became one of us, he was automatically bound to our code—and he knew it. Yes, he did. There was no question of our having to track him. If he did not come back, it meant he was unable to. If he was not dead, he was as good as dead. The day my heart knew he wasn't coming back was the day I ceased being a wife and became a widow. After which my energies were completely directed to raising my son."

"You have a son?" Nelith asked.

"When he left, he did not know a child was on the way." Kairi answered the unasked question first. "Yes, I have a son. He lived with me until a few years ago. When the government banned hunting, my son and his friends cultivated a patch of land. They grew yams and gourds and *kurakkan* millet and we got by, but we had a huge problem if the crops failed or we couldn't sell at a good price. So he moved to a more stable job in Ampara. He married a Tamil lady but she won't leave that town."

"Have you heard from him lately?" Poromala asked her.

"No," she said, and her eyes clouded.

"He's a good boy," Poromala told Nelith in a low voice. "He would visit his mother every month but she hasn't heard from him in a while. She lost her husband. Now she's terrified she's lost her son as well. We're afraid he may have been killed—the war has affected Ampara badly. Not a day without gunfire, they say, and half the town in smoldering ruins. The poor boy may've been conscripted to fight for one side or the other. Can somebody find out how he is?"

"Give me his name and address," Nelith said. "I'm not sure what I can do but when I get back to Peradeniya, I'll check what's feasible."

"Does the lady know any English?" Paul asked Nelith, wondering if any conversation without a translator was possible.

No, her husband had been so fluent in the Vedda tongue she had no need to learn English. She only knew two English words.

"And what are those?" Paul asked.

Kairi answered him directly, in English: "Shut up."

THE TIME FOR the Kiri Koraha drew near. They left Kairi, walked back to the village and across it to a large meadow where the dance was to be held. Poromala had withdrawn a few moments earlier. Several men with bare torsos and knee-length skirts made of twigs and leaves had spirited him off, barely hiding their resentment that he had wandered off to Kairi's hut without informing anyone where he was going. Many distinguished visitors had arrived; they needed the chief to receive them.

Metal folding chairs had been set up in an uneven circle around the meadow, and even from a distance they heard the noisy gibbering of the spectators. The expected vanloads of people had finally reached the village. Jeremy stopped, his eyes fixed straight ahead. Paul followed Jeremy's line of vision to find out what had transfixed him so. He found nothing striking about the rows of faces, white and olive and brown. Jeremy, ablaze and breathing heavily, punched Paul on his biceps.

"I say, do you think he could possibly be Old Tommyrot?"

"Who?" Paul barely made out the faces in the crowd.

"Come on, Pauly, remember that frightful show on the Beeb a couple of months back? Sir Thomas spouting all that baloney, and everybody slobbering over him saying how great he is?"

"What about him? He's not in this crowd."

"D'you think Sir Thomas is the fellow who married Kairi?"

"Bugger me." Paul's breathing became audible as the idea took root. He looked at Jeremy; the excitement was diabolical. Sir Thomas Rye-Brooke, a professor at Cambridge, was by popular acknowledgment Britain's foremost expert in linguistics. The big man had been recently interviewed at length on BBC, and later in the same program, others took turns hailing his achievements. Even his interviewer fawned over the professor, bestowing such titles as "Master of the Tongues of Men" and "Lord of the Languages" as though the knighthood were not sufficient enough distinction. Rye-Brooke clearly reveled in the homage; his making light of the tributes he received was patently phony.

"I thought Tommyrot won his laurels for his work in Polynesia and Melanesia." Paul said.

"Yeah, but on the show somebody did say he learned his trade with the Ceylon aboriginals. *Two* Tommys here, Pauly?"

"I wonder if that lady has photographs. We'd recognize him all right even as a young pup."

"He's a married man with two children, they said. And grandchildren too. What a stir it would create if people discovered he had another wife in Sri Lanka. Who he abandoned."

"And a son, half-English, half-aboriginal."

"Who might right now be fighting in a civil war. Could be on either side, with the Sinhalese or the Tamils. Could be dead."

"But Jeremy, there's no record of this wedding. No registry office that cranks out marriage certificates or keeps any records, y'know."

Jeremy gave a short laugh. "Think *that'll* stop the tabloids?"

"The whole thing is bloody hard to digest. This man plays in the premiership league—caviar, champagne, cuisine bourgeoise, antique chaise longues. He has a grand house on the river. Can't imagine he could have lived in a primitive hut any time in his life, been a Tarzan in the jungle, and scarfed down the arse of a lizard cooked medium rare."

"Oh, it's him all right."

They had slowed down as they conversed and Nelith waited till they caught up with him.

"Isn't this a shame?" Nelith waved at the crowds and at the Vedda dancers who carried a large clay pot and wooden sticks to the center of the circle. "At one time the Kiri Koraha was a sacred ceremony. When they went through long spells unable to hunt any game, they conducted this ceremony to appease *Né yakka*, the spirit of their dead kith and kin, and pleaded for a few animals to be sent their way again. Today they dance for the tourists, like any actor in the street theaters of Kandy and Colombo. Have either of you been to America?"

They shook their heads.

"I want to go there some day. I'm reading whatever I can find, and when I read about the Indians that once had nations there—Apache, Cheyenne, Cherokee, Navajo—I wonder how they're doing today. Have they also been reduced to tourist attractions, putting on—what's the expression—a dog and pony show?"

The two sociology honors students ignored him. They were still preoccupied with Sir Thomas Rye-Brooke, how to corner and expose him to the world.

AFTER THE VISITORS had left, Kairi sat down and stared vacantly at the tree tops, something she had often done lately. In recent years, the village had seen a stream of callers who seemed interested in the villagers' lives but who failed to help them in any concrete way. Kairi was glad she rarely saw these curiosity seekers. When her heart told her Tom was not coming back, she moved her hut outside of the village, seeking out solitude, the companion of isolation. It was also a gesture of atonement to the *yakkas* for her unorthodox marriage.

The visitors she met before she moved out of the village had all furiously scribbled into their notebooks whatever they were told at random. Anything they wrote was bound to be similarly disjointed. If somebody ever wrote about her life, people would find it an unsatisfying read, an incomplete story. But what was life if not a fragmented affair? All stories were incomplete, as life itself was.

She, the most beautiful girl in the village, combination of gazelle and butterfly and gentle breeze, had been reduced to a plight she once could hardly have imagined. The day the Englishman married her, the two of them had outshone the sun. The sun still rose every day but the radiance had since ebbed out of the village. The villagers no longer lived and worked as they once did; they had turned into a pack of lazybones, a bunch of performing monkeys on display.

These two English boys had deliberately sought her out today. That was frightening. It was a bad omen, really bad. After her son moved to Ampara, she had become naked. Now, with her cloak of anonymity stripped away, she also felt defenseless. Who else would come after her? Why? Why wouldn't they leave her alone?

When Tom first came to the village, he'd been about the same age as these two English boys. But he was so confident. These boys looked lost, unsure of why they were here, unable to convey their thoughts except through the mouths of others. This, despite having it much easier than Tom, for today, the villagers had become accustomed to visitors. When Tom arrived, most of the villagers had not seen a white face, and when he addressed them in their own tongue but in a stilted accent, they had been terrified, wondering if this man were an outlandish personification of one of the *yakkas*. Although it was strange and without precedent, and there were layers of misgiving, they allowed Tom to live in the village.

Tom learned quickly and adapted swiftly. In a matter of days, he exchanged his constricting clothing for their scant waistcloth, moving among them by day like an albino, by night like a pale ghost under the moonlit skies. Yet for all of this, how much vulnerability lay under that bold front. Kairi couldn't imagine journeying to the land of the white people to live as they did.

One day she noticed red, raw welts on his shoulder. The Veddas carried their ax with the blade on their shoulders, the handle on their chests. Tom did not know how to place and balance the flat end of the blade and had scraped his skin right off.

Tom's eyes loved to stray her way though he averted his gaze if he realized she was observing. When the village boys gave her the eye, Kairi knew how to snub them with a single glance, offer a caustic comment, or just walk away. With this white Vedda, she was not too sure. But she could minister to gashes and lacerations on anybody. A wound was a wound.

"That better, Dhom?" she asked, concealing her shyness under a nurse's authoritative tone, after she bathed his sore shoulder in cold water and applied a coarse salve of crushed herbs and leaves.

"Yes. Aaah," he said, wincing as the salve stung his flesh. "And it's Tom, not Dhom."

"I'm happy you're feeling better, Dhom."

"Hmm, so your lips have trouble making the T sound." He flashed a smile that displayed two rows of even white teeth. "OK, call me whatever you want."

When Tom and Kairi began spending a great deal of time together, the elders looked at each other, as though expecting one to guide the other on whether to be revolted or pleased, which stance to take in public and which in private. The village youth were not smiling.

"Kairi, be careful, be very careful." Badini, Kapuru, Thuthie, and the other girls were stern. They told her she was stepping into a pit cleverly concealed by a mat of twigs and leaves, the kind used to trap elephants.

"Kairi, this is madness." Handunna, Tikiri Banda, Kadira, and the other boys admonished.

"Why?" Kairi played innocent. "He's a good boy, like any of you."

"Like us! He's *not* one of us, how can you be so blind, mad girl? When the thrill wears off, he'll no longer want to live here."

"I'll go with him, then, to his island."

"What demon has possessed you, Kairi? Have you not heard him speak of his island? A blanket of gray clouds always covers the sky so the days are as almost as dark as the nights. It rains all the time and the demon clouds still aren't spent. How can you live, Kairi, without ever seeing the sun, without enjoying its warmth on your skin? And in the cold season, the water turns into hard white rocks, which are colder than the waters of all our rivers combined. You'll die within weeks."

"Don't worry about me." Kairi dismissed them with a smile flavored with just a hint of mockery. What an ignorant bunch! Tom had come from a faraway corner of the world, traversing many lands and seas. He possessed a brand of wisdom that she—any of them—could not fathom. He spent his evenings, hours upon end, scribbling away in his notebooks. On humid nights, his face became beaded with sweat but he would not even bother to wipe it away, so absorbed was he in his writing, a man controlled by spirits, filling the pages with hard little scratches and loopy squiggles. She could be standing right next to him, breathing down his neck, and yet he was as unaware of her presence as he was of the deerskin mat on the floor.

On other days they existed only for one another, idling away the long, languid hours on the mountainside. Ahead of them the ground sloped steeply into lush valleys and rose again to become stately mountains, behind which stood other brother and sister mountains. Their solidity made it easy to visualize the ethereal spirit they personified, the *kandé yakka*. When she and Tom exchanged long and passionate kisses, the eternal *kandé yakka* was a witness.

"Oh, *kandé yakka* is pleased for us," Tom murmured, as his tongue sought Kairi's. "All the *yakkas* are happy. Can't you feel them blessing us?"

Indeed, the sheer joy in the air was invigorating. Paradise had descended from the firmament to merge with the earth and at this moment it was hard to tell them apart.

There were days when Tom prattled as they lay side by side on the grass, their immediate passion spent. He talked of things that didn't quite fit into the world she knew. He also told her if she turned into a little bird and flew east she'd encounter one island after another—Sumatra, Java, Bali, Kalimantan, and the myriad islands of the Indonesian archipelago. Then, Papua New Guinea, and a truly gigantic beast called Australia with its cuddly little baby, Tasmania. Beyond, the two islands of New Zealand floated on the waters like hungry lovers groping for each other. And then a vast ocean, the largest in the world, spreading out as far as the eye could see, pockmarked by many little islands, every island having inhabitants with a distinctive culture.

"So the world is nothing but a boundless ocean, full of islands," Kairi said, dreamily, raising her head from Tom's chest to look at his brown curls, clustered in bunches like tendrils on a vine, so different from her straight black hair. "And every island has villages with people just like us."

"I made it sound that way, didn't I?" Tom's laughter rolled up from the depths of his stomach. "It's because I see the world like many oyster shells glued together to form a sphere. And each shell contains a pearl, and no pearl is like another. How I long to pluck them, pearl by pearl, to study each one, to admire that which makes it different from its fellows. Of course the world is much more than islands floating in an ocean. There are large land masses as well, North America, South America, with their own ancient cultures. And each and every one of these groups is being ripped up, wiped out, if they haven't already been."

"We're still here."

Tom raised himself on an elbow and stroked Kairi's cheeks. "Yes, right now. But you are slowly disappearing and you don't even recognize it."

Kairi laid her hand on his forehead in an exaggerated gesture to check how high his fever ran.

"Look, guess what I'm discovering the deeper I study your language? That many words are from Sinhala. And more are creeping in, even replacing existing words."

"What can we do? The Sinhalese are plenty, we are few. We can't avoid dealing with them. They won't learn our language, so we have to learn theirs, just so we can all get along."

On another occasion, Tom fumed, "When you lose both your language and your traditions, you cease to exist as a people. I can't make the elders understand this. They don't care. You even call yourselves Veddas. The Sinhalese imposed that name on you, and it's loaded with contempt—it puts you on the level of the primitive cave dwellers who lived thousands of years ago. Your own name for your people is Vanniya'leto, those who belong to the *vanni*, the forest. It offends my ears to hear you call yourselves Vedda."

Kairi recoiled from his words. He was no longer a stranger. He lived with them. He was smart. He experienced all the pressures that made them behave as they did.

"Stop bullying our elders, Dhom," she snapped at him. "Shouldn't you instead be talking as forcefully to the headmen on *your* island?"

"What do you mean?"

"Didn't you once tell me your language was spoken all over the world? Why did people in all the corners of the earth have to learn English, Dhom? What does this say about *your* people?"

From the way the blood inflamed his face, she knew she had scored. But she didn't feel happy. For the rest of the day they both retreated into the glum silence of those who felt hurt without being able to say why. Not too long after, Tom left for the Andaman Islands. He appeared wound up but in high spirits, sure he would learn many things from the Andaman islanders that could help the Vanniya'leto.

"Are you going in a big boat crammed with people, Dhom?"

"Passenger ships don't go to remote places like the Andamans, Kairi dear. But the cargo ships sailing between Colombo and Rangoon stop at the Andamans to drop off goods. I'll talk them into giving me passage."

"Should I come to Colombo to see you off?"

"Entirely unnecessary. How will you return to the village from Colombo? It's not like I'm going to be away for long. Only for five or six months."

But he never came back.

Why didn't she guess immediately when she discovered that, although he left some of his clothes behind, he had taken his oilskin bag in which he kept his notebooks? There was not even a scrap of paper with his jottings he hadn't taken with him. She had no keepsake of his handwriting, the symbol of his erudition, his wisdom. Seize me, she shrieked to the elements after she knew he had departed forever. Wind, blow me up to the sky and as I plunge, Earth, take me into your bowels and make my flesh one with my bones. A few days later the spirits murmured in her ear they could not do any of that, for she was with child.

Kairi was jolted out of her reverie by the drumbeat that came floating through the air and exploded over her head. The Kiri Koraha had started. They would have erected a tripod made of wooden sticks and placed an earthen pot on it. They would have filled the pot with betel leaves, areca nuts, and tobacco. She pulled out her own pots to prepare her meager evening meal that would see her through to the next day.

Another drumbeat wafted along. Old Randunna hurled his energy at the drums, and Kairi marveled at how his wrists and fingers remained so strong and supple, so young, while the rest of his body shriveled and withered. When it came time for him to enter the world of spirits, the Kiri Koraha would be diminished, for there was none in the village who made a drum talk the way he did.

The drumbeats grew louder and they flung themselves on the surrounding mountains, becoming more powerful as they assaulted the rocks, multiplying many times over and bouncing back to the village. And now the beats and the echoes became fast and rhythmic and resonant, encapsulating the whole world in their sound: *Dhom-mmm, Dhom-mmmm, Dhom-mmmm.*

ANDREW GRETES

ARTIE AND THE VEIL OF MAYA

alloween night. Six o'clock. The father, impatient, enters the bathroom to inspect his son's costume. The son is wearing a frock coat and a latex bald cap with white sideburns; he's holding a bridal veil in one hand and a book titled *The World as Will and Representation* in the other.

THE FATHER: Martin Van Buren?
THE SON: Arthur Schopenhauer.

The father experiences a familiar feeling—somewhere in between fishing and failure—mind coated in the slime of a thought that's slipped away. The father listens to his ten-year-old son explain how Arthur Schopenhauer was a nineteenth-century German philosopher who believed we are all unwitting pawns of a blind insatiable vortex called "Will."

THE FATHER: Scary.
THE SON: Boo.

The father ushers his son out of the bathroom and down the stairs. He visualizes his to-do list. The list is filled with checkmarks, even to tasks the father has yet to accomplish:

- ✓ chaperone son's trick-or-treating
- ✓ call ex-wife and demand favor for taking their son this weekend on such short notice
- ✓ acknowledge that parents don't typically demand favors for raising their own children
- ✓ prepare dinner for current wife who, despite being eight months' pregnant, is stuck at her firm, working late on a case
- ✓ update real estate blog with a post titled, "Ever wonder how to prepare for a buyer's home market?"

The father and son walk outside. The night is filled with witches and pirates and zombies and Arthur Schopenhauer. They ring the first doorbell and demand a tribute of high-fructose corn syrup.

THE NEIGHBOR: Oh, and what do we have here?
THE SON: A messenger. *(holds up bridal veil)*
THE NEIGHBOR: Bad news?
THE SON: We live in the worst of all possible worlds.

The father and son thank the neighbor for the peanut butter cups and continue along the sidewalk to the next house. The father thinks about previous Halloweens: his son dressed as 1) gravity, 2) divorce, 3) the heat death of the universe. He blames his ex-wife for encouraging their son's precociousness. He asks about the significance of the veil.

THE SON: It belongs to Maya.
THE FATHER: Maya? Your stepmother?
THE SON: Maya is the Sanskrit word for illusion.
THE FATHER: So this has nothing to do with my wife?
THE SON: We're all wed to illusion.

The boy mumbles something about the remote possibility of peeking through the veil of illusion: how a sudden shock—a simple boo—can lead to an out-of-body objectivity, an intermission of self, Will, vortex, where the lights flicker to reveal a roomful of eyes all privy to the same show.
The father nods and thumbs the keypad of his smartphone.
They ring more doorbells, raise more eyebrows. No one recognizes Arthur Schopenhauer. The son blames the father.

THE FATHER: Me?
THE SON: You're throwing people off.
THE FATHER: Is that right?
THE SON: Schopenhauer wouldn't go trick-or-treating with his father.
THE FATHER: Too mature for that?
THE SON: He wasn't around.
THE FATHER: Deadbeat?
THE SON: Suicide.

The father doesn't have time for this. He's thinking about his checklist, dinner, his current wife, his future daughter, bills, etc. He wants to do everything right this time. Marriage 2.0. Husband 2.0. Father 2.0. Career 2.0. And why not? Students write rough drafts. Pilots use flight simulators. Schools do fire drills. *So too*, thinks the father, *so too*... He equates the last decade of his life with a dress rehearsal.

THE SON: Dad?
THE FATHER: Huh?
THE SON: This man says he knows you.

The father is facing an open door. An old man with impeccable posture stands on the threshold. The man was the father's AP English teacher, Colonel Tyler. At the sight of the seventy-three-year-old retired colonel, the father's neurons transmit inadequacy, shame, terror.

THE COLONEL: Hello Steven.

Names never escape the colonel's grade book.
The father exchanges pleasantries. He smiles. He watches his grammar. He imagines the colonel correcting the spelling of his spoken words.
The colonel examines the book in the son's right hand.

THE COLONEL: Arthur Schopenhauer?
THE SON: I go by Artie.

The colonel and the son strike up a conversation about how humanity is a dwarf riding the shoulders of a giant idiot named "Procreation."
The father stands there. Dumb. Listening. He experiences an unfamiliar feeling—somewhere in between nakedness and objectivity—mind stripped of its host, like a brain in a vat. He watches his son converse with a man who led airstrikes over the Ho Chi Minh Trail and earned a doctorate in education from Brown University. He watches. The father's not there. A beam without a flashlight.
What the father sees: a ten-year-old boy wearing a bald cap, conversing casually with a seventy-three-year-old colonel. The boy's synthetic white sideburns are the texture of Brillo pads. The sideburns appear more natural on the boy than they should. The boy's eyes are round, discolored, glassy, as if they belong to a puppet in a thrift shop. The boy too has a list:

- ✓ call Mom and demand favor for spending Halloween with Dad
- ✓ acknowledge that sons don't typically demand favors for spending time with their biological father
- ✓ unlock Nintendo World Championship mode on Super Mario Maker
- ✓ hold your breath and see what shade of blue your face becomes before Dad remembers you exist
- ✓ don't beat high score: cadaver blue

CYNDY HENDERSHOT
WHILE MY SKIN ROTS AWAY

Every day more skin comes off when I take off the bandage. I look at the chunks and throw the bandage in the trash. Necrosis, they call it. No doctor knows the cause. When the leg wound rots to the bone, I will have an operation.

Tired of doctors' offices and blank stares on nurses' faces, I search for the explanation. The dungeon is dark and smells of smoke. The tall, thin man leads me to an office as I gaze dumbfounded at the devices—Iron Maidens, racks, iron chairs, cat o' nine tails.

He is dressed in a black turtleneck and black jeans. His face is sallow and his hair shockingly white. He smokes a cigarette in a holder. He gestures for me to sit down in a plush red velvet chair.

"Call me Dr. Robert," he says in a gravely voice. "Tell me what you want."

I hold my cane firmly in my hands. "I want to know what caused this." I lift up my trouser leg and show him the bandage.

"Take it off."

I remove the bandage and he moves closer to me and stares. He sits back behind his desk, lighting another cigarette. "I know what caused that. I don't think you want to know."

I clear my throat. "I do want to know and I am willing to pay you for it."

"Money isn't my concern. I have plenty. I just don't think you want to know."

"I promise you that I do."

Dr. Robert stands up and puts on a jacket. "Put on a fresh bandage and we will go."

"Right now?"

He nods. I quickly put on a fresh bandage.

In his limousine, Dr. Robert is very silent. He stares straight ahead and takes no notice of me. I start to ask a question, but then think better of it. He is taking me to an answer. *Any* answer is better than ignorance, I think to myself. I feel a wave of excitement and elation sweep over me.

We drove for over an hour, we stopped in front of a pet store. This is it. I looked at him, astonished.

He put his face close to mine, "You still have time to refuse this."

"No. It is a gift to me."

"Maybe."

We walked into the small pet store greeted by a talking parrot, mewing kittens, and barking dogs. A serious young man sat by the cash register. "Hello, Dr. Robert."

"Hello, Malcolm. You know why I'm here."

Malcolm nodded and gave him a set of keys. "Another one," he said plaintively.

I followed Dr. Robert to a heavily bolted room. He slowly unlocked all the padlocks.

The room was empty except for a single metal box on a white linoleum table. We approached the box slowly.

Dr. Robert put his hands on the lid. "It will strike again. You must know that and accept that."

I nodded. He opened the box and I tried to see it. Part human heart, part eel, and covered in places with a strange brown fur. Although apparently eyeless, it still winced at the light.

I stepped back, feeling nauseous and strangely sorry for it.

"What is it?" I whispered.

Dr. Robert lowered his head. "It is you."

ROBERT HINDERLITER
THE LEPRECHAUN

The rainbow that day, arcing over the forest, seemed like a cruel joke. Winter would be here soon, and in Oregon that meant endless days of rain and gloom. Even in happier years, the months without sun took an emotional toll. But now more than ever, the changing season filled me with dread.

I'd set out in the midafternoon, thinking I'd just take a short hike, but the eerie calm after the rain drew me deeper into the woods. Soon I found myself trekking past the rotting log flume, past McKenzie Pond teeming with newts, much farther than I should have gone. In the week since Talia and I had returned from the hospital, I'd wandered through the woods searching for moments when the beauty of nature—the sun broken by pine needles into a thousand shards of light, a smooth black pebble resting in a stream—could bring me peace. But on the day of the rainbow I hiked without thinking, letting the silence of the forest and the endless repetition of trees clear my mind. By the time the shriek of a nearby hawk brought me to my senses, an orange hue was already creeping across the sky, and I realized I'd left the trail behind.

Being out in the woods at night is something even an experienced hiker should avoid, so of course I turned around immediately. I knew I'd have to hurry to beat the darkness. But I'd only taken a few steps back toward the trail when a movement through the trees to my left brought me to a halt. I often came across deer and wild turkey while hiking, so it was with only mild curiosity that I angled for a better look. But what I saw through the mossy branches was something I could never have imagined.

In a clearing on the forest floor, pawing at the ground, was a small, human-like creature. It was around two feet tall, bent on bony knees. Its head—pointy ears, squat nose, big eyes—bobbled on its gangly body as if the weight might cause it to topple over. Its sickly green skin was stretched tightly over its rib cage.

I let out a gasp, and then, terrified I'd been heard, clutched a hand to my mouth. But if the creature heard me, it didn't flinch. Its entire focus was on the soil in front of it. I squatted down and frantically searched for a stick I could use as a weapon, keeping my eyes on the creature. The word *monster* immediately came to mind. Whatever it was, it didn't belong here. I'd spent decades in the area and knew every living thing that called the forest its home. This creature was an intruder. I felt around until I found a stick—two and a half feet long, sturdy, jagged on one end where it had broken away from the tree.

My heart was pounding, my breath shallow. I wanted to run. But I forced myself to slow down and think. The creature didn't seem aggressive. In fact, as it kneeled in the dirt, slowly scraping at the ground, it appeared docile, even clumsy. As I watched, my breathing became deeper, my heart steadied, and slowly my thoughts began to turn.

Whatever this thing was, animal or alien, it had to be worth something. The government or some scientist would be interested in my little discovery, and they would pay. Maybe a lot. I'd been out of work two months, and although Talia's piano lessons kept the lights on, we'd come home from the hospital with a medical bill we couldn't begin to cover.

For several minutes I watched, gathering my courage. And then, making as little noise as possible, I parted the branches and stepped into the clearing. The creature didn't look up. It continued to dig its hole, which looked around four inches deep. I took a few cautious steps closer, gripping the stick. Every animal has a defense mechanism. The weakest run. Those that don't run usually have a trick up their sleeve. A sudden lunge, a mouth full of fangs? As I grew nearer and it still hadn't reacted, I began to feel confidant. It seemed so meek, so feeble, that I was sure I could handle it.

When I was five feet away, I knelt down for a better look. The creature's bony chest rose and sank with each breath. A few strands of black hair swirled on its skull, and a small green penis dangled between its legs. Its hands and feet were large, with long, soiled nails. It clawed at the earth with both hands, grunting softly with the effort.

"My god," I whispered.

At the sound of my voice, the creature turned for the first time to meet my gaze. Its eyes, large and slightly cloudy, were green. Tilting its head, it examined me for several seconds, and then, glancing from the dirt to me and back again, began moaning loudly and pointing downward with one long finger.

I took a quick step back, holding the stick in front of me. Was this some kind of warning? "Easy now," I said. "Take it easy."

The creature continued to point down and moan. With its free hand, it scraped a fistful of dirt from the hole. After a few moments I realized what was happening, and all I could do was stand there stunned.

It was asking for help.

What kind of animal was I dealing with here? It seemed to have no innate fear of humans, and in fact seemed glad that I'd stumbled by. But why would it ask me to help it dig, and what the hell was it digging for? The idea came to me again that maybe I was dealing with something extraterrestrial. This discovery could reshape our world, and it would certainly change my family's life forever. I could deal with the hole later. Now, I had to get the creature home.

"Hey little guy," I said, taking a step forward. "Why don't you come with me?"

Despite sensing the creature wasn't about to attack me, I was still reluctant to touch it. For all I knew, it could be radioactive, or have poisonous skin. I took off my jacket, stepped behind the creature, and scooped it up. It gave a surprised yelp as I lifted it, and then began frantically clawing at the jacket.

"It's OK," I said, trying to calm myself as much as the creature. "I'm not going to hurt you." The creature thrashed around and emitted a thin wail. It pried at my hands through the jacket and tried to bite me, although it didn't have teeth and only gummed and slobbered on the fabric. I struggled to hold it, but its squirming and cries were finally too much, and I had to set it down. It crawled on its hands and knees back to the hole and looked up at me fearfully. Then once more it began moaning and pointing down. Apparently it wouldn't come anywhere with me until I helped it dig.

Shaking my head, I put on my jacket, picked up the stick, and jabbed it into the ground. The creature moved aside and watched me. I turned over clumps of rain-loosened dirt. Thick earthworms writhed in the soil. Every so often, the creature would lean over and peer into the hole, or scoop loose dirt away from its edges. About eight inches down, the ground became hard enough that I couldn't make much more progress with the stick. I stepped back and tossed it away.

"Sorry," I said. "There's nothing down there."

The creature gave an alarmed whimper and crawled to the edge of the hole. It reached down and began pawing at the dirt.

As the creature continued to dig, I looked up at the dimming sky. It was a long hike back to the house, and I didn't have a flashlight. The wind had picked up, rustling the trees, and with it had come a chill. I needed to leave now. But what about the creature? I watched it scrape at the ground—its digging seemed almost desperate, I thought. I doubted I could carry it back to the house against its will without accidently breaking one of its frail limbs. I needed a way to restrain it gently. And I remembered that back at the house I had just the thing.

From the creature's actions so far, I was confident it wouldn't leave the hole. But night was coming soon, and the darkness would bring predators—foxes, coyotes, bobcats, and even the occasional mountain lion or black bear. The creature wouldn't stand a chance. I had to hurry.

⚓

I MADE MY way as quickly as I could through the woods. Crickets and frogs had started their nightly songs, and in the distance I heard the yipping of a coyote. The light soon faded away. I trekked the last ten minutes by moonlight, tripping over roots and holding out an arm to protect against low-hanging branches.

When I reached our backyard, the porch light was off, but I saw a flickering through the curtained bedroom window. I crashed through the back door and clomped to the bedroom in my muddy boots.

It looked as though Talia hadn't moved an inch in the time I'd been gone. She lay in bed with her head propped on a pillow, Nintendo controller in her hands.

"Honey, I saw..." I said, my chest heaving. "There's something out there. I don't know what it is."

She didn't look up. "I'm glad you saw something interesting," she said. "You've been gone long enough."

"Listen to me," I said. I stepped over to the bed and stood above her. "I found something in the woods—some kind of creature."

"Ray, could you just not?" she said, still staring at the screen. "Could you just not do this right now?" From the TV came playful music and cartoon sound effects—beeps and boings, and one character saying *Yeah, ha ha ha!*

I reached down and pulled the controller from her hands.

"Give it back!" she cried, scrambling up in bed. "What's wrong with you?" She snatched at the controller. Her face, warped with anger, was almost unrecognizable. I staggered away from the bed, dropped the controller, and stumbled out into the hall. The door slammed behind me.

My mind spinning, I made my way to Joseph's room. I hadn't set foot in there since we'd returned from the hospital. Joseph's crib sat in the middle of the room, a mobile with plastic planets and moons hanging over an empty mattress. Stacked along the wall were unopened boxes of diapers, and above me were hundreds of glow-in-the-dark stars I'd stuck to the ceiling the night before the delivery. And there, in the corner, was what I was looking for: Joseph's red baby carrier.

With the empty carrier strapped to my chest, I went out to the shed and grabbed a big plastic flashlight and, after a moment's thought, a shovel. I took one more look at the bedroom window—light still dimly flashing through the curtains—and set off into the woods.

⚓

THE FOREST AT night was much louder than during the day. Trees creaked and leaves rustled in the wind. The sound of awakening nocturnal life filled the air, and every few minutes a small animal would scurry into the underbrush as I approached. Somewhere near me a woodpecker hammered on a tree. Deeper into the woods, a coyote began to bark, and soon another joined in with a long wail. I walked faster, trying not to think about the defenseless creature alone in the clearing. Instead, I focused on the sound of my own breathing and the metallic scrape of the shovel dragging behind me.

In the flashlight's beam, the path seemed unfamiliar, winding in places I hadn't remembered. I shined the light out into the maze of trees but couldn't recognize any landmarks. After thirty minutes, I came across a large branch blocking the path. Had the wind knocked it down, or was I going in the wrong direction? I stepped around it. Suddenly, a dark shape appeared from the darkness and careened toward my face. I dropped to my knees and swung the light wildly. It was gone. Just a night bird, or maybe a bat. I trudged on.

The baby carrier jostled against my chest. It was thick with padding and equipped with sturdy harnesses. It would be perfect to secure the creature and take it home.

As for Joseph, he could never come home. The doctors rushed him out of the delivery room and came back twenty minutes later with a tiny blue lifeless body. Our son. They asked us if we wanted to hold him, and Talia did, but I couldn't bring myself to touch him. What would be the point?

The abandoned flume, at last. I was going in the right direction. At McKenzie Pond, the moon's reflection trembled in the wind-rippled water. Dozens of newts crawled along rocks by the water's edge.

The trail ended fifteen minutes past the pond, and after another five minutes of trekking through untamed brushwood, I reached the clearing. I shined my light through the branches. The creature was still there, bent over the hole, digging. As I approached, it looked up for a moment, wincing and shielding its eyes from the light, and then turned back to the hole. It had cleared away maybe three more inches. I set down the baby carrier and balanced the flashlight on a rock a few feet from the hole.

Now that I had the carrier, the creature would be coming with me whether it wanted to or not. But I was still curious about the hole.

"All right, little guy," I said, swinging my shovel into position, "let's see what's down there."

The creature scampered to the side as I stepped up to the hole. One shovelful after another, I dug into the earth. The crickets were wild around me, an owl hooted in the distance, and again and again the shovel broke through the soil, first with small popping sounds as the blade cut tiny roots, and later with a gravely scrape as the earth hardened. Two feet down, three feet down. I was standing in the hole up to my waist, hands blistered, muscles burning. The creature clasped its knees and moaned with anticipation.

I kept digging. It felt good to push myself, to exhaust my muscles. My mind, as I dug, was clear.

And then, more than five feet down, after what must have been over an hour, sweat running down my temples and a huge heap of dirt next to me, the shovel's progress was arrested with a resounding *clunk*. A thrill shot through me. The creature lunged to the edge of the hole and peered down into the darkness. I scooped out a few more shovelfuls and climbed from the hole to get the flashlight.

There, at the bottom of the hole, still half-covered with dirt, was the lid of a chest—dark wood reinforced with thick metal bands. The creature clapped its hands and grabbed at my shirt, pointing down frantically.

"Not yet," I said.

For another five minutes, I continued to dig around the chest's edges. It was about three feet by two feet, its lid now fully exposed but its main bulk still buried. On the front was a metal latch. I climbed from the hole and lay down, jammed the shovel blade below the latch, and pried upward. The lid creaked open. I grabbed the flashlight and shined it down. The creature, lying beside me, squealed with delight.

"Oh my god," I said.

There, gleaming in my flashlight's beam, was a glittering pile of treasure. Gold bars, jewels, goblets filled with coins, diamonds catching the light and tossing it in a thousand directions.

The creature teetered over the edge of the hole, lost its balance, and toppled down into the open chest. It rolled around rapturously, sifting gold coins through its fingers, a huge smile wrinkling its face.

And watching the creature there with the treasure, the puzzle pieces jumbled in my head began to fall slowly into place: the rainbow, the small green creature, the buried gold...

It couldn't be. The thought was ludicrous. I'd never believed in Bigfoot, the Loch Ness Monster, or any of that nonsense. Hell, as a boy, I'd never even believed in Santa Claus. And now this? I must be having a breakdown. But my mind seemed sharp, all my senses clear. I stood there and laughed. I dropped the shovel and howled with laughter.

A fucking leprechaun.

Still laughing, I jumped into the hole.

Reaching around the creature, I began filling my pockets with gold and jewels. My jacket and pants quickly became heavy, overflowing with riches. What I took would be enough to get us through more than a few winters. But I wanted to dig deeper, to search through all the wonders in the chest, and the creature was in my way. I grabbed it by its waist to move it aside.

But before I could set the creature down, my breath caught in my throat, and I stopped.

Maybe it was its weight in my arms, or the way its big eyes—*his* big eyes, I thought—blinked up into mine, but I couldn't let him go. I scooped his legs under my arm and cradled him to my chest. He looked at me with bewilderment and reached up and touched my shoulder. Very slowly, my hand shaking, I ran my fingers across the thin swoop of his hair. He lay motionless, staring at me, forming an O with his toothless mouth. I brought my hand to his face and touched his cheek. He murmured softly and nestled his face against my palm. I closed my eyes.

A single sob escaped my throat. I held the rest inside. For another minute I just stood in the hole and held him that way, his body against my chest, his soft face in my hand. I wanted that moment to last forever.

Soon, though, he began to fidget and glance down. "I know," I said. I lifted his face to mine and kissed his forehead. And then, lowering him into the chest, I told him goodbye.

He lay on the treasure and curled into a ball. I climbed from the hole, reached down with the shovel, and slowly closed the lid.

ALLEN FORREST
CITY LIFE, UNHAPPY

LA LANTZ

HAIR OF THE DOG

The train from Antequera to Madrid ran only once a day, in the evening. We sat in the small station on hard benches that looked like church pews. During this trip it had become clear that we were no longer a young couple.

Now, for instance, Frank didn't suggest that we find a bar and knock back beer from tall, narrow glasses or impossibly cheap, strong mixed drinks. We English-only speakers had finally realized that we were too dependent on each other to dare speak or hear what words might be freed by the alcohol.

Also we were too embarrassed to awaken again with cheek pressed against a beery table and see smirks from other drinkers. That was how we missed the train to Madrid last night.

The train station was mostly empty. The morning sun began to dazzle the white walls of the train station, dust rising from the still-cool cement. The light hurt my eyes so we moved inside.

After a while a few people arrived and formed a line in front of a closed ticket office. I felt anticipation. It seemed like there was going to be something to see in the same way I'd read that a line in Soviet Russia had been a thing to join. The ticket office opened and did a brisk business. The ticketholders moved outside to track 3. Just after the train departed, the ticket office closed. The station was again empty. The process repeated itself exactly twice while we were waiting that morning. Antequera was not a large town.

"Fifteen minutes," said Frank, looking at his phone. "The ticket office opens only fifteen minutes before each train."

"Wonder what the ticket seller does the rest of the day?" I asked.

Before lunchtime, I pulled our guidebook from the bottom of my backpack. It was ten years old; I got it used. We followed it with a grain of salt.

"It says there are dolomite caves outside of town. Ancient."

"What's dolomite? How far?"

I shrugged. "Stone? Makes me think of black comics, but I can't think why. About a mile." We decided to walk. We had nothing but time.

As we walked out of town along the shoulder of a quiet highway, a dog joined our party. She trotted beside us, matching our pace although she limped slightly. When we reached the path to turn off, she came along. The path was lined with a stately double row of poplars, tall and angled by what must be a very consistent breeze. I thought that we would soon come to the manor of the landed gentry, but there was no house, no buildings at all. The dog vanished when we reached the stones.

"You're sure the book said caves?" Frank asked. He lifted his sunglasses to his forehead and blinked in the sun. He looked like something nocturnal.

The caves were not caves at all, but weighty, simple structures like shelters or tombs or sanctuaries. A relative of Stonehenge. A guard or guide, who'd been sitting in his car playing Bon Jovi, got out as we walked up. He held his hand out toward the structures and said that no one knew. Which was not actually an answer to anything that we had asked.

"They're impressive either way," I said.

Frank shrugged. "In a mute, caveman sort of way."

"Yeah? I'd like to see you move these into place." Frank didn't answer. He walked around the back of the guard's car to read the make.

The guard rummaged around on the passenger side seat of his car. He located a sheet mimeographed with old-fashioned purple ink. I remembered winning the opportunity to crank the handle of our mimeograph machine in the third grade. Why did a mimeograph print in purple; why not black?

The guard read with an accent so heavy I couldn't understand him. I don't mean it as an insult. Then, we three watched each other blankly.

Finally, I thanked him. I gave him a coin and he returned to his car. A Renault 4 Frank told me at some point. It was old, square-ish, and squashed-up looking.

"Man," said Frank, staring again at the car, "I wonder if he gets paid whether anyone comes here or not."

"Stuck here all day, just sitting around?"

"Paula, do you have to make everything a big fucking deal? It was a simple question."

When we sat down to rest on the side of a hill, it was very peaceful. The sky overhead was blue and cloudless. It didn't make my head hurt. What was wrong with working here? Why did I think that an office was so terrific? My growing email inbox? Which food truck I might lunch at? I looked at Frank, ready to apologize; his eyes were closed. I didn't speak.

In front of us was a range of mountains. One mountain was shaped in perfect profile of a stereotypical American Indian chief or warrior. Reclining like me, watching the sky. Strong brow, hawklike nose, high cheekbones. It was a benign interpretation, but I didn't tell Frank.

"Doesn't Spain have modern photocopiers?" I asked.

"Maybe he was reading from a really old copy," Frank said. He knew what I was talking about, which gave me a good, restful feeling.

"It can be slow here, but it doesn't seem especially poor. Or rather, it seems like things are happening. Economically."

"There is a lot of construction," Frank agreed.

"Also people sing as they work." We had both noticed this during our trip.

When we stood to go, the dog rose from the shadows and came near. She didn't seek attention. Her fur was golden, but dusty, matted, and dull. Her frame was strong, but bony. When we walked back to town, I could see that her limp had increased.

I waited and waited until I was beaten, then finally asked, "What do you think is up with this dog?"

"Weird, huh?" he said. I felt my irritation dissolve in another a glow of shared sympathy.

Back in Antequera, we stopped at an antiseptic restaurant, distinguished by being open and air conditioned. It was empty although it was not yet 2 p.m.. We had trouble deciphering when people ate in Spain. If we went to a bar, no one else was there until we left. If we settled on a restaurant, it was often closed. We were like senior citizens in a nation of nightclubbing youth.

Our menu had also been more unvaried than I'd hoped. In department stores, we bought cookies that thought about being flavored lemon. In bars, we ordered dark, oily tapas by waving at a plate whose contents we could not see and even if we asked, we never knew what we ate. The experiences were unfulfilling in many ways.

From the sidewalk outside the restaurant the dog stood and watched us. What did she think we were? How could she imagine we could help her? I ordered a hamburger and fries.

"Wow," said Frank, "What's with the sudden carnivore urge? Should I be scared?"

"It's not for me," I said sharply. To my shame, a tear rolled down my cheek.

"It sure has not improved your mood." Frank was not the sort of man to react to tears. As a rule, he avoided routes and conversations and decisions that would lead to crying. When the waitress brought the hamburger, I carried the yellow plate outside without saying a word. The waitress said something in Spanish, likely along the lines of what the hell are you doing. I didn't answer her either.

The dog wasn't near the door anymore. The afternoon streets were hushed, gently dusty from some of that construction we had seen throughout Spain. Dust drifted over the hamburger. Had the dog gone? Abandoned me after I'd cried in front of Frank?

I walked a block one direction; all the shops were closed and shuttered for lunch. The narrow sidewalks sometimes gave up, and melted away into equally narrow streets. I walked the other direction, where I found the dog. She was resting out of the sun in a shop entryway. Dust had settled thick as a blanket over her body.

I hesitated. Would it be kindest to creep away and leave the dog in peace? I lay the plate with the hamburger quietly on the tile floor near the dog's head. The dog was not startled, but lifted her head the minimal amount she need to open her mouth, inhaled the meat. Her head dropped back and her tail slapped the tiled floor twice.

I left the dog and returned to the restaurant for a coffee cup. I poured a glass of water into the cup and went back out. The waitress and Frank were watching television. Frank was talking. "I've been saving for this trip ever since I got out of college. My brother did some study abroad here and he was always telling me how great it was." The waitress nodded while never looking away from the screen. As I left again, he was saying, "I don't know. Maybe I'm too old or the world's gotten smaller, but it's been a bit of a disappointment." I hoped that the waitress didn't speak English.

The dog watched me as she drank from the water, then laid her head back down. I couldn't read her expression, but, then again, she was a dog.

In the restaurant, Frank said, "Nelson Mandela died today."

The afternoon still wasn't over. After lunch, Frank looked at his phone. "Knicks won in overtime. We've still got six hours before the train to Madrid. What is there to do here? Didn't we see a pool hall?"

"Do you think that women are allowed in pool halls here?"

Frank laughed softly, but not kindly. "Why? Are you trying to impress someone?" I began to walk away from Frank, away from the dog, but Frank wouldn't follow. "Paula. Paula." He called. "This way."

"Let's just walk around the block this way." I wouldn't tell him why because he would laugh at me. He just looked at me as if I was crazy now. I watched as he walked back the way we had come. He walked past the dog. She sighed, but pulled herself up awkwardly, dust clouding her for a moment and hobbled after him.

I followed. I couldn't leave the dog to Frank. He paid no more attention to her than he did to me. "We've been down this road before," I called to Frank, who offered me a deep condescending sigh, then shrugged. "What a long, strange trip it's been," he said. It was my turn to sigh.

This trip was supposed to be the prelude to us living together. I had let my apartment go before we left—to save money—though I'd known that Frank hadn't given notice on his. Why hadn't that seemed suspect to me? I struggled to remember his exact words, but could not remember where we had the conversation. Had he urged me to keep my apartment?

I caught up with Frank and looked back at the dog. Her brown head bobbed if my arm moved or Frank began to whistle, ready to serve although her limp slowed her.

In the middle of a block, in sight of a big church under scaffolding, I stopped at an arched wooden doorway the size of a small truck. It was open, and resembled the entry to a medieval convent, so I imagined. Inside, pulling me through the darkness, was a dazzle of light. I stepped up and into the entryway, while the dog hesitated, looking from me to Frank. Who marched on as if nothing were wrong.

I stepped far enough into the darkness to see that the courtyard beyond was green and gold, a shady oasis hidden behind bare walls. It was an architectural style that didn't care about impressing the passerby, different than at home.

I urged the dog to follow me. She whined, placing her front paws on the entryway, but not willing to abandon Frank. She was the most faithful. Finally, I learned out the door and called into the street, "Bastard, come here." Frank stopped, like the dog, ambivalent, and finally turned back. The moment he turned, the dog relaxed, and heaved herself over the entryway.

Quicker, I stepped back out and over, closing the door on the dog. Without patting her goodbye or reassuring her or explaining.

Frank neared me. "What is it?" I was crying too hard to answer. I could hear the dog inside, scratching the door and testing little yips as if she didn't quite want to accuse us of anything yet.

I had to get away before she began to howl. "Are you hurt?" Frank asked. When I shook my head, he said, "Well, what is it?" I was touched, but I didn't answer. What could I say? He must hear the dog. The dog should lay down in the shade and rest. Someone would open the door or the inside door and she would at last be in the care of someone who would have the capacity to provide for her.

"Well?" His eyes registered disgust and weariness.

"I can't help the dog," I said. These were difficult words to speak.

"Of course not. You don't live here. You can't take her home. Imagine her in customs." He looked to see if I had smiled. The weariness crept forward again.

"I'm done," he said and walked toward the train station. His shoulders slumped for a while beneath his backpack. Then, a few blocks ahead, his back straightened and his pace picked up.

I didn't want to argue over who might have said what and what either of us had meant before we'd come to Spain, if anyone lied. Still, I couldn't help but wonder if, rather than simply telling me that he had no intention of moving in,

Frank had intended this overseas vacation to provide us an exit strategy? Why not just break up?

As I walked behind Frank toward the train station, I could hear the dog howling. Her pain was hard to listen to, but I quieted my steps and didn't hum so I could hear better even as I got further away. I had done the right thing. I resolved in the future to always try to listen even if I didn't hear what I wanted to.

RAIMA LARTER
THE INITIATE

A bell sounds in the cold, quiet morning. Guan Lee pulls his robe close. Saffron and burgundy folds swirl around his legs as he runs. Perched on the hillside, the temple sits silent, waiting.

Fatigue tugs at the corners of Guan Lee's mind. The bell sounds again. He must be in his place by the third chime. The young initiate hastens his steps, hopping over the stream that plunges beside the steep path. Ice hangs in suspended sheets along its rocky banks.

A sudden flurry in the bushes brings Guan to a stop. There, beside the trail—a bird, barely visible on its nest. Something else rustles in the branches. Guan Lee sees only the bird. A low rumble comes from the undergrowth. It is dark—tigers are dark. The hairs on Guan's neck spike to attention.

Guan gathers his robe tight and runs to the temple. His breath puffs from his mouth as he approaches the ancient wooden building, kicks his sandals off by the door, and enters. A giant golden Buddha, three stories tall, sits silent, waiting, filling the front half of the room. Squares of folded carpet form neat rows across the polished floor. A dozen boys, each wrapped in robes like Guan's, sit yawning on the carpet squares. Their teacher, a tall man with a shaved head and a round face, holds a switch. He frowns as the young monks enter, one by one. All of the young monks are, like Guan, initiates to the monastery's order, not quite the real monks they will, one day, be.

Guan Lee finds his assigned spot in the middle of the back row. He stands beside his carpet square, presses his hands together, and bows to his teacher. He turns and bows again—to the giant gilded Buddha, the Awakened One.

One of Guan's classmates tends to the fire in the blackened stove at the Buddha's foot. Guan curls onto his carpet square and gazes, as he does every morning, at the Awakened One. Half-closed lids shroud enormous eyes. The Great One looks down on the young monks, golden fingertips of one gigantic hand touching, forming a mudra whose meaning Guan Lee cannot remember.

The third bell sounds. Guan squeezes his eyes closed and waits for instructions. Every day Guan and the other boys must sit in meditation, not talking, not moving, not thinking, counting their breaths—one count for each inhale and exhale. The teacher announces the starting number: today they will begin at one hundred and count backward all the way to zero. Yesterday, they started at ninety, the day before it was eighty. All of these are beyond his ability. He knows that. The last time Guan succeeded in reaching zero, the starting number was only twenty.

Fighting the pull of sleep, Guan Lee begins to count. *One hundred, ninety-nine, ninety-eight...* He yawns. *Ninety-seven, ninety-six, ninety-five...* Thoughts of his warm sleeping pad return. He imagines snuggling under the heavy blanket, imagines Mama cooking warm porridge, the bubbling pot perched in the coals of a crackling fire. It is almost as if she is really there. He can even smell the smoke from her fire.

Guan Lee flinches, startled. He is awake now. Smoke curls from the stove at the Buddha's feet. He has been dreaming. He has lost count. Teacher says one's thoughts have a way of distracting from the practice. When that happens, teacher says, one must start over.

Guan begins again. *One hundred, ninety-nine...* The floorboard creaks beside him. He opens one eye. His teacher, standing nearby, clasping the switch behind his back, glares at a young boy who is scrambling onto his carpet square, late.

His teacher smacks the stick into his own palm and walks toward the Buddha, kicking at the hem of his robe, whacking his hand, one tap for each step. Guan Lee draws a deep breath. What number was he on? He cannot remember. He must start over. *One hundred, ninety-nine, ninety-eight...*

Guan Lee is happy to be here, and he should be happy even though it's cold and his stomach rumbles with hunger, even though he is bored, so bored. Teacher says that boredom is the gateway to enlightenment, but Guan Lee has no idea what teacher means by this. If boredom is such a gateway, surely Guan Lee should be enlightened by now, maybe even a bodhisattva. Instead, he is just a bored boy.

Guan Lee is happy—he must be. He is living the life he told Papa he wanted more than anything in the world, so he must be happy, even though he thinks he is probably sad. He's freely embraced his calling, renounced the life his father always said he was wasting, the life Papa said would amount to nothing, since Guan Lee himself is nothing, nothing but a lazy boy who prefers playing dice with his friends to helping Papa in the shop.

Guan Lee catches himself thinking. He sighs, returns to the beginning... *one hundred, ninety-nine...* This time, he gets all the way to eighty-nine before Mama's face enters his mind. She is smiling, offering him a steaming bowl of porridge. Mama is pleased that Guan Lee has chosen the life of a holy man, a life of tranquility and retreat, according to Mama, whose own life was so hard she refused to accept any more babies after Guan was born, aborting every one. Each little death has etched another line into her deeply creased face.

Once he asked her why she didn't want more babies, and she said the choice was not hers to make. It was the authorities, she said—but Guan Lee doesn't believe this. He knows, or thinks he knows, that it is because she, like Papa, grew disappointed in Guan Lee and wanted no more children like him.

He said this to her as they walked to the train that brought him to the monastery. Don't be silly, Guan Lee, she said, tugging on his ear. How could any mother be disappointed in a son like you?

It has happened again. He is thinking and must start over. Guan Lee shifts his position and recrosses his legs. He is bored, so bored, but he must count. The numbers help. When he counts, he doesn't think of Mama. He doesn't think of Papa. He doesn't think of the tiger outside, the one he heard in the undergrowth, the one whose growl—if that's what it was—sounded a lot like his stomach, rumbling again with hunger.

He imagines the tiger now, waiting for him, patient. It is hiding beneath the same bush where the nest sits. The nest is empty now. Guan wonders where the bird has gone. Dew drips from the branches onto the tiger's striped flanks. It blinks its large eyes in the dim morning light, searching for Guan Lee.

Guan Lee, Mama said, as the train pulled up, do not think we don't want you. She held her hand out to the monk who met them that day. Guan saw money pass between them. It is your calling, Mama said. Your father will be proud, she said, when he sees what a great monk you have become. In a few years we will welcome you home. She handed him his bag then, and he turned away before she could see him crying.

He is thinking again. He has let his guard down. This time, the tiger has noticed. It sees what Guan Lee has done, how Guan Lee is thinking about Mama, her hand stretched toward the monk at the train. Guan has yet again forgotten to count his breaths. The tiger knows that Guan has abandoned the lessons his teacher repeats each and every day. Maybe Papa is right. Maybe Guan Lee is a worthless, lazy boy.

The tiger sees its opening. It approaches the door, pausing at the threshold between forest and temple. Outside, the air is filled with bird sounds and the music of the tumbling stream. Mist rises from the forest floor. Inside the air smells of incense. The tiger steps out of the mist and into the temple, padding on soft feet across the wooden floor. Its breath comes out in tiny puffs, like smoke, filling the chilled temple air with its warm breath.

The tiger stops at Guan Lee's side. Guan Lee has not opened his eyes, but he can see perfectly—through the tiger's eyes. The floorboard creaks again as the tiger approaches, but Guan Lee keeps his focus. Fear pulls at Guan's eyelids.

Is it his teacher standing there? He is about to open his eyes to check when he senses the beast beside him—an enormous being with hot breath that rumbles deep inside a large striped chest. The tiger walks in tight circles around Guan Lee. Guan can see himself, through the tiger's eyes, sitting motionless on a square of carpet as the tiger circles, once, twice, three times—one circle for each of Guan Lee's breaths.

Now, somehow, Guan Lee can see both tiger and boy, as if he is watching the two of them from a distance. The tiger turns its big tiger head toward the Buddha. Tiger gazes at the Awakened One, who looks back and sees the tiger circling Guan Lee. The Great One gazes through his enormous gilded eyes, watching the young initiates breathe and count. They sit in neat rows on their folded squares of carpet, Guan Lee one among many.

The train stands waiting. Mama reaches toward the monk. She accepts a large stack of bills from him—payment for the boy she has just sold.

Guan's heart becomes a frantic bird inside his chest, a tiny frightened being who does not want to see the truth—the truth the tiger has just delivered. Boredom has given way to something excruciating, yet thrilling. Guan Lee breathes. Counting, counting, counting without numbers.

The tiger closes its soft tiger eyes and stretches out upon the floor, curling into Guan Lee's side like a kitten. The Awakened One watches them, tiger and boy. A rumbling comes from deep inside the massive creature. Guan Lee breathes—counting, counting, counting without numbers. The tiger, as still as the morning, powerful beyond measure, presses its warm face against Guan Lee's knee, yawns, and begins to purr.

CHRISTINE MA-KELLAMS
DAVE

By the time he was thirty-four years old, Dave Kellams was living at 22 San Federico with seven children and his fourth wife. If he was the introspective type, he might've considered this somewhat of a bad sign. He wasn't and he didn't.

At this point you are likely to jump to several conclusions about this Dave, all of which would be inaccurate, not because you are stupid but because true stories always defy expectation.

Conclusion #1: Dave Kellams is a Mormon. You are unversed in Mormon theology but you remember your Mormon neighbor from when you were in the fifth grade and even though she was just an overweight middle-aged single mother with curly hair and a slight Middle-Eastern accent—plus a singular, very round son named Nigel—you were always under the impression that her kind—Mormons, that is—had a lot of children.

Conclusion #2: Dave Kellams is a Catholic, a legit one. You know a bunch of Catholics, and on average they are childless or have two kids, which, empirically speaking, does not support your theory, but you read somewhere that Catholics don't believe in birth control. You are a scientist but a crappy one, so in this particular case you'll disregard the data and go with what you read online.

Conclusion #3: Dave Kellams is from one of those parts of the world that can't stop procreating and it's making all the Americans nervous. You are not a racist so you refuse to specify which exact "parts of the world" you have in mind, but you and I both know you are thinking about countries south of Texas.

Conclusion #4: Dave Kellams is terrifically rich. This would not so much explain the immense number of kids but more explain the immense number of wives. Poor men collect things—stamps, cars, knives, guns, vinyl—but rich men collect people—subordinates, shareholders, nannies, wives. Frozen versus liquid assets, or whatever it is economists call them.

Wife #1 doesn't have a name. None of the seven kids remember her, knows what she looks like or whether she still lives in Santa Barbara, lest we worry if she is the woman who gave us free tea at the downtown Starbucks that one night when it was raining on Christmas Eve, or the lady with the newly fake tits who passes out the flyers at Calvary Chapel. You call her Cherry; it's your favorite stripper name, and also the name of the tight little Filipino woman at the gym whose ass looks like two perfect loquats superglued together. Cherry and Dave lived in West Campus Family Student Housing at UCSB in 1968, the year both the rest of the world and their marriage ended, almost as quickly as it started.

It all started with the laundry. By the time he was living in 22 San Federico, Vicky—Wife #4—was washing all his drawers, but in 1968 Dave still liked the idea of redemption, and that's why doing his own laundry seemed like a nice idea. Shit could always be washed off, and that was a good thing; he was happy to redeem himself in whatever form he could.

You could tell who was a routine laundress versus a sporadic one by the content of what they were washing. The sporadic laundress always washed tons of underwear, unanimous underwear, because without an utter lack of them she could not be moved to do laundry in the first place; new undies cost a buck a piece at Robinson's May on sale but a whole load was only fifty cents. The routine laundress had a unified selection of clothing items—inner and outerwear, men's and women's, at least two of each kind, like Noah packing his boat. Systematic, that's what God told him to be, you (mis)remember.

Then and now, West Campus consists of a series of twenty-something army barracks arranged Tetris-style, some facing East, or North or South, though never West, where Stork Road devolves into Isla Vista, home of the natural blondes and on-campus janitorial staff. The blondes share rooms but not wombs, while the janitors and their families and their families' families share both; such was the irony of social dominance. The only thing that has changed since 1968 is the color of the janitors; they used to be white, but now they are brown. Everything else—including the laundry machines—has remained the same, but they don't make things like they used to.

"David, right?" Debbie asked. Her hands were held shut but her face was wide open, like a papaya.

"Yes!" Dave said. "How'd you know?"

Debbie pointed East and squinted, pretending to count. "You live two buildings down, kitty-corner to the largest pine tree on campus," she replied. "I've seen you around."

"You're good," David said. He was yelling, but didn't know why.

"I am," Debbie said into her cavernous dryer. Her breathing began to fog up the outside of the glass, even though it was June.

Dave liked her right away and only afterwards did he see the baby by her foot, chewing on his own cotton booties and eyes aflutter, like they were looking for a new daddy to land on. "How many months?" he asked.

"Nine," Debbie said. "I just love them at this age, don't you? They're all milk and sugar and no tea."

Dave nodded, not really understanding. He was smart but not intellectual, Debbie would accuse him decades later, long after the divorce, but what she really meant was this: he never asked enough questions; no, what do you mean by that, or do you still love them when they're fifteen, or four, and what happens when the tea shows up?

No, at this point Dave was marveling at Deb's face. It was very Tess of the d'Urbervilles. Marveling at her breasts would come later, though not by much.

"I used to be a nun, you know," Deb confided, smiling for the first time.

"Wow," said Dave. "How long ago was that?"

"Nine months," she repeated. "Joking," she added, after letting him do the math.

"You're very funny," Dave told her.

"And good with names," she reminded him.

"What else are you good at?" he asked. And that was the start and end of it.

All the apartments at West Campus consisted of little boxes stacked four to a row, two rows per building, built vaguely Spanish-style to mimic everything else in Santa Barbara, lest the tourists get confused when they visited UCSB and realized that technically, the university wasn't in SB at all, but rather, in a neighboring shithole nicknamed—ironically—the Good Land—that only began to gentrify four decades later, after Oprah moved just South to Montecito and drove all the housing prices within a fifty-mile radius up.

One consequence of living in a box was that decorating was impossible; Deb, Dave, and their respective spouses each had a ten-foot-by-ten-foot square with which to stake out their entire domestic arrangements, which typically meant eating next to the TV and having the dining table end where the couch started. Those who dared to bring in a coffee table had never heard of fire hazards. Lucky for Dave, Deb did not believe in feng shui and instead opted for her own brand of practical minimalism: a single double bed occupying one side of the *cajita*, with brown jersey sheets that could hide just about anything.

After he folded all his underwear, and a few of Cherry's panties too—that was his idea of holding up his end of the stick, at least in marriage—Dave followed Deb back to her place.

"Show me what you're good at," he asked.

Deb ignored him and trekked instead into the kitchen—another, even smaller box nailed to the front of the living-dining-room combo. She filled the white tea kettle she had received as a wedding present and turned on the gas stove, waiting for the spanking sound of the gas valve to transform into a ring of taurine blue but deciding, at the last minute, to leave the cap of the kettle off. She didn't want the impending whistle to disturb what would happen next. In the meantime she had to demonstrate that she could boil water, that she was no dummy.

"My name is Debbie, or Deb," she said, through the drywall. She was a thin woman, and were it not for her spongy breasts men might've mistaken her for a coat hanger, or a hard lay, but they didn't; she wasn't. When she talked she sounded commanding and just on the edge of falling apart, or divulging some black secret, so in this way she was also hard to ignore, even if you learned, over the decades, not to take her too seriously.

"Of course," said Dave. He didn't apologize for not asking earlier.

"How old are you?" she asked.

"Probably the same age as you," Dave guessed. "Though you look twelve."

"People usually guess seventeen," Deb answered. "Just shy of legal." Deb did not smile when she said this, did not appreciate this gift of the gap between real and perceived age, until Husband #4 died suddenly and violently in a parking lot in Lompoc, but by then the gap had disappeared altogether, and it was too late anyway.

MARK MAXWELL

THIN PLACES

ACCORDING TO MAX

My friend Luke is the forty-nine-year-old son of a man who was, until his death, the highest-ranking deacon in the Archdiocese. When his father died, Luke gave a eulogy in front of the Cardinal that made everyone in the church weep. Even the undertaker. Then my friend Luke blew a kiss toward his father's casket.

When we were kids, Luke was the one who was good at everything. Pinball, billiards, card tricks, Ping-Pong, baseball, guitar, brewing homemade beer, procuring bottle rockets and Black Cat firecrackers, making people laugh. You name it, he could do it and do it better than anybody else in town.

Now that we're older, Luke is still good at everything he does. In midlife he's taken up kickboxing, woodworking, piano, and drawing, among other things. Everyone loves Luke.

Luke and his wife of twenty-five years own a yoga studio and boxing club in a strip mall in the suburbs, and they do quite well for themselves. They have a swimming pool in their backyard and have built a three-bedroom addition to their home. Their mortgage is almost paid off, and they have no credit card debt.

The other night, I met Luke for a beer. He asked me to meet him at a bar in between where he lives and where I live.

When I entered the place—a dumpy little dive bar—Luke was on a stool already with his back to me. He was chatting with the bartender, a beautiful redheaded woman who looked to be a good ten years younger than us and who was smiling at Luke with a little twinkle in her eye—her thin, pale arms reaching out between the beer tappers and across the bar. As I stepped up to my stool, I noticed that the bartender was holding Luke's hand.

The bartender's name turned out to be Evie. She had the biggest, most soulful eyes I'd ever seen and the body of a nineteen-year-old. And she was clearly smitten with this man who is good at everything. She was in love with Luke, I could tell. But so what. Everyone loves Luke.

When Evie stepped away to serve another customer, Luke told me that he was deeply embroiled in what was now a steamy, two-year affair with this gorgeous thirty-eight-year-old bartender from Ireland. He said he still loved his wife, but also loved the bartender.

After a few more beers, I suggested that maybe Luke ought to either shit or get off the pot. I mean, it's only a matter of time before his wife figures out what's going on since this Irish bartender also teaches yoga part time at the studio that Luke and his wife own. If you love your wife, I said, you better get off the pot before you lose her. If you love Evie more, than you really should come clean with your wife.

But I can't do it, he said. Too much Catholic guilt, he said. I don't want to hurt either one of them, he said. I just can't put them through that.

Luke likes to be loved. In addition to the bartender, it turns out there was also a long-legged psychologist he was seeing once a week. He told his wife he was going for therapy to sort through some shit that got stirred up when his dad died. In truth, Luke fucked the therapist weekly on the plaid sofa in her office. The therapist's name was Margaret. She was a student at the yoga studio. She gave Luke his therapy in exchange for free yoga classes.

And then there was Beth, the receptionist at the yoga studio, a hot young mom of twin girls. Luke fucked her in the back of her minivan on her lunch break. There may well have been others. I expect there were. These were the ones Luke told me about—Evie, Margaret, and Beth.

I love them all in different ways, he said.

Luke told me something else that night at the bar. He told me that a while back he was diagnosed with cancer. The same kind of cancer that killed his father. The kind of cancer that requires surgery to remove the organ in question. The kind of surgery that makes it difficult to get an erection without the aid of a little blue pill. The kind of surgery that makes you shoot blanks—if you're lucky enough to keep it up and have an orgasm at all.

I'm living on borrowed time, he said.

We all are, I said.

After a few beers, we stepped outside for a cigarette. In the parking lot, Luke showed me his new car—a twenty-first-century version of the '70s muscle car. It's got all the beef you'd expect under the hood, but it is aerodynamic and it has four doors and lots of electronic bells and whistles. Luke can program the car to start from his smartphone. He can check its tire pressure from anywhere on the globe. He showed me how this works—all that power right at his fingertips, and he doesn't even have to be behind the wheel. He told his phone to start his car and unlock the doors. The engine purred. We hopped in. Luke wanted me to see the glowing dash, feel the supple leather. The radio was on full blast when we got into the car, tuned into a satellite station called Sex Talk Radio. Two women were discussing their preference for men with shaved balls. "I don't want to floss my teeth when I'm sucking a guy's nut sack," one said. The other woman laughed and agreed wholeheartedly.

I suspect Luke imagines that when he dies, his son will offer a beautiful eulogy for him, and everyone gathered at the funeral will weep. And then his son will blow a kiss toward Luke's casket. And everyone else in attendance will follow suit.

There's not much distance between where Luke lives and where I live. It's only about fourteen miles, actually. The bar where Evie works is practically smack dab in between our two houses—his, almost paid off, mine a two-room apartment above a drugstore.

When I left Luke, he was still sitting at the bar, holding Evie's hand.

At home, I climbed into bed with my wife of six years. She spooned me and moaned a little, and then we both silently drifted off to sleep under heavy blankets and the cover of night.

ACCORDING TO LUKE

Women want to make love. Men just want to fuck.

It's a matter of human physiology. Women have a finite supply of very patient eggs, which make themselves available for a limited time by involuntarily tumbling down the fallopian tube on cue once a month. These eggs wait quietly to be fertilized, and if they don't find a taker, they involuntarily flush themselves out of the uterus. This is why women want to make love rather than just fuck. It is, quite simply, because they have no control over the body's release of eggs. For women, orgasm does not send the egg on its mission. Their bodies will force an egg down the chute one way or another, with or without sex. So sex becomes an expression of love rather than an expression of a simple and always-urgent physical need. Men, on the other hand, have an infinite supply of very eager seeds, which can be made available at a moment's notice, but of course, not without a little coaxing. This is why men need to fuck. The coaxing. And the fact that ejaculation is required if the seed is ever to find its home.

So women want to make love, and men just need to fuck. This is not universally true of course. There are always exceptions—soft men who like to make love, hard women who like to fuck—but they are rare exceptions; they defy nature; they are, quite possibly, mutations.

I tried to explain this phenomenon to the woman I married over a quarter of a century ago. We were sitting on our bed on our frilly, floral bedspread. She was on her side of the bed. I was on mine. She sat cross-legged like a yogi. I sat back against the white headboard with my legs extended out in front of me, hands folded in my lap. The plasma TV above the dresser was tuned into *The Big Bang Theory*, but the sound was turned off.

I tried to tell her about how the prostate and the ovary are very different animals. The latter is a cozy nest, I told her, while the former is a rocket-fueled launch pad. I told her that a man needs to fuck the same way he needs to pee. When ya gotta, ya gotta. She said it hurt her to hear me say such things. She said it was degrading to women. She said that if I really believed such a thing, I must be demented. She said that if all I really wanted was to fuck, then maybe what I needed was a fuck buddy instead of a wife. She said all these things, and then she cried. Then I held her in my arms for a while. Then she gave me a blowjob.

There's nothing quite like a great blowjob. My wife has gotten pretty good at it over the years. She has given me blowjobs on trains, in my car (while I'm driving), and under the table in our kitchen. She even gave me a blowjob in a broom closet at church during Mass once. Since her hysterectomy, she doesn't have much appetite for actual intercourse anymore, but she satisfies a fair number of my urges with her mouth. It suffices for the time being, but it doesn't stop me from fantasizing about all those little nymphs down at our yoga studio.

One day, when I was watching this little butt twitcher stretch her limbs over her head at the studio, I started thinking about my wife's fuck-buddy idea. The more I thought about it, the more I saw the genius of it. Now, my wife hadn't actually said that I should go out and find myself a fuck buddy, but she had been the one to bring up the idea, and who was I to question her?

So I did what I always do when I face a dilemma: I turned to the Internet for advice. Turns out "fuck buddy" is a real thing. People do it all the time—men who aren't getting any at home hook up with mutant women who want to fuck as much as men do, or with women who are unsatisfied with their husbands, or with women who are so young that they still confuse fucking with lovemaking. These people pair up for a night or for a long-term, fuck-buddy relationship. In theory, there are no strings attached. It seemed like a great idea to me, so I visited a fuck-buddy website, and I found myself a mate right away.

There was plenty to choose from once you sifted through all the fat, desperate chicks. There were young ones, old ones, tattooed ones, pierced ones, curvy ones, black ones, white ones, even pregnant ones—pretty much whatever you could want was available. I decided I wanted to find somebody who at least had a better body than my wife. Or a better face. I figured as long as I was going to go through with it, I shouldn't settle for anything less than what I already had.

I finally selected a girl who was twenty-five, a little plump, but cute enough, and though her butt was large, it was round enough and firm enough to keep me happy during those first early days of marital indiscretion. I've always been a booty man. Unfortunately, my wife has no ass at all—just two flat Frisbees that perch dumbly atop her veiny thighs. So my fuck buddy's plump ass was a welcome sight despite its considerable size, and it ended up being the deciding factor that clinched the deal.

My fuck buddy, whose name was Patty, worked nights as a nurse, so she was home on Wednesday afternoons—my day off—and we hooked up at her place weekly for about three months. I would go to her place—a girly bachelorette pad with a country farmhouse motif in the type of apartment complex that attracts young singles and large Mexican families. I'd let myself in with the key she had given me, and climb the three flights to her apartment, where I would find her spread-eagled on the dining room table or masturbating in the shower. We would smoke a little dope before we started spanking. She always wanted to get baked before we did it, which was fine with me. When we were sufficiently stoned, I would explore her, mount her, deposit my seed, then wash my face and my crotch in the kitchen sink, and take my leave. It was an ideal arrangement.

Sure, I was violating my marriage vows—the vows that had been administered by my father. As a deacon in the Church, my father could perform many of the sacramental rites of passage. (Just about the only thing he couldn't do was hear confession, thank God.) So it had been my father who had officiated at my wedding, and it was he who asked me if I would have and hold Lisa till death did we part, for better or for worse. It really was a beautiful ceremony, and my old man did a great job with the homily, telling the story of how he had met the Pope and how he had kissed the Pope's ring and how the Pope had told him that the majesty of eternal forgiveness could transcend all mortal failings. I damn near wept.

Eventually, Patty, my fuck buddy, got switched over to the day shift at the hospital where she worked, and the fun ended. I found a few other fuck buddies on the Internet, and after a while, I got brave enough to start fucking some of the women who frequent the yoga studio. That's how I met Evie, my Irish Goddess.

Evie teaches hot yoga by day and works as a bartender at night. Evie is a redhead with the body of a centerfold. She said she wanted to take kickboxing lessons from me, which was a real turn-on, as anyone can imagine. By day we would pummel each other in the ring, and then before she went off to work at the bar, before she had even showered, I would bang her beautiful sweaty body (from behind) in my office with the blinds drawn like a foaming-at-the-mouth mad dog who had just been released from the pound after six weeks in solitary confinement.

The problem is, Evie and I have been banging for two years now, and I think I've sort of fallen in love with her. I guess I fall in love with all of them along the way, but usually it's the kind of love that's easy to fall out of. With Evie, it's different. I can't seem to shake her out of my system. Even when I'm fucking one of my other fuck buddies, I'm thinking about Evie.

During the past two years, while I've been with Evie, I got my cancer diagnosis, had my prostate plucked, recovered, and got back into action. Evie was right there the whole time, coaxing me back to manhood. It's hard to walk away from something like that.

My friend Max told me that I should shit or get off the pot with Evie. He's my oldest friend from childhood. In truth, he's probably my only true friend. He knows what an asshole I am, but he still treats me like a brother anyway. I tell him stories about me and Evie doing the nasty, and he just giggles and shakes his head. I can't tell if he's shaking his head out of disbelief or disgust, but I know what the giggles are about. He's a married man, but first and foremost he's a man, and not some kind of soft mutant man either. He understands about the needs of the launch pad.

Actually, I think maybe Max is a little jealous of my arrangement with Evie. As far as I know, he's never been unfaithful to his wife, but then, he hasn't been married as long as me and Lisa. Maybe his time will come. Maybe I'm paving the way for him. But I doubt it. Max really isn't the type to do the kind of shit that I do even though he'd probably like to.

I've always admired my friend Max. In a way, I hold him up on a pedestal. Some people are good at doing stuff like kickboxing or Texas hold 'em or racquetball. Some people are just good at being people. That's Max. I think I tell Max about my indiscretions because I want to see his reaction. I guess you could say he's my barometer. If he ever stops giggling and just shakes his head in disgust, I'll know I've gone too far.

When Max said shit or get off the pot to me the other night, I thought maybe I had reached that crucial juncture. But then a little while later, Max asked me if my Evie shaved her pussy, and I knew I was probably still OK in his book. Even so, the truth is, I know I'm going to go to hell if I keep this up. Something's got to give.

ACCORDING TO MAX

The morning after I had met up with Luke at Evie's bar, I told my wife about Luke's dilemma. We were still in bed, staring up at the ceiling. She laughed a little when I offered the details. She was not nearly as repulsed or shocked as I had expected her to be. Afterwards, we made love.

A few days later, I got a call from Luke.

I'm gonna do it, he said. I'm gonna tell Lisa about Evie.

What about your Catholic guilt? I asked.

I'll just have to deal, he said.

Good luck, I said.

After a week or so had passed, I called Luke to check in with him and see how it had gone. I didn't reach him.

I figured he would call me when he was ready to tell me about how it went, but a month went by and I still hadn't heard from him, so one day after work, I stopped off at the gym behind the yoga studio, where he trains kickboxers.

Luke was in the ring with a blond kid twice his size. The kid was shadow boxing. Luke was coaching him on his left hook. I watched for a while until Luke noticed me standing at the edge of the ring. He nodded toward me and told the blond kid to take five.

Luke was wearing a sweaty wife beater and long boxing shorts. As he made his way across the ring toward me, I noticed for the first time how old he looked. He was still fit, but somehow he seemed thin and frail and a little stooped. And because he was dripping sweat, I could see clearly just how far his hairline had receded over the years. It wouldn't be long before Luke was doing the full combover.

He gave me a fist bump and motioned for me to join him over in his office. I walked across the gym, entered his office, sat down in the chair opposite his desk, and noticed a photo on the bookshelf behind the desk. It was a picture of Lisa arm in arm with Luke's son. This is the office where he fucks Evie, I thought. And I wondered if Evie had to stare up at that photo while Luke poked her from behind.

Luke came in and stood in the doorway.

You want to know what happened with Evie, don't you? he asked.

I am a little curious, I said.

I couldn't do it, he said. I couldn't tell Lisa.

So you're still banging Evie? I asked.

No, he said. That's over. I told Evie I couldn't do it anymore.

Luke paused then, entered the office, sat down at his desk, put his feet up, and ripped a fart.

So what now?

What now? he said. Now I start acting like a man who prefers lovemaking to the good old, red, white, and blue buddy fuck.

So that's all Evie was? A buddy fuck?

No, man. But I don't know what she was. That's the problem. I can't trust my judgment anymore. I been driven by my cock for so long that my heart, if I ever had one, has fallen into some kind of hallucination. Things are never what they seem. I think maybe I loved Evie, but I'm not sure I even know what that means.

Luke stopped talking, looked out through the window of his office to see what his latest prodigy was doing. The kid was skipping rope. Luke seemed pleased.

Then Luke said, I keep thinking about my old man and how when I was little, he would cook up a big pot of his famous chili and bring it to the widow down the street. He didn't bring her that chili because he wanted to bang her; he brought it to her because she was poor and she was a member of our parish and she was raising two kids on her own. That was love, man. And I've never felt that for anyone. But I figure I've got a better chance of feeling that for Lisa than I do for Evie.

He didn't say anything else, just sat there staring out the office window with his feet up on the desk. Finally, he said, I really got to get back to this kid I'm training. He's gonna be a champ.

We shook hands then and I watched as Luke went back to work. I thought about Lisa, who was probably teaching a yoga class in the studio next to the gym. I thought about stopping by to say hello to her, but I decided against it.

As I walked out to my car in the parking lot, I noticed the sun was beginning to set over the strip mall. It was autumn. In another week, we'd be setting our clocks back for Daylight Savings Time.

I thought about Luke and Lisa and Evie, and I wondered if Luke had made the right decision. And I wondered if I would have made the same decision.

They say that in order to really understand somebody, you have to walk a mile in their shoes. I've been wishing I could walk in Luke's shoes most of my life, and while I still don't fully understand how somebody makes the leaps that he's made with regard to women and fidelity, I do understand the impetus. To be honest, I'm not sure I would have gone back to Lisa if I were Luke. But I'm not sure if I would have chosen Evie over Lisa either. Most likely, I would have carried on with both of them indefinitely, hoping not to get caught.

Shit or get off the pot, I had said to Luke that night at the bar, as if I were talking to him from some altar of morality, but the God's honest truth is I probably just wanted to cast an evil spell over Luke's good fortune. I didn't want him to have his cake and eat it too. After all, he's been having his cake and eating it ever since we were kids. This was my opportunity to feel superior to him, to make him look up to me like I was the big brother figure for a change.

Apparently, it worked. And now, as I climbed into my car and started the engine, I felt a sinking sensation in my chest. Maybe it wasn't exactly Catholic guilt, but it was guilt, that's for sure.

I drove home to my wife that night as the sun sank out of sight and the temperature dipped to near freezing. The trees were almost totally bare, and as the streetlights buzzed to life, I weaved through traffic a little recklessly, eager to get back to where I lived, back to where I belonged.

ACCORDING TO LUKE

Max came sniffing around the gym today. I knew right away what he was after. He wanted to know what became of me and Evie. I fed him some bullshit about how I had decided to be a good boy and stay with my wife. I think he bought it. It was what he wanted to hear, what he needed to hear.

I could have told him the truth, and he would have understood, but to be honest, I was a little worried about him. He's the kind of guy who could fall from grace if somebody showed him the way. And I don't really want to see him end up like me. I mean, I still need him to be my barometer. I don't want him following me down the rabbit hole.

I used to rely on my old man to be that voice in my head, reminding me that it is possible to transcend mortal failings. Now all I've got is Max. Where he lives is a different place from where I live, and I need it to stay that way.

So for the time being, I'll ride out the lie. Max might see through it eventually. But probably not. I'm pretty good at keeping secrets. The trick is to convince yourself there is some filament of truth in every lie you tell. If you cling to the true part, you can get people to believe just about anything. It's not until you start believing it yourself that you are in trouble. I'm not there yet. Not quite, anyway.

For now, I'll just keep saying my prayers and hoping that someday somebody will deliver me from myself. And for now, no matter whose bed I find myself in, I'll sleep well knowing that at least my old friend Max is right where he belongs. For now, I'm where I belong too. For better or for worse.

ACCORDING TO MAX

My wife tells me I am not a very good communicator. She says I am too passive, too indirect. She complains that I either don't know what I want, or I am afraid to say what I want. The truth is I'm afraid to say anything. I just don't have much faith in words. They always seem to fail me.

I have long believed that lovemaking is the ultimate form of human communication. It is the communication of spirit, heart, and mind. Without words. It is, as the Sufi poet Rumi once said, "the spreading union of lover and beloved." He called this spreading union "the true religion." (Once every few centuries, words succeed, I guess. Just not usually when they dribble over my lips.)

Luke and I were introduced to the poetry of Rumi in our world literature class at St. Adalbert's High School, though I doubt Luke could recall any of Rumi's poems. Besides reciting Rumi from memory, our lit teacher—an old Irish dude, who wore the same gray wool sweater every day—used to talk about Celtic traditions all the time. I remember he told us once about the idea of "thin places."

He said that in the Celtic tradition there was a belief that heaven was not a space shuttle flight away, but was instead "always at hand." He said there was a veil that separated heaven from earth. The good news, he told us, was that there were these thin places where the veil was nearly transparent. The thin places marked the times when you encountered spiritual clarity or even religious epiphany. Luke told me once that he had decided to have the words "thin place" tattooed on his foreskin. I don't know if he ever went through with it, but I wouldn't put it past him.

Last night I took my wife out for dinner at this little place on the town square. We were celebrating because my wife had just told me that she was pregnant. We both secretly hoped we were having a daughter—a little girl who would say, "Beep beep," whenever a car passed, a little girl who would play Candy Land with an imaginary friend, a little girl who would hoot at toy owls in the window of a toy shop.

The Village Café was all decked out for Christmas that night—candy canes and garlands and stockings and blinking lights. While we were there, eating fish tacos and mousse cake, I think maybe I encountered a thin place of sorts. As my wife chattered on about work and family and friends and the deaths of our friends' parents and the impending birth of our baby, I stared over her shoulder at the woman sitting at the table behind us.

The woman, who was wearing a floppy newsboy hat, was at least ten years younger than me. Long, brown, zaggly hair, big wide smile, the lips of a magazine model, the perky young body of a Barbie doll—with slightly more realistic proportions. And she was wearing that ridiculous floppy hat that was just about the sexiest clothing accessory I have ever seen on a woman—lingerie included.

I had smiled at the woman in the hat when my wife went to the washroom earlier. Now the woman was smiling back as I stared at her over my wife's shoulder and pretended to listen to the latest workplace drama.

Later, after we had finished eating, I went to the rest room at the back of the restaurant. I had to pass by Floppy Hat on the way. She ignored me, playing coy. As I entered the tiny men's room, I wondered what Luke would do in this situation.

In the bathroom, I found myself searching my pockets for a scrap of paper. Then I saw the paper towel dispenser. I thought long and hard. There was a pen in my pocket. What would be the right words in this situation?

I imagined myself walking past Floppy Hat's table and slipping the folded-up paper towel into the soft pink palm of her delicate hand. I imagined her unfolding it hours later, alone in her apartment. I imagined her reading my perfect words. I imagined her picking up the phone and calling my number. I imagined us talking and planning. I imagined us meeting. I imagined us kissing each other hungrily. I imagined us tearing each other's clothes off. I imagined us making love. But then as we came—together—I heard myself saying, "I love you." And with that, the fantasy imploded.

This is the problem for me. It has always been the problem for me. Sex is love— the true religion. I express love and connect with love through sex because words are never enough. And when I make love, I am in love. For that fleeting moment, I am certain that this ecstasy I am feeling must be love. What else could it be?

So I need to be selective about partners when it comes to lovemaking. Since I am likely to fall in love with whoever it is, I cannot allow myself to partner up with the wrong women. (I already made that mistake more than a few times. Before I met my wife.)

Maybe this is the real reason why I remain faithful. I know I have found the right woman for me, and I don't want to make love with anybody else because I don't want to *feel* love for anybody else. Whoever they are, they will not be her. They will not be this woman who moans as she spoons me at night. They will not be this woman who does not freak out when I tell her about my friend's infidelity. They will not be this woman who challenges me to be a better communicator. They will not be this woman, who is having my baby. Most importantly, they will not be this woman who would never wear a stupid newsboy hat in a blatant attempt to look sexy.

Needless to say, I did not write anything on any paper towels. I went back to our table, avoided Floppy Hat's gaze, then went up to the counter to pay the tab.

There was a little crèche set up by the cash register. The three wise men were there—one on his knees offering frankincense. The shepherd was carrying his lamb. The star twinkled above. And the baby Jesus, oblivious to His majesty, had a stray piece of silver tinsel wrapped around His neck.

As I slid my credit card out of my wallet, I thought about Mary and Joseph. And miracles. And the bizarre ways in which the thin places manifest themselves. Then I paid the tab, went back to the table, gathered up the doggie bag, and helped my wife on with her coat.

When my wife and I walked out the door, arm in arm, I felt myself hovering somewhere between heaven and earth, somewhere between here and there—the thin veil almost transparent.

I didn't look back.

JEN MICHALSKI
GREATER GOOD

She will love him, honor him, comfort him, keep him in sickness and in health, forsake all others, be true to him as long as they both shall live. She will tell white lies, that she doesn't mind if he wears the ugly green and blue stripe golf polo to the museum or to the garden party; or that his feet stink, yes, monstrously so, does he ever wash between his toes; or that the smell of beef and vodka on his breath, ruffling the air around him like waves of heat, makes her ill. She will not tell him she is not sure what love is, if she ever felt it, if she feels it for him. She will make him broth and cold compresses when he is sick even if, when she is nauseous, when she is heartsick, when she is depressed, she will zip her lips together, tight as violin string, and laugh yes, she's fine. Go ahead to your thingamajig at the club. She will smile like a doll even though her insides do not feel like stuffing. They feel like the wrought-iron sculpture in the garden at the Baltimore Museum of Art. She will not tell him she lies in bed awake at night, wondering why it is so hard to translate this vague unhappiness, this cloud of exhaust that chokes the base of her throat with every breath she takes. The girls are grown. The dog doesn't favor one of them over the other, and the cat likes neither of them, so she should just leave, but what if she's having a midlife crisis, what if everyone feels this way, this desire to leave, to be alone, or maybe to be alone with their intense love for something else entirely, whatever it is?

You should be grateful. Her mother ingrained gratefulness in her every day like a child cleaves a ditch in the sand. Grateful you have enough food to eat and you weren't in the camps (even though they were not Jewish) or some minority who always was the only black person/Asian person/Indian person at the faculty parties, at the opera, at the wedding. Grateful you live in the first world, in the new millennium, that men are less sexist but maybe more secretive about it. Grateful you have tenure and are not teaching at three community colleges. Grateful grateful grateful grateful. You should be grateful for your health. Your good looks. Your good job. Your good girls. Your good husband.

He was a good husband, occasionally jealous, occasionally angry, mostly (very) dull, very handy with the bills, the taxes, the cars, the appliances, the deck staining, the DVD and cable hookups, the mattress flipping, the showerhead fixing, the vacation booking, the chauffeuring, the snow shoveling, the gutter cleaning.

He was bad at personal conversation, romance (slippers for her birthday and an iPhone cover), reading her mind, gray areas, emotions other than irritation and anger. He was endlessly fascinated with golf and sports and card games. He left all the big talks with the girls to her, never bonded with Emily's husband or the conveyer belt of shiftless boys that Jennifer sometimes brought to holidays or parties, switched out with the same frequency and care as her numerous forays into alternative diets, cleanses, yoga, psychotherapy, cognitive behavioral therapy, animal rescuing.

On paper, she should be grateful. Grateful grateful grateful. Grateful for being so unhappy, so wishy-washy. So frowning with cake in her mouth. So unable to even know what happiness was, except that she did not feel it.

The little burps you make while you eat disgust me. She wrote it down on the pad she kept in her purse for groceries, and then she ripped it up and dropped it into the wastebasket in the women's rest room. All around the city, for the last year, wastebaskets in restaurants, grocery stores, her office at the university, crumpled and torn pages concealed the shame of her hatred. *The way you pat my arm like a dog's head annoys me.* Sometimes she burned them with the pack of matches she'd taken from that steakhouse in Mount Washington, the place he always had the ribeye on his birthday, disfigured the notes so thoroughly that no one else could read the contents, could feel the insult of her careful, tightly wound penmanship.

You fuck like you dance. No rhythm. When she got through the pad of Post-Its, she always told herself she would leave. But then she'd run out and the sump pump would flood and he would be down there in the muckety-muck, in his galoshes (yes, he called them that), taking care of the muckety-muck. You should be so grateful, her widowed sister tells her, to have someone to clean up the muckety-muck. And she would buy one more pad of Post-Its, one more yellow mountain of chances he got, crumpled in the Royal Farms, Trader Joes, the rest room at the Towson Town Center.

Can't you tell how much I despise you? Why is she still buying white bread, twenty years later, when he can't be bothered to try the pumpkin seed, the oat bran, the cheese bread, why didn't she just buy what she wants and make him eat it? Because the look, the way he'd look at the bread, and look at her, like a nine-year-old child, passive-aggressive. You know what I like, I like white bread. I've always liked white bread. Why do you have to go and change everything up all the time, things that don't need changing?

Do you even know me? But she had never once told, him, had she? She'd always been afraid, of course, that he wouldn't have married her if she did.

TERESA BURNS MURPHY
THE TREE HOUSE

atherine and Andrea lay on their backs, head to head, on the slick side of the sleeping bag they'd spread across the floor of the tree house in Andrea's backyard. A soaking rain had fallen overnight, clearing away the pollen and suffusing the air with the semen-scented blossoms of the Bradford pear trees that grew along the fence row bordering Andrea's property. The trunk of an ancient oak provided the foundation for the tree house. Washed clean, the tree's leaves were shifting from the yellowish-green of spring to a deeper shade. An atmospheric change was in the air, but Catherine barely noticed. She lifted her head and flipped her coppery-brown hair off her damp neck, the ends touching Andrea's loose blonde curls.

Without sitting up, Andrea extended her slender arm and handed the joint to Catherine. "You take the last hit."

Catherine took the joint and sucked in the sweet smoke as Jim Morrison crooned from the CD player Andrea had carried up to the tree house. When Andrea and her husband, Drew, had bought the 1960s-era fieldstone house on some acreage about a mile outside the city limits of Kennerly, Arkansas, Andrea had insisted that Drew fix up the tree house, long abandoned by the sons (now grown men) of the woman they'd bought the house from. Drew had replaced the rotten floor boards with bald cypress and built a three-foot-tall circular wall around the perimeter. It seemed to Catherine as if she were lying in a flat-bottomed boat that had fallen from the sky and been speared by a giant oak tree.

Catherine and Andrea tried to sing along with "Light My Fire," but they couldn't even get through the first verse. They laughed like a couple of teenagers until the sound of a screen door slamming shut snapped them out of their hysteria.

"Hey, Andrea, I know you're up there, and I know you've been in my weed," Drew yelled from the back porch.

Catherine sat up and peered over the tree house wall. Drew's full cheeks and plump body made him look boyish despite his thick moustache and curly brown beard. At thirty-seven, he was ten years younger than Andrea and had lived in Kennerly his entire life. Andrea had met Drew when she moved to Kennerly after completing her doctor of fine arts degree in dramaturgy and dramatic criticism. Andrea told Catherine she had wanted to stay in the Northeast where she'd been raised, but tenure-track theater jobs were hard to come by so she'd taken a position at Byrne, a small liberal arts college hoping to expand its theater program. Drew had attended the local community college when he met Andrea at one of her student's parties. He'd played guitar in a band that had shown some promise, but after he married Andrea, he'd quit the band and become an appliance repairman. Though he made more money than Andrea, her position at the college was more prestigious, and Andrea always seemed to have the upper hand.

"Go away, Drew," Andrea said without getting up, "unless you want to come up here and have a threesome with Catherine and me."

Catherine watched Drew shake his head and shove his hands into the pockets of his faded jeans. "Cut it out, Andrea."

Andrea propped herself up on her elbows. "Oh, come on, Drew, you're always telling me how much you love Catherine."

"I'm going now, Andrea."

"You're missing out," Andrea said and flopped back down on the sleeping bag.

Catherine heard the sound of Drew's truck engine fire just as Andrea said, "Drew is such a pussy. He talks about you all the time." Andrea screwed up her mouth and, in a mocking voice, said, "Is Catherine coming for supper tonight? I got an extra steak." Then she added in a slightly agitated voice, "You know what I say to him?"

"No, Andrea, what do you say?" Catherine said, focusing on a ladybug crawling up the front of her shirt.

"I tell him you only eat organic food and you wouldn't be caught dead eating *his* meat." Andrea laughed, an elfish chuckle that always made Catherine smile. "One of these days I'm going to tell him what happened to your husband. That'll shut him up."

Catherine sucked in air, and the ladybug's carapace split open, its translucent wings emerging as it took flight. "No, Andrea, really, you can never say anything about that."

"Just kidding," Andrea said. "I fuck him with the lights on so I can look into the eyes of Jim Morrison."

Andrea had taped a poster-size photograph of Jim Morrison to the ceiling of her bedroom. She told Catherine he was the sexiest man who had ever lived. After hanging out with Andrea for the past three years, Catherine knew every song Jim Morrison had ever sung. The obsession with Jim Morrison, especially the poster, was just another indignity Catherine had seen Andrea inflict on Drew. And yet, Andrea's outrageous behavior was usually funny, an antidote to the dullness of working at the college and living in the conservative town of Kennerly. Had it not been for Andrea, Catherine didn't think she would have emerged from the deep depression she had fallen into after her husband's death. When she took the job teaching at Byrne, her plan had been never to tell anyone about her husband, Carter, fearful someone might find out about the disturbing details surrounding his death. But one evening when Andrea had come by Catherine's apartment and found her in tears, Catherine told Andrea everything.

"Today would have been his seventy-seventh birthday," Catherine had said, showing Andrea a photograph of Carter.

Andrea had looked at the man in the photograph. He had blue eyes that at a certain angle looked bright and daring, but at another appeared dull and resigned. His cobalt blue shirt seemed to have been deliberately selected to match his eyes. The man appeared to have a stocky build, and he had thick, curly salt-and-pepper hair and an almost-white beard and moustache.

"Your father?" Andrea had asked.

"No, my husband, well, he was until about a year before I moved to Kennerly." Catherine remembered how Andrea's eyes had widened. "You were *married?*"

"For almost twenty-five years. Carter was a lot older than me, but when I think about him, it's like my body hums."

Andrea had listened intently as Catherine told her the story of meeting Carter, a divorced lawyer in her hometown of Olive Branch, Mississippi. One afternoon, he'd come into the library where she worked during the summer. Catherine said she wouldn't go out with him at first because she was eighteen and he was forty-eight. But then, she found she couldn't stop thinking about him. She told Andrea her marriage had caused a scandal, but, in time, everything blew over.

"What *happened* to him?" Andrea asked.

Catherine's eyes filled with tears. "It's so embarrassing." She hesitated and looked down at the photograph. "I came home from teaching my classes one afternoon and found him hanging from a metal rod in a closet just off our bedroom. He wasn't wearing any clothes."

She closed her eyes and held in a breath for a time before letting it go. "I didn't know what to do, so I called Carter's best friend, Jim. He's a doctor in Olive Branch, and Jim said he didn't think Carter had meant to kill himself. He pointed out that Carter had used a hand towel to pad the inside of the belt he hanged himself with and he had semen on his thighs. Jim thought it was..." Catherine took a deep breath. "He said he was almost sure it was autoerotic asphyxiation and men sometimes did this when they had trouble getting an erection. He said people die because they don't realize how little weight it takes to collapse a carotid artery."

"I'm sorry," Andrea had said.

"Please don't ever say anything about this."

"No," Andrea had promised. "I won't."

⚓

NOW, THE TWO women had fallen asleep in the tree house. By the time they woke up, the azure patches of sky that had laced their way through the lobes of the oak leaves had gone dark, dotted with a few stars blinking their eyes open. Catherine listened to the sound of Andrea's soft snoring, accompanied by a tree frog having a fit about something. She sat up and pressed the stem of her watch, illuminating its face. It was past eight o'clock, and they were late for a party at the Byrne College president's house.

Catherine tapped Andrea's arm. "We've got to get going."

Andrea made a smacking sound as she unstuck her tongue from the roof of her mouth and murmured, "I just got to sleep."

Catherine shook Andrea's shoulder. "Andrea, wake up."

Finally, Catherine got Andrea to go inside. Catherine retreated to the guest bathroom to brush her teeth and shower. She dressed quickly in the black linen pants and cream-colored blouse she'd brought to wear to the party and went downstairs to wait for Andrea. When Andrea came downstairs, she was wearing a hot pink satin top and a tight black miniskirt. Andrea was a few inches taller than Catherine, but the black suede heels she wore made her much taller. Andrea had fluffed out her curls and put on so much makeup her eyes popped like the blooms of a chicory plant.

"Wow!" Catherine said. "You look great."

"Maybe I'll pick up a couple of johns at the party tonight," Andrea said and laughed.

By the time Catherine and Andrea arrived, all the parking spaces around the house were taken, so they parked on the street in the suburb bordering the Byrne College campus. Andrea had revived herself by washing down four aspirins with a can of Coke and listening to a Doors CD all the way there, but Catherine had a dull headache. She cursed herself for letting Andrea talk her into smoking dope *and* drinking white wine.

Catherine followed Andrea down the asphalt lane leading to the president's illuminated red brick mansion. Andrea pressed the doorbell button repeatedly until the president's wife, a bone-thin woman with chin-length blonde hair and a pinched mouth, came to the door. She smiled at Catherine, but barely greeted Andrea. In the foyer, the president was talking to Matt Landers, a young art professor whose office was next to Catherine's.

The president, an overweight man in his early sixties with wispy sand-colored hair dusted white around the edges, had a jowly face and a look of friendly gullibility. He was one of the few people on the Byrne campus who didn't seem to find Andrea offensive. As soon as he saw her, he turned his attention from Matt and flashed Andrea a lopsided grin.

"I gave him a blowjob in his office," Andrea had once told Catherine. When Catherine expressed disgust, Andrea had said, "Just kidding," leaving Catherine to wonder which of Andrea's stories were true.

As the president took Andrea's hand, Matt turned his attention to Catherine. "He just likes you because you listen to his boring stories about his middle-aged mom students," Andrea was always telling Catherine. To clear the sound of Andrea's voice from her head, Catherine concentrated on Matt's appearance. His gray suit fit his small frame snugly, and he had paired a crisp white shirt with a yellow silk necktie.

"What a beautiful tie," Catherine said.

"You like it?"

"It's perfect with your suit."

"One of my students brought it to me from Italy. She's been making mosaic placemats from bottle caps ever since she got back. Her motto is recycle, recycle, recycle."

Catherine tried to stay attentive, but out of the corner of her eye she saw the president's wife summon him away from Andrea. Students often helped the dining staff serve at college parties, and Catherine watched Andrea lift a glass of wine from a tray balanced on the palm of Travis Meyers's hand. Catherine heard only snatches of what Matt was saying. She thought about the things Andrea said about Travis, a sweet-faced boy who had been Catherine's work-study student for the past two years. Travis had a round behind and typically wore tight jeans, which hadn't escaped Andrea's notice. Whenever they walked past Travis on campus, Andrea made jokes about how she wanted to strap on a dildo and take Travis up the ass. As Andrea strolled past Catherine, she patted her mouth in a fake yawn, hoisted her glass of wine in the air, and thrust her pelvis forward. Matt turned around just in time to see Andrea jut out her rump as she left the foyer and walked down the hallway to join the party.

He turned back toward Catherine, clicking his tongue. "I don't know how you put up with her, Catherine. She's nothing but a perpetual child."

Catherine shrugged and said she was famished and headed toward the dining room to check out the food.

Gillian Perkins, one of Catherine's colleagues in the English department, stood just inside the archway between the dining room and the great room. Tall and slender with pale skin and dark hair and eyes, Gillian was the kind of person who seemed too eager to be liked. Andrea had once told Catherine she found Gillian to be the stupidest creature she'd ever met. "And that includes animals. Even reptiles are smarter than Gillian Perkins." Catherine had said Gillian wasn't stupid, just naïve and a bit clueless when it came to reading other people. Andrea had smiled. "My point exactly."

When she saw Catherine, Gillian waved. The two had worked together on an accreditation plan, and Catherine had stayed late at the college several nights meeting with Gillian and other members of the committee.

"Better watch out for Gillian," Andrea had said. "She's secretly a slit licker."

Before Catherine could get to the buffet table, Gillian cornered her and began talking about how the dean had sent back their latest report, demanding a rewrite. Catherine felt as if her head were attached to her body with a spring. All she seemed to be doing was nodding. Just then, Andrea, carrying a plate of food, walked behind Gillian. She caught Catherine's eye and lifted a plump shrimp from the plate, suspended it in front of her face while licking her tongue all the way around her lips, and then popped the shrimp into her mouth.

Catherine rolled her eyes at Andrea, and Gillian, obsessed with her story about the dean, said, "I know. He's really a pain."

By the time the party wound down, Catherine had only been able to swipe a lamb chop from the buffet. She began looking around the house for Andrea. Through a window in the great room, Catherine spotted her out on the deck. Andrea's animated face was bright in the moonlight, and she was standing with two men on the faculty Catherine had heard people on campus sarcastically refer to as "Andrea's boys." Though Catherine didn't really like spending time with either of these men, she felt a slight affinity for Wade Williams, an English professor in his late fifties who had been kind to her when she'd first arrived at Byrne. He was a deeply tanned man with thick gray hair and green eyes. Dressed in a pair of khaki shorts and a button-down shirt, Wade had the look of an aging frat boy. Next to Wade was Richard Eastlin, an economics professor who was about the same age as Andrea and Catherine. Richard made Catherine nervous. He had dark hair, coarse and straight, and his blue eyes seemed too close together, his cheekbones too wide, and his white teeth too wolfish. At six feet four inches tall, he towered over Andrea and Wade.

Once, during a party, as Catherine had come out of the bathroom just off Andrea and Drew's bedroom, Richard had grabbed her by the elbows and pushed her down onto the bed. She had struggled to get away and yelled for him to stop. The party was outside, but Drew had come inside the house and when he heard the sound of Catherine's voice, he'd rushed into the bedroom, grabbed Richard's shoulder, and said, "Hey, dude, come on now. Let her up."

Richard had stood and put his hands in the air. "Be cool, man. We were just playing around."

Catherine had seen Richard "play around" with Andrea, especially when he got plastered. Andrea always said he didn't mean anything by it, but Catherine didn't know what Richard would have done if Drew hadn't come into the room. She only knew she'd fallen a little bit in love with Drew. They'd stayed inside the house for a while, and Drew had shown her some music he was writing. Andrea had never mentioned that Drew wrote music, and Catherine never told Andrea about the time she'd spent with Drew.

Catherine made her way through the dwindling crowd and out onto the deck. As soon as she was outside, she heard the sound of Andrea's voice. Andrea was talking about Travis Meyers and how she had a dildo with his name tattooed on it. When Catherine walked past Travis, he wouldn't make eye contact with her. She wanted to say something to him, but she didn't want to make him feel any more self-conscious. She kept walking in Andrea's direction, wondering how she was going to get her to leave the party and go home.

When Andrea looked up and saw Catherine, she called out, "Here comes Miss Popularity."

Wade and Richard turned, their eyes following Catherine's every move. Catherine thought Andrea was so beautiful, and she wondered why the men would even take notice of her. She'd mentioned this once to Andrea, and Andrea had laughed. "You think they can't see that ass of yours beneath those loose-fitting clothes you always wear."

Catherine was used to this kind of talk coming from Andrea, but the other thing Andrea said had disturbed her. Andrea told her men and women were attracted to her because she had a softness engendered by her Southern upbringing. "If I'd grown up in the South," Andrea had said, "I'd be crazier than I already am from just living here."

Richard leered at Catherine. "How does it feel, Catherine, to know every man here has his cock up because of you?"

Catherine felt her face getting warm, and she wanted to keep walking down the side steps of the deck and out to her car. She wanted to drive away and never, ever step foot on the Byrne College campus again.

Wade said, "Now you've done it, Richard. You've embarrassed her."

"She's not *embarrassed*," Andrea said, swaying in Wade's direction. "She knows she's hot. Whenever she comes over, my husband has to excuse himself so he can go jack off."

Andrea and Richard laughed, but Wade seemed aware that something inside Catherine was collapsing.

"You guys think I'm kidding about Catherine and Drew, don't you?" Andrea said.

"I'm sure that's *exactly* the way it is," Richard said, grinning at Catherine.

"It is!" Andrea said, lifting her empty wineglass in the air as if she were delivering a toast. "Nobody wants to fuck me when Catherine's around."

"Nobody wants to fuck me either," Catherine mumbled.

"Everybody wants to fuck *you*, Catherine," Richard said.

Andrea went into a fit of laughter and when she recovered, she said, "Well, they better be careful. Her husband wanted to fuck her so bad, he killed himself."

Catherine felt the air being sucked right out of her as the two men turned their stricken faces toward her.

Without saying anything, Catherine took off toward the steps. She heard voices calling her name, but she couldn't stop running. She kicked off her shoes and ran faster, feeling nothing but the lush grass beneath her feet until she hit the asphalt and finally got to her car. As soon as she turned on the ignition, the sound of Jim Morrison's voice blared out, "When the Music's Over."

"Damn you, Andrea!" she screamed and turned off the CD player.

Catherine drove out of the subdivision past the huge brick houses and into a neighborhood of small frame houses. She thought about Carter and bit the edge of her lower lip to keep from crying. Sometimes, she thought she heard the sound of his footsteps on the stairs in her apartment. Other times, she was sure she felt his hand on her shoulder. Catherine didn't really believe in God. Still, she couldn't help thinking there was something beyond this life. All that energy had to go somewhere. Or maybe it was just wishful thinking to keep from feeling so alone.

Finally, she came to the sharp turn that put her on the highway to Andrea's house. She drove past an abandoned drive-in where kids in the 1950s had danced in the parking lot, past a shuttered munitions plant that had closed when the Vietnam War ended, and finally to the Quik Mart, the landmark that signaled the turnoff to Andrea's house. Catherine passed a few houses with their lights still on, but as she got closer to Andrea's house, the road grew darker, the stars shined more brightly, and the fireflies flickered more brilliantly in the fields beyond the road.

When she pulled up in front of Andrea's house, she heard, amid the crickets' chirping, the sound of someone strumming a guitar and singing softly. Catherine got out of her car and walked across the dewy grass toward the music, which seemed to be coming from behind the house. As she made her way around the corner of the house and into the backyard, she saw Drew sitting in a lawn chair beneath the tree house. A citronella candle in a silver bucket next to his chair spread a muted glow over him.

When he looked up, he seemed startled. "Andrea's not back from the party yet."

Catherine stopped the way a person might pause to look at a deer in the woods. Drew's body was curved over the guitar, and the earnest look in his warm brown eyes made Catherine want to reach out and stroke his cheek. She had planned to tell Drew he needed to go to the party and get Andrea, but she found she was unable to say those words. Her body had started to hum as if bees were buzzing beneath the surface of her skin.

"I didn't come to see Andrea," she said as she walked toward Drew. "I came to see you."

She focused on the wooden ladder Drew had hammered into the trunk of the oak tree. Placing her hands on the second rung, she pulled herself toward the opening of the tree house, certain Drew would follow.

ERIC ANDREW NEWMAN
DOWN THE MISSISSIPPI

Whenever I tell people that I work on a boat piloting down the Mississippi, the first thing they always think about is Mark Twain, Huck Finn, and all that bullshit. Just some barefoot kid in a straw hat standing on a raft made of logs and lashed together with rope, using nothing but a tree branch to guide where he's going. But I work on a towboat and it's nothing like that. Most people think towboats are what tow bigger ships behind them down the canals, but those are actually tugboats. Towboats are what push barges in front of them down the rivers. I know it doesn't make much sense to call them towboats if they're not really towing anything, but that's just what they're called. You figure it out.

You can make pretty good money working on a towboat, but it's definitely not for everybody. A lot of guys sign up because all you really need to get hired is a high school diploma and a good back. Those are the kinds of jobs that are always in demand these days. But some guys start to go kind of crazy after a few months. I always chalk it up to the lack of sleep. When you work on a towboat you work in four-hour shifts. Four hours on working, then four hours off to rest. You do three of these cycles in a twenty-four-hour period. I guess you could technically get eight hours of sleep, but since it'd be broken up by four hours of hard labor in between, most guys only sleep for four. When you have to go back to bed after working a rough shift in the middle of the night, you're so exhausted that you can't even fall asleep. All you can do is lie awake and stare up at the ceiling.

When you work on a towboat, you have to work outside in all kinds of weather. Most people think it's about working in the hot sun when it's a hundred degrees out, stripped down to the waist and sweat dripping into your eyes. You know, the whole construction worker, Coke commercial thing. While that's certainly a part of it, it can really be in any kind of weather, whether it's rain, sleet, or snow. Kind of like that old Postal Service slogan. If it's below freezing, your fingers will go numb in just a couple of minutes. If you're working on the hook, you can't wear any gloves because you need to be able to grip the pole as tightly as you can. So what you do is put your hands in the pockets of your coat every couple of minutes to warm them up, while holding onto the hook in the crook of your arm. That's how it is working on a towboat. Four on, four off. Two in, two out. Everything is in shifts, even eating, drinking, and shitting.

But what I really want to talk about is the body. I was working on the hook one night near the end of my shift about three thirty a.m. when it happened. We were getting ready to catch a shipping container at the next terminal and I saw something strange floating in the water amid the chunks of ice between the side of the boat and the pier. The snow was coming down hard and the wind was blowing fast, so the visibility was pretty lousy even with all of the floodlights on. What I did know was that it wasn't the usual debris you'd find floating around in the river near a wharf, like a worn-out car tire or an old unlaced shoe. I reached out with the pole and hooked what looked like some sort of cloth on the end of it.

Once I pulled it closer and still couldn't figure out what it was, I called it in to the watch. While I waited for the first mate to get there, I held the pole in the pit of my arm and lit a cigarette from the pack in my coat pocket. Then I turned the pole around in my hands, trying to get a better angle on whatever it was. After the first mate arrived in front, he peered over the side of the boat and squinted into the wind and snow.

"Yep, that's a body all right," the first mate said.

"A body? Should we pull it up?" I asked.

"Nah, it's probably just a jumper. We get them every so often on this side of St. Louis. They jump off the Eads Bridge and get swept down river."

As he was talking, the first mate pulled a shiny metal flask, which I knew from my time working the night shifts with him was filled with whiskey, out of his own coat pocket and took a big swig. Of course, you weren't supposed to drink on the job, but the crew did whatever it took to get through the long, boring nights in the freezing weather.

I took another look on the end of the hook and if you squinted real hard you could see the outline of a human form underneath the coursing surface of the water. It turned out that the piece of cloth I snagged on the end of the pole was a torn jacket. I could also see a stream of long hair floating in the current just under the water like a shiny oil slick, which meant the body most likely belonged to a girl or a young woman.

"Are you sure we shouldn't pull her out and take her to shore?"

"Nah, I'll just call it in to the Coast Guard. They wouldn't want us to mess around with it too much. If it wasn't a suicide, it might have been an accident, a drug overdose, a homicide, or who knows what else. They're going to want to investigate it, anyway. You probably shouldn't have moved it as much as you already have."

"Sorry, I didn't know. Should I let her go?"

"No, we don't want it to drift too far down the river and go getting lost again. I'll keep an eye on it, while you hit the sack." He took another swig from the flask, which I knew by now was more than half empty.

Just then the whistle blew, signaling the end of one shift and the start of another. The first mate motioned for me to hand the hook over to him and I did. I took one last drag on my cigarette and flicked the butt out into the river. While I couldn't hear the hiss of the hot embers hitting the icy waters over the sound of the wind, I knew it was there drifting just above the surface like a long, melancholy sigh.

Once I got back to my bunk, I took off my hat and coat, and lay down on top of the covers still fully dressed. I didn't even take off my work boots, since I knew I wasn't going to be able to sleep anyway. I lit another cigarette, even though you're not supposed to smoke in the crew's quarters. While I looked up at the ceiling and thought about my girlfriend back home, I took a long drag and blew a plume of smoke that wafted upwards like a stream of long hair floating in the current.

JANET OLSONBAKER
ONLY MEMORY

G rant called shortly after Donna received the mailing about the reunion. "It's forty-five years," he said. Grant had been the student body president while she was the secretary at South Puget High, where she'd met her husband, who in their last years together bought a gun to sleep with.

Grant said he'd drive. "You won't have to brave the evening alone." He knew she would never drag her boyfriend to a reunion. For over two decades she'd not attended one, though she'd not told Grant why: She was afraid Alex would shoot her. But the divorce was eons ago, and he might not come. She wanted to see Marietta, who'd taught her how to dance. And Grant, of course. He knew Alex, too. Grant's mom let Alex sleep on the sofa when he'd show up late at night, his parents drunk, fighting, and maybe, Donna thought, those times when his mother had messed with him, though Donna didn't know about that back then; probably no one did. Donna hadn't told anyone likely to attend the reunion about the gun.

September, the weather still warm in the early evening, the sky carrying feathery ripples of cloud. Grant and his wife had driven up from Long Beach, where he had a law practice. Donna met them at their downtown hotel. When it was time to get going, they left his wife waving on the sidewalk on her way to Nordstrom, delighted not to have to go to another reunion. Grant drove around one of the city's numerous construction sites, a crane swiveling high overhead, and turned toward the freeway.

"I'm not looking forward to this," Donna said, her fear of Alex having returned, uneasiness in her gut.

"Me either. On my way to one of these things I wonder why I agreed to go. But then I have a good time."

"I can't imagine that happening," Donna said.

"If Alex is there, I'll stay close. There'll be so many people you won't have to run into him."

THE COURTYARD AT the Puget Golf and Country Club was partly enclosed by rhododendrons. Unrecognizable faces at tables glanced at them. Floor-to-ceiling windows and sliding-glass doors opened wide into a reception area. Old people everywhere. Maybe two hundred of them. Donna didn't see Alex. She mingled, enjoying her classmates, happy they were excited when she told them she'd become a chef in a downtown restaurant. Marietta was grinning when she found Donna. Her face appeared narrower, turned in on itself as if she'd met up with a vise. They talked about the senior girls' camping trip after graduation until someone over the sound system was telling them to find a table and take their seats. Donna recognized the voice and turned toward a podium on the other side of the dining tables.

The master of ceremonies was Alex.

Still somewhat handsome, slender, but bald with white hair like bristles along the lower part of his scalp, and a tight-clipped white beard. He stepped away from the podium and she saw a long-sleeved plaid shirt with shiny snaps down the front, and a wide belt, turquoise-jeweled buckle: the man who slept with a loaded gun like any cowboy on the prairie. While they took their seats, Alex introduced himself and his wife Wendy, a petite, pretty woman who'd also graduated with them. He welcomed his classmates, said he'd retired to Arizona where he and Wendy played a lot of golf. An announcer's voice, eloquent, easy, a voice Donna could never forget.

The first reunion Donna attended was with Alex. They hadn't been married long. Before they walked in he'd grabbed her hand, looked into her eyes, the way he did, all serious and in love, and his smooth voice told her how much he admired her. They'd not dated in high school but sat next to each other in Mrs. Harold's English class. He would ask about Donna's weekend, what she thought of *Othello.* Did she think he had good reason to kill his wife? He asked Mrs. Harold if she thought murder was ever justifiable. Donna was drawn to him, how smart he was, and particularly with each rumor she heard about his home life—the poverty, brutality. His wounds started a place in her heart. She'd been attracted to their danger, her own childhood uneventful, a father always working, a mother dutiful but distant. After he'd finished with the army, then college on the GI Bill, they ran into each other. They fell in love, his voice making a sonnet of his feelings. They married, Donna unemployed at the time. But he sold life insurance, a talker, could talk even young couples into buying a policy. He was good at painting the dire circumstances necessary to make the sale, a different person than the one who came home and sank down inside himself or became inexplicably pissed off. Or downright angry against a known opponent: the neighbor's yapping dog, the Democrats in the Senate. These outbursts became more frequent, eventually aimed at her, until after sixteen years, the two of them were no more.

TED, THE STUDENT Body Vice President, sat between Grant and Donna. He wore a handsome charcoal gray dress shirt. He was the same: loud, laughing, funny, endearingly talking about himself, his hard life fishing in Alaska. They talked about how good the chicken was, moist, flavorful. "The béchamel sauce is just the right consistency," Donna said.

Alex was back at the mic. Ted turned out to be Alex's good friend and occasional golfing buddy, when he could get to Arizona, about once a year. Alex made jokes and jibes at Ted; Ted returned them. The crowd clapped at the repartee, golf talk, crude jokes, stupid stuff, Alex enjoying himself, looking her way, knowing at every moment where she was in the room.

He had his classmates pass the cordless mic, introduce themselves, tell where they lived, what they'd done in their lives. He liked to organize people, get them to do things they might not ordinarily do.

He had wanted Donna to start a business involving postcards. Go into establishments, talk to the owner, arrange for Alex to photograph their operation—he was an excellent photographer—and then within two weeks deliver 5,000 postcards. "It's a real moneymaker," he said. Donna picked restaurants instead of the used car lots, auto repair shops, and hardware stores Alex had mapped out. She went into a lot of restaurants, ordered coffee in every one of them, sometimes pie, but never had the courage to talk to anyone.

"How're you going to earn your share?" Alex yelled when he found out. She got a job in one of the restaurants: dishwasher. She moved up to salad maker, and then moved on to another restaurant as a cook—burgers weren't tough—one place after another. She went to cooking school, graduated, eventually becoming head chef at an upscale eatery.

"I suppose now we'll never get chili dogs for dinner," Alex had said.

WHILE INTRODUCTIONS WENT on, Donna turned toward the whispering on the other side of her. A woman, Donna barely remembered her, but evidently they'd been lab partners in chemistry. The woman told about her many grandchildren. Without Donna noticing, Alex left the podium and came around and leaned down between Ted and her. She didn't know he was there until she heard him, his words deep and soft in her ear, "I have your grandmother's painted tea set. Don't get away without my giving it to you."

Then he was gone, back to the podium without a gun or anything else poked into her ribs. Closed up in a room with him and she was still alive, unharmed. Had the man of their perplexing marriage changed, righted himself? The man who three years before their divorce maxed out his credit card on a small handgun with a polished, dark wood handle?

He'd put it into her hand. "Doesn't that feel good?"

He loaded it and tucked it under his pillow.

"If anyone walks through that door, I'll shoot first and ask questions later." He meant the bedroom door; they were lying in their big bed, Alex on his side, Donna on hers, lights out, downstairs the dishwasher drumming. A shiver shook her body, all the way down to her feet. She told herself to be careful entering rooms, any room. With a gun on the loose she was glad to be infertile, no children to worry about.

She tried to listen to her classmates give snippets of their lives lived away from her, but visions of her grandmother's two hand-painted tea sets took over: the Satsuma tea set and the miniature set she had painted for Donna's mother when her mother was a girl. Both were in Donna's china cabinet. Safe at home. Donna didn't remember any others.

Alex took back the mic. He wanted to take them on a journey through the neighborhoods he'd walked to school. "I'd like ten or fifteen minutes of your time." He described the bowling alley, the cleaners, Marietta's corner where she waited for him every morning, the Castle, a dancehall where Timmy Brewer and Cash Coleman, both dead now, duked it out with anyone who dared, and Hoffman's Bakery. "I never got enough to eat at home, but when I could scrape together the money, Marietta and I would stop on our way to school. We'd get a four-part loaf right out of the oven, drop in a quarter-pound of butter. Now that was living."

His classmates hooted. Ted stamped his feet. Donna didn't remember ever having gone to that bakery.

"At school there were normal people who came from nice homes," Alex said. "My home wasn't like that. We had drunken brawls. Windows got smashed, curtains ripped from their rods. My old man threw glasses against the walls. Stains the next morning to prove it." Alex paused, looked around the room. For a moment he appeared at a loss to continue.

"We need to remember each other, cherish each one of us, because that's what matters. You." He left it at drunkenness, appropriately failing to mention his father threw him across the room when he was six. And his mother. He'd not directly told Donna about her, but she'd found a page ripped from his journal and left on the desk as if he wanted her to read about his mother pushing him onto her bed, his mother on top of him, his anger at his arousal, the confusion of hate and love, wanting to be free of her, afraid to upset her, hoping later he'd feel OK about nakedness and a mother, seeing her flesh, pink and beige and puckered, and her pulling at him, entering her.

Not a parent himself, Alex congratulated those who were, and admonished all of them to take care of their parents. "Marietta came to say goodbye to me when I went off to basic training. I didn't have the money then to go to college. My mother saw me off, too. This surprised me. And she cried. I'd never seen my mother cry. We don't know a parent's heart. We have to honor them," he said with conviction.

He told them how wonderful Arizona was, how much golf you could play under the sun, invited them down out of the rain. "All of you are welcome," he said. Donna wondered if he thought a visit to Arizona could wipe out bad memories.

ALEX WAS DRIVING. They were on their way to Canada for the weekend. He wore a black T-shirt. Donna reached over and rubbed her hand along the back of his neck where his weightless, honey-brown hair stopped at the neck of his shirt. His jaw tightened, lips turned inward. He kept his eyes on the road. She felt anger coming from him like a thick fog moving in, enclosing him.

She jerked her hand away. It was trembling. "What's wrong?" she said.

He didn't answer, didn't even speak until the next day when he got up, wished her a good morning, and they went about their day as though nothing had happened.

But something had before their trip. The week after they got home, Donna broke out with herpes. A doctor had to tell her what it was, how one got it. Alex had it too. Since they'd married, she'd not been with another man. She confronted him. He threw up his arms, pointed a finger at her, yelled, "How can you think that? Your own husband?"

He scared her. He talked about viruses being tricky, lying dormant for years, and then rising up. "What do doctors know?"

Maybe he was right. Donna didn't speak of it again.

AFTER AN HOUR, Alex gave up the podium to hearty applause. Donna clapped, too. She wanted to make him feel better about his boyhood tragedies that kept reappearing no matter how many golf balls he hit.

She looked for him afterward. She wanted the tea set ordeal over with. She wanted to skedaddle, discuss the evening with Grant, put it behind her. Alex seemed to have disappeared. She left the others gathered at the tables and walked into the deserted reception area, the light outside diminished now. She looked around, studied the sign-in sheet. A figure moved outside, came into the courtyard. The figure headed toward the sliding-glass doors now closed against the evening air. Now Alex wore a sports coat over the Western shirt, and held a box out in front of him. A brown cardboard box the size of a layer cake, flaps unsealed, could easily conceal a gun, as could a sports coat. Donna stood fixed to the place her feet found themselves. He hurried. Would a man wanting to kill her run to her?

He might.

He was in the room, the box moving toward her. He was saying again the tea set was her grandmother's, hand painted. He stopped before her. Up close, his head and face were as round as a melon. She'd forgotten that. His rugged skin, strong facial features, pleasing even. But he didn't look like anyone she knew or ever had known. He didn't feel familiar. Strange scalp, hair, he looked like somebody else.

He held out the box. She lifted back the flaps, looked inside. Another smaller box: her father's Van Dyck cigar box, the lid raised as if what was inside had been hastily packed. The thought that Alex could be doing her a kindness didn't figure in her machinations. Not the man who'd been unfaithful, careless. A cigar box, after all, was big enough to house a small handgun. But would a man planning to shoot her shove the gun toward her hidden in a box? More to the point, a man who needed the approval of his classmates would not risk shooting his ex-wife in their presence. Yet he could be that crazy. He could require an audience to commit the act she knew he'd been contemplating for years.

"I remember this cigar box. Where'd you find it?"

"In my things when I moved."

He bent slightly forward from the waist and pressed the box into her hands as if he wanted no more to do with it. But that was not quite right. Something else. His bearing and stance were that of a supplicant's as if he regarded this box as an offering.

"Where's the pistol?"

"What?"

"The handgun you bought when we lived on Lowbury Lane."

"I still have it. In Arizona."

She noticed something else. It lasted only a moment. His face held its usual tension, mainly in the jaw line, but his stance, the forward bend of his body, was protective. He was keeping the rest of himself back and away from her. After his mother died, four years before the divorce, he withdrew, stuck down inside himself. Donna suggested counseling, offered to go with him. He shouted, "Who do you think you are wanting into my business? You think you're so much better." That's how he saw her, on a higher plane than himself. She'd not noticed this posture before tonight.

"Thanks for coming," he said. She was above all a classmate from his best, fondest years.

He turned, walked away, but stopped, looked back, his countenance more relaxed. He paused there for a few moments, and she wondered what he might do. "You look lovely, lovelier than ever," he said.

Donna stood still, holding the box, trying to take in what he had said.

He turned all the way around and came toward her. Slowly, almost a strut, confident, unlike his usual guarded manner she remembered, as if he'd kept something in reserve, off limits. He stopped a foot from her, hands out, palms up.

She did not know this man. Sixteen years hadn't made a dent. She knew his favorite beer, how he liked his potato salad, but she didn't know what he thought about or how it felt to live in his bones.

"Come talk with me," he said. He touched her elbow, guided her outside. Maybe she could trust a man who brought her a forgotten tea set from her past. They sat at a table in the courtyard. The light was quickly leaving the sky. Stiff leaves on the rhododendron bushes moved together in a breezy fit.

He talked more about Arizona: continuous sunshine, dry air, warm nights much of the year. "Most of the time we wear the same clothes all day and evening," he said. He asked after her father, her career. Was she still working? She lied and told him small catering jobs. She kept her answers brief. He didn't need to know about her. She noted at that moment she was not afraid of him.

"I found some old pictures of you. Remember when we went to the rodeo in Montana? You were beautiful then, too."

"I never knew you thought that."

"Donna, yes. I should have told you every day."

A mole, just a dot, sat on the side of his nose, dark, contained, like a beauty mark. He didn't have the mole when they were together.

Donna felt a change. It had nothing to do with fear, as if a long-held emotion could go poof. Probably it was his words: *...should have told you every day.*

Now she remembered, felt her Alex, the one she fell in love with, the man whose mission in life was to be with her. She also felt the boy back in high school, the troubled boy Grant knew, the young man who tugged on her heart, who might have need of her. As though it were nothing, the simplest thing, they were talking like old friends.

And yet... She knew he could easily shoot her now, at least hurt her. No one saw them go into the courtyard. He could do the deed, drag her body into the corner behind the outdoor bar, leave, be on his way. Her boyfriend wouldn't know what had happened to her. No one would find her until the next day. A young worker unable to imagine how such a thing could happen.

But her body was telling her this wouldn't happen. She felt a kind of relief, a settling. She wasn't here to be killed. Life wasn't as portrayed on TV. Not her life. Some other reason had brought her here.

He reached into his sport coat.

She flinched. Now she was certain he'd pull out the gun, point it at her. It would have a silencer mounted on it. She upbraided herself for being so stupid as to have abandoned her long-held reasonable belief that he meant to kill her.

He rummaged through his inside pocket.

He had planned the murder down to the tiniest detail. He already had her alone in the dark. She should never have let him lead her outside.

She pushed back her chair.

He pulled out a photo and a miniature flashlight. He turned on the flashlight and handed it to her. A very young, smiling Donna. Donna in front of a hayrack in cowboy hat and boots, foot propped on a wagon wheel, Bitterroot Mountains in the background. The mountains were familiar, and her once flawless face, but not the Western garb, the pose, that moment. She couldn't recall it.

"Donna." His voice came in a rushed, husky whisper. In the past he'd not used her name, didn't refer to her as if he had no need. He put his hand on hers. She recalled the feel of his long fingers, the tough skin that now wrapped around the back of her hand. She could see him at her mother's funeral. He had rubbed her hand over and over. She hadn't remembered him like that until now. Yet he did not seem to be the man she knew in that memory. More like someone you meet on a crowded bus, get into conversation with when the bus swerves and you fall into each other, no one you have anything in common with, and once you get off the bus, no one you would ever know.

She held the photo, kept her eyes on it. His fingers reached out, touched the edge of it, gave it the slightest push. "You can have this," he said. "I brought it for you."

LATER THAT NIGHT, alone in her kitchen, she placed the cigar box on the counter. She ran her hand over the lid's rough surface: shiny paper, cherry brown, beige trim, with the logo of a painter's palette, brushes sticking out of the frame. *Van Dyck* in cursive was scrawled across the palette and *Perfecto* along the front of the box. Her father had kept his cigars on the table next to his big chair. She'd coveted the Van Dyck box; after he'd smoked the last cigar, he gave her the box.

Inside were small clumps of wrinkled, discolored tissue paper. She peeled away the paper and found what remained of her doll's tea set. Exquisite colored glass, the colors thick, chalky, opaque, but translucent too. Yet not. More like skim milk can be one color yet hint at another: white that isn't white, but blue, and blue that isn't blue, but white. Not painted China; Alex remembered her grandmother had painted China, not what it looked like. This was Donna's very own tea set. Likely given to her when she was six or seven, probably a Christmas gift from Auntie Madeline—she gave terrific gifts.

All in miniature: Four sage green plates, three pale, palest pink, almost flesh-colored saucers, three not-so-blue cups and creamer and sugar bowl and teapot with handle, spout. The spout had a chip, worn smooth, and the pot came with the palest pink lid you could almost see through.

MEREDITH POND

ANNIVERSARY PARTY WITH GATSBY IN MIND

It's the idea of him, really, theoretically masculine, muscular under a soft linen suit, a ghost from the Lost Generation, recently back from Paris, or returned from a leisurely sail around the Mediterranean, sun drenched, wholehearted, loved. You are watching the door for the woman of *his* dreams, the woman others might call a dame from a remake of *Damn Yankees*, or nowadays, question the origin of her gender. Born a woman? Why would anyone really care? Especially, baby, if she's a dream lover, a dirty talker, and certainly good enough for him. And for you? Well, she's all you've ever wanted, and you remember that as you keep your eyes on the door at the top of the stairs, smiling to yourself, as you try to imagine the moment she saunters through, making her appearance as if from nowhere and filling the room with open sky, the scent of hibiscus flowers, iridescent scarlet birds. You must remember this: Only yesterday she called you, out of the blue, and she asked you to meet her here tonight, at the bookstore at 15th and U for the long-awaited F. Scott and Zelda seventy-sixth anniversary party, complete with meticulous brass rubbings from the Fitzgerald gravesites, up the Pike at St. Mary's Church in Rockville. Great Gatsby and his madwoman buried side by side covered in red and white rose petals. Of course you agreed. With grace and gratitude and the hope for some quiet moments together afterwards. Of course she agreed. And now, above all the silvery shoulders, boas and tweeds, she glides down the staircase, her grand entrance unforgettable in sequins and a twilight of blue silk. She scans the room for you, catches your eye and the deep rhythm of the party, and she moves towards you, one beat at a time, touching and kissing the other guests as if they are her chosen family, a crowd of stars, and like the notes of an exquisite well-played saxophone, easy, unpredictable.

NICKALUS RUPERT
THE WORST MILE

A nne hasn't jogged in weeks. Legs: untempered glass. Arms: sandstone. She might get dizzy and quit before she makes it to the overpass. Or, she might run all the way to Lake Baldwin, then all the way back. Ten miles. Eliott, her dying boyfriend, never ran farther than nine.

Anne gets passed by a mother-daughter bicycle duo.

"His mother used to say bicycle seats were sinful," she shouts at their backs. They keep pedaling.

She passes a series of ponds, several blocks of grassy backyards, and a factory that seems to produce only gravel. She and Eliott used to speculate on the crude swampland that bubbled and stank here before industry drained it. The carnival-sized reptiles that must've slithered and warred and sunned their inflated bellies.

Q: What do you say to your dying boyfriend?

A: Relax, sweetie. It's only temporary.

A mile in, she reaches the overpass. Anne's butt muscles tense up at the top of this breathless incline—Eliott's favorite part of the trail. He used to laugh at the gridlocked drivers on Forsyth.

Deep into mile three, the sweat runs into her eyes, her skin full-on weeping. She passes a small cemetery, neat little headstones dark with yesterday's rain. Eliott's parents are Baptist, which means they'll want to do the whole embalm-and-bury routine. No ashes, no urns.

Anne doesn't think of Eliott again until mile four, as she comes upon the nicer houses with terraces, Victorian turrets, tomato vines gripping bright trellises.

"Place gentrifies right before your eyes." He'd say that every time, as if she might forget.

Not that he was wrong. Near the lake, the joggers all wear Newtons and the yoga moms powerwalk behind self-propelled strollers. There's a tidy lawn for picnics. Around the corner, a strip of jewelry shops, a high-end ice cream joint, a bistro. She and Eliott would walk the rickety dock and stare down at whatever fish were brave enough to stare back. Afterward, they'd lie on the lawn. She'd lean her head backward into his lap and he'd knead her neck while he talked about playing Bonnaroo a few years summers past. Eliott's was one of the lower-tier acts that year, but he still got to play Tom Petty's X-Box and smoke his weed. Or so he said.

So often, Anne has tried to imagine—as if through a microscope—the delicate cellular warfare that's taking place inside Eliott. Viral shapes lighting on his cells. Primitive mosquitoes that pump material in rather than suck it out. They never get tired. *Never.*

A cut-out cloud rides over the lake. Anne can't see past the water's shine, can't see what's beneath the surface. If she passed the lake and kept north, she'd end up at the hospital where she left Eliott, attended by a mother and father who are not only convinced that his was a *Christian* band, but that Anne is somehow responsible for his illness.

She sits on a bench and waits for her heart to settle. Eliott sits beside her, or someone who could be Eliott. A lot of men could be Eliott. This guy wears shirt, tie, and beanie—a style collision she finds odd.

Q: What do you say to your dying boyfriend?

A: Later, gator. Thanks for all the Tupperware. XOXO.

Anne's hands quake. With every heartbeat, the blister on her foot pings. Forty-three pings before she catches his eye.

"Eliott's an Aquarius," she says. "You?"

"Leo. That's pretty much the opposite of Aquarius."

Anne was expecting Capricorn. "The main thing," she says, "is whether or not you can stand the other person."

Mr. Beanie-Tie fixates on that lonely cloud over the lake, and not without envy, it seems to Anne. But maybe if she can keep him listening for just a little while longer, he'll understand.

"It's easy to forget," she says. "Movies he refused to watch. Art classes he wouldn't take. I'm not one to use the word *prick* lightly."

Beanie-Tie doesn't bother with an excuse. He's off toward the cottage-style houses or the bistro. But she's not finished.

"His nickname for me?" she shouts at his back. "*My little goat.* G-o-a-t. Not sweetie, not honeypie."

Two miles into her homeward run, Anne passes another runner—an older, squatty guy who trots with a stiff cadence. He is not Eliott, not at all. She slows to match his pace.

"Not saying I don't have regrets," she says.

The man pulls two plastic buds from his ears.

"Would you?" she asks. "Would you visit him if his nickname for you was based on a farm animal?"

"Well, I—"

"What are you listening to? What's so important in there?" She pokes the flat black surface of his phone. Her finger leaves a sweat spot.

"It's Queen." He takes long, ragged gasps.

"Their singer died early, right? So you've got to wonder about his lovers. The ones who didn't visit because he was too proud to ask. Just assumed they'd show up, like Pavlov's dogs."

"Whose dogs?"

"I'm saying, if he *knows* that he's dying, and he still doesn't ask for you. If he's too afraid—"

"He's right to be afraid," the man says. "I watched my brother die, and it brought me no comfort." In go the earbuds. The man nods as he passes, another placeholder for kindness.

Anne stops, but not because she's tired. Where does this bowlegged creep get off giving life advice to *her?* She faces north, the direction of the lake and the hospital beyond. She doesn't want protection. Not from nosy joggers, and not from Eliott. She can set her own terms.

Anne doesn't stop when, for the second time, she reaches the park benches and the well-mowed lawn. Stopping is another kind of exertion. The hospital will make ten miles, with distance to spare. Eliott never made it farther than nine.

Q: What do you say to the dying man you've loved?

A: Not so fast, handsome.

CURT SALTZMAN

THE OBSERVER AND THE OBSERVED

The ramshackle house he called home for a year, the graveled roadway where no one ever passed, he abandoned quickly. He raised the red signal flag on the curbside mailbox, deposited the note scrawled on a sheet of the girl's notebook paper inside, folded in two, just a few words admitting guilt without euphemism or remorse, penned in his erratic cursive. Then he started out on foot for the mountain range which surges abruptly above the valley like a giant wave, filling the sky.

Reaching the thicket of conifers, his footsteps are muffled by fresh needles of pine, the soft forest humus. As the sun declines so does the temperature. The wind, smelling of summit ice, bringing weather in from the north, freshens. He spots the hunters' cabin with its rude chimney of stone between trees in the distance. A dog is moving toward him along the trodden path leading there, a hobbled stray. The animal has caught the scent of him, approaching in a measured, limping gait. It is a large mongrel with a yellowish coat. Some critical juncture is attained; the animal breaks into a crabwise run, halting a few feet away from him, where it remains as frozen as a gun dog pointing at prey. The tail is rigid, the russet eyes fixed, imponderable. He tosses over a few slices of the beef jerky he carries in his backpack and the dog hunkers down, salivating, eating with the sides of its mouth in great chomping motions of the mandibles. It allows him to pass. The land is flat here and undisturbed, the sky beyond the crowns of trees the deep, lovely indigo of dusk.

Firewood has been cut and piled next to the cabin beneath a blue tarp, where he also finds an ax. He gathers logs, chops kindling. There are newspapers bound with twine and stacked under an awning at one end of the structure; he scans obsolete headlines while tearing off pages faded by time and the elements. He totes everything inside, places crumpled paper in the foyer of the cast-iron stove, positions kindling, starts a fire. The play of flames in the belly of the stove produces a hypnotic effect upon him. Soon he adds two logs, crossing one over the other, prepares his suspension from the overhead beam, and sits at the table in the lone wooden chair. When he begins feeling the warmth of the fire he rolls a cigarette. He rises, leans over, and lights it off the hot metal of the stove, before sitting back down again. As he smokes he replays the death of Sherry's daughter in his mind. They ate lunch together at home while Sherry worked the noon shift at the diner. They'd always flirted, but today she seemed ready for more. At some point he found himself strangling her to stop her squirming. She was still raw, only fourteen.

He gets up and lets the dog in, who's been scratching at the door. The animal heads directly for the scatter rug spread before the stove, curls its body into a tight circle, closes its eyes, begins to whimper. The muzzle and ears twitch. Electric currents course the musculature. He watches, grateful for this undemanding company. He puts his feet up on the table, plummets from some high precipice within himself, and sleeps.

When he awakens night has fallen hard over the mountain, the boundless, inhuman, fearful night of the wilderness. He strikes a match, touches the flame to a candle's wick, revealing the backpack in a corner, the dog sleeping still before the warm stove, the length of rope dangling from the rafter. Outside, it has been snowing silently. The landscape is covered in a glittering film. He thinks of Sherry. A woman without beauty, lean, hard muscled. He has only seen her cry once in all this time, when he mentioned he might be moving on one day, testing the waters. He never understood what they were doing together.

They met at the honky-tonk off the interstate: two pool tables in the back, a Formica counter with a dozen stools lined up, a picture window overlooking the dusty highway. Music-wise the jukebox standing against one wall spun three forty-fives for a quarter. Every half hour or so you heard that song by Patsy Cline again. "Haven't seen you around here," she said to him. He happened to be sitting next to her at the bar that night. "Because I would've noticed you a bunch." He smiled, though he isn't the sort of man who smiles at all, even when conversing in barrooms with the opposite sex. She was drinking screwdrivers, smoking the kind of slender cigarettes women who are not entirely serious about smoking will puff on. He was ordering draft beer and rolling his own. He has the hands of a pianist rather than a cowpoke, deft, lithe, and it soothed her observing him work on his quirleys, like when she used to watch her mother knit. "Roll me one of those things, OK?" she asked him in a tender voice, which was about as intimate as you could get after a minute or two of idle talk down at that dive.

He stands on the chair, performs the act whose purpose is to destroy the world.

An hour later, framed in the rimed pane of glass, men emerge from out of the growing flurry in a galaxy of flashlights, carrying firearms and restraining the enthusiasm of hounds. The lament of the tracking dogs carries across the wooded plateau, as do the wrenching cries of the trapped and terrorized stray. As the men pad closer through the deepening drifts they perceive the candlelight guttering in the window, the shadow cast by the hanging figure, and reaching the threshold know there is no need to prepare their arms, that the only living creature left is the crippled animal, which flees like a ghost as the door is flung open, pale form vanishing into the immortal darkness.

ALLEN FORREST
LONDON NOIR, #1

NICK SANSONE

WEEKENDS

Thank you for seeing me. I get that you'd rather not be here so I'll make this quick as possible, just give you what you came for so you can be on your way, beat traffic if you're lucky. Before we start, though, I wanted you to know that you're the only reporter I'd ever agree to talk to.

This interview is a first for me, so I'm not sure how best to proceed. I'm told you should lead with an interesting or unusual fact. Maybe that's the rule for speeches I'm thinking of, but whatever, I have one anyway—a fact not a speech. Were you aware that the adult entertainment industry publishes a trade magazine? Like what *Aviation Weekly* is to pilots or *American Banker* is to American bankers. I no longer subscribe, in case you were curious, zero reason to anymore, but even if I had a professional use for the periodical, it's not as though I could get it delivered. In here it's considered contraband. Back when I owned the club, however, I browsed each month's issue in order to stay current on trends within the business. Basic entrepreneurial due diligence is all. And believe me, the mag kept me up to date. Their coverage was very thorough. The contents mostly focused on product previews and reviews—the latest films, toys, and other assorted bedroom paraphernalia that had or would hit the market. But there were also insider scoops, such as which actresses would be signing exclusivity deals with what production companies or whether popular performers had public appearances in the offing (I booked numerous acts over the years for special events like the Super Bowl or Halloween using agency contact info posted in those calendar notifications). What impressed me most about the magazine's scope, though, and I hadn't truly appreciated it until my trial, were the twenty or so pages dedicated to the law.

Toward the back, under a section titled "Legal News"—the name itself a display of commendable editorial restraint; I don't know how, given the audience, they resisted calling it "Legal Briefs"—readers found in-depth analysis of free speech and obscenity cases before the courts, the articles written by former defense attorneys and dense with legalese. Seems a random inclusion, perhaps, but makes complete sense. Short of a journalist like yourself, you won't meet a more enthusiastic group of First Amendment supporters than pornographers. For the same reason, too: their jobs depend on it.

Your mother has been telling me about your new career, speaking of. She's mailed me some of the stories with your byline. "Green Truck Sought by Authorities in Hit and Run" is my favorite, have it on the wall next to my bunk, which my cellmate thought was weird until I explained it to him. I'm just so crazy proud of you. Sorry if I'm getting off topic—what was I saying? The legal reports, right? So the articles approached the cases from a business operations perspective, scrutinizing the logistical impacts of potential rulings, how an unfavorable opinion would expose industry stakeholders to steep compliance costs or criminal liabilities. It's fascinating, arcane shit. Actually, I just enjoyed reading about myself. It's fine. I can confess to an ego. Besides, the consequences of my trial were low enough that I could get a kick out of the minor, fleeting celebrity my case brought. The emails, the phone calls, the requests for comment—it was all so stupid, so out of proportion. On the advice of counsel, I turned down anyone who contacted me to talk, including multiple inquiries from your paper. You weren't working there yet, and I wouldn't have wanted to violate the temporary gag order regardless. But hey, with the case adjudicated now—the verdict rendered and the appeals denied—that's been lifted. So fire away.

Is the recorder on yet? It feels a bit strange introducing myself to you, I'll be honest, but I understand the formality. It's not for you, it's for everyone else. My name is Bob Brantley—former owner of the Glass Slipper in Maitland, Florida—and I'm currently serving a four-year sentence in the Seminole County jail on multiple counts of public indecency.

I'd rather you called me Dad, though.

NO DOUBT YOU'LL do your own research, but some background for you if it helps. Shortly before my arrest and subsequent legal entanglements, local officials approved an ordinance enacting strict new regulations on adult recreational establishments. I can't prove it, maybe it's an angle you want to look into, but I suspect more than a few council members (along with some of their developer buddies) were eyeballing the real estate where my club resided when they OKed the legislation. It's an excellent location. Close to the interstate, lots of visibility, plenty of parking. From what I hear, there's a gym and spa there now, and, to no one's surprise, it's making a killing. Maybe I'm being unfair. They could've passed the ordinance with the sincere belief they were improving the community and doing right by their constituents. Why not? People make dumb but well-meaning decisions all the time. That's a shortcoming near and dear. Hell, life is complex, they could've been plotting a land grab *and* believing they were doing the selfless, civic-minded thing.

Anyway, the ordinance banned public displays of nudity in commercial enterprises. Slight obstacle for a strip club. Then, in pathological detail, for close to five pages, the statute went on to define what parts of anatomy, when exposed, qualified as nudity in the estimation of Seminole County legislators and was therefore subject to the penalties later delineated in the bombastically named subsection of the ordinance called "Transgressions of the Moral Code." Can't you just see that garbage chiseled into a stone tablet? It's an extraordinary document. Here's how they described boobs (and yes, I memorized it; not on purpose, just saw it enough in court documents that I couldn't un-see it). *Breasts: a portion of the female mammary gland including the nipple and the areola (the darker colored area of the breast surrounding the nipple) and an outside area of such gland wherein such outside is reasonably compact and contiguous and contains at least the nipple and the areola and one-quarter inch of the outside surface of such gland.* Someone actually *thought* that. Someone thought that and put it to paper. Then a roomful of grown-ass men—it's all men on the council, of course— negotiated amongst themselves whether that passage accurately characterized what a *breast* was. They deliberated the measurement of one-quarter inch—why not a half-inch or a full inch?—and concluded that that was the appropriate point at which one crossed over from being clothed to nude. They even included a metric conversion! I lose sleep knowing such people exist.

And like that, the ordinance turned my club—a fixture in Maitland since the '90s—into a bikini bar with a giant neon-trimmed stage in the middle of it, took a hatchet to my employees' earning power (less skin equals less tips), and forced me to talk to my attorney. In other words, forced me to talk to your mother. For a lot of guys, that last bit alone, requiring they interact with their exes would be worth waging a blood vendetta over, but hard as it might be for you to believe, January and me remain on cordial terms. Professionally, at any rate. She appreciates the billable hours I bring her, I respect her courtroom prowess, and we both acknowledge the boundaries of our relationship. Attorney-client.

Present circumstances notwithstanding, I'm fortunate to have her representing me. My punishment could've been much worse, but Jan's a devastating lawyer—combative, whip-smart, and immune to normal human emotions like mercy or compassion. Has a real instinct for the jugular, that one. No exaggeration, I've seen your mom make dozens of adult males cry like children (uncooperative witnesses, your old piano teacher, *me*). When pointed at someone else, her skills are a marvel to behold. Like watching a snake unhinge its jaw to eat a rabbit.

Now, the amateur psychologist in me would love to blame how unforgiving Jan is—and by extension our divorce—on her upbringing. It was TV-movie hard.

Drunk mother, imprisoned father. Falsely locked up, no less, to hear her tell it. So it's easy enough to draw a straight line from a youth spent passing through security checkpoints to see her dad to a ruthless attorney conquering the system that unjustly put him there. That's simplistic, though. It'd be just as understandable, if Jan never wanted to set foot inside another correctional facility again, if she grew up and became a librarian or a computer engineer or a medical transcriptionist and broke out in hives going through metal detectors at the airport. And that's because you can make connections between any two points—that's math. Say, for instance, the estranged daughter of a strip club owner so valued freedom of expression that she chose to study journalism in order to take full advantage of the liberty her father, by stoic if distant example, instilled in her to cherish. A nice fantasy. You're your own person, like Jan is her own person, like I'm my own person. Maybe you just figured it'd be cool to interview famous people—and if that's the case, I regret disappointing you again—or maybe taking Journalism 101 allowed you to fulfill an English credit while sleeping in on Mondays and that's all there ever was to it and now you're stuck. That's possible, too. Who knows why anyone does anything? You can puzzle about the motivations of others forever, so I'll avoid the speculation wherever I can.

I'll only observe one last thing about your mom. I mentioned it many times during our marriage, sometimes meaning it as a compliment, but more often than not, you know, *not*. Women whose names derive from the calendar usually get buoyant and airy months of spring (April, May, June), but not Jan. She gets the coldest of the year.

WHEN THE COUNCIL passed the ordinance, I left a message with a receptionist at Jan's firm to have her call me and talk me off the ledge. The next morning, Jan visited the club unannounced. Actually, it's more accurate to say she *materialized* there, as if reconstituted from the wings of a thousand bats. I was sitting at a table a ways back from the stage, close to the DJ booth, eating breakfast. The club didn't open for the early birds and the just-clocked-out night shift crowd until ten, but our executive chef, Guillermo, and the rest of his crew showed up well before then for their prep work. (FYI, I've heard all the jokes about food at strip clubs—*don't order the crabs, ha ha ha*—but while Guillermo may not have been the most upscale or avant-garde chef in town, he was one of the cleanest. You could perform heart surgery in that man's kitchen. The appliances gleamed, the counters reeked of disinfectant.) Anyhow, Guillermo was always good about putting together an omelet or scramble or fruit plate for me or anyone else on the day shift willing to get to the club by nine o'clock for a meal on the house. One of our performers was on the other side of the room in street clothes, having pancakes, relaying instructions to a babysitter over her phone. I hadn't seen Jan enter the club. I didn't even notice her until she was standing in front of me, her presence altering the level of lighting in the room, her shadow darkening the space around us.

I looked up. "I thought I felt my blood turn to ice," I said.

"You have cheese in your beard," she said. Jan took a seat across from me and helped herself to half my mug of coffee. She hadn't had time to brew a pot at home. "On my way to court so can't stay long but got your message. Figured I'd pop in and make sure you hadn't set this place on fire or something. Heard from Theresa lately?"

In retrospect, I realize that Jan didn't mean her question the way it sounded to me, because at the end of the sentence, I appended an implied *because I haven't*. I'm an optimist by nature. Or, according to your mom, I hear what I want to hear. And during that hopeful moment of misunderstanding, I did. It pleased me to think Jan hadn't spoken with you anymore recently than I had, that the reason you and I talked so infrequently wasn't specific to me but just because you're an adult and adults are busy. Not that I don't want you to have a good relationship with your mother. But yes, I feel a little competitive about it. I've never stopped envying the time she got to spend with you growing up, how close you two were. *Are*. Whatever.

I wiped my face with a crumpled napkin. "Called her last month," I said. "She had to run, but she's doing an internship for a paper this summer. Think I heard that right."

"The *Tampa Bay Times*. Gary knows one of the editors," Jan said, flaunting the details of your plans I wasn't aware of, tossing in the added rebuke of your stepdad's involvement in arranging them. "She'll be home for a couple weeks before then, though. We should all have dinner."

"Sounds great," I said and meant it. An opportunity to catch up with you would be well worth sitting through a meal with Jan (whose company in very small doses I enjoy) and Gary (whose presence in any duration is a test of my patience). I know that sounds like jealousy, but it's not. If it were, I'd cop to it. I'm glad your mom found someone who seems to make her happy and gets along well with her. It's wonderful. It's rainbows and unicorns and puppies. What bothers me with Gary is hearing him talk about his work, listening to him describe acanthosis nigricans or pityriasis rosea—no way to know if I'm even pronouncing those right—or any of the other gnarly skin conditions he sees at his clinic. Those conversations eradicate my appetite. It's to the point he doesn't need to say anything, looking at him produces visions of rashes and blisters and warts.

"However," I added to Jan, "that assumes I'm not locked up."

"Then don't break the law."

"Good idea. I was planning on sending everyone home, anyway."

"Have faith. I'm worth what you pay me," she said, opening her briefcase and removing a copy of the ordinance streaked with multicolored highlights.

OF COURSE, CLOSING us down was exactly what the council members behind the initiative intended. The politicians framed the issue in moral imperatives, talked about safeguarding our communities and threw around phrases like *adverse secondary effects*. The more apocalyptically oriented in their ranks emphasized the urgent need to protect our children from the corrupting influence of yada yada. Never mind that the Internet exists. Never mind that no kids could see through the tinted windows of the club, the glass as dark and impenetrable as limousines'. Never mind that no minors could set foot inside and would have to be insane to even try with my bouncers stationed on the door. Have you ever seen them? Tattooed necks, weapons-grade biceps, not one of them south of two twenty. Their mere presence on site deterred incalculable mischief. Seriously, if I hadn't already seen their background checks, worked with them night in and night out, known what absolute sweethearts they were, they'd scare the piss out of me, too.

Regardless of their reasons, though, the council members got the ordinance on the books. Near-unanimous vote. Once they did, they weren't shy about their favored outcomes. They wanted to drive operations such as my own out of business—or, failing that, out of their jurisdiction. We had no place in *their* community. Points for honesty, I guess.

The ordinance, however, provided exemptions where public nudity would be permitted. The first was for breastfeeding. I commend whatever wife or intrepid female staffer asked to have that included, because no way do I believe it crossed the minds of any of the sitting council members. The second exemption was for exhibitions of *genuine artistic performance*. No doubt they were presaging angry calls from theater owners worried about running afoul of the law for screening the latest horror flick where some coed gets knifed while skinny dipping. It's a reasonable exception to make, as far as there was reason to be found in the ordinance at all, but guess what, it's also a loophole big enough to drive a strip club through. It took your mom all of five minutes to find it, scanning the document at traffic lights on the ride over to the club. Just erased months of legislative time and effort. She did that before her morning coffee—that's the kind of legal chops she has.

You asked me once why I didn't fight her for custody. That's why.

Actually, you never asked me. It's more correct to say you *accused* me of not fighting her for custody, and beyond the one time you came out and said it aloud, the allegation has been implicit in a lot of our interactions, an insinuation that because I, in your opinion, didn't choose you, then you weren't going to choose me right back. I'm not thick. Calling me "Bob," inviting Gary to play in the father/daughter softball game, putting him down as your second emergency contact after Jan. Yeah, I picked up on the subtext. Your mom divorced me, but that was more or less mutual, so who cares. When you divorced me, though, not going to lie, it fucking stung.

I remember catching you coming home after sneaking out with friends to party God knows where. You were sixteen-ish. Your eyes were red, you smelled of liquor, and you fell through the screen climbing into your bedroom window. It wasn't the stealthiest of break-ins. When I asked where you'd been, you told me it was none of my damn business. I wasn't your guardian. I was just some guy you were forced to stay with once in a while. If I wanted to be your boss, I should've done something about it when I had the chance. It was mostly the booze talking, but the ease with which you said it, moments before you collapsed onto your bed and passed out, it was obvious how often it'd crossed your mind before. I hope you don't still think that way, though having barely seen you since your eighteenth birthday when my visitation rights expired, you probably do. To be clear, the reason I didn't take your mom to court was because she would've torn me apart. And I'd have lost you entirely.

Sure, I could've ignored the warnings of my attorney and contested custody, sent him into the courtroom on a kamikaze mission, but he was very upfront with me about the odds of success: nil. A strip club owner with a handful of arrests on his record petitioning for primary guardianship of a nine-year-old girl? Not going to fly. Not when the other parent was a successful professional.

"But I'm a successful professional, too," I said.

"Take the weekends," my attorney told me. "They're a gift."

⚓

SO, THE LOOPHOLE. When Jan drew my attention to the relevant passage in the ordinance, she said, "Who are they to say what counts as art?" I slid aside my breakfast plate and squinted at the document. "It's not stripping, it's interpretative dance," she continued, already standing, gathering up her briefcase. "I'm being facetious, but you get my point. Look, if you really want to be safe about it, respect the spirit of the law and make sure whatever your girls look like in the club they could look like at the beach. But if you go by the letter of the law, you can have your girls dash off a few lines of *Paradise Lost* or *Hamlet* before getting to the main event and be just this side of legal."

Thus was born Strip Theater.

Doubtless, that's what you're most keen on hearing about, that's why your bosses sent you up here for an interview. That's what all the other reporters wanted to talk about whenever they called. It's what every article focused on—with the notable exception of the ones that appeared in the trade magazine, of course; those were deeply substantive dispatches. But whatever, it's racy and salacious and fine, I more than most get it, sex sells. Every dime in my bank account confirms that much. Every child-support check, every contribution to your college fund, validated that truism. It's why interest has come back now that my appeal to the state supreme court was denied, gives everyone a chance to cover the quirky strip club story a bit more, write a couple more columns, move a few more papers, pull in a few more clicks. I don't care how superficial or sensationalized your report is, though. Go wild. Make shit up. Put words in my mouth. I'm just thrilled you're here.

Anyway, Strip Theater went a lot farther than I intended it. I meant to keep operations as routine as possible. Here's what I envisioned: a brief programming note from the DJ at the beginning of the acts explaining that, in accordance with the asinine Seminole County regulations, all performances would include a short reading from Shakespeare—that way we wouldn't alarm anyone. The balcony scene from *Romeo and Juliet* isn't something you can spring on a crowd like ours unawares. Not when you're wearing neon stilettos and a vinyl miniskirt, not when the audience is all four drinks' deep into the night. You have to warn folks about things like that.

What I didn't consider, though—and I should've—is that for a lot of the women on staff, we're talking about aspiring actresses, singers, musicians. Girls who auditioned for reality shows and plotted trips to Hollywood and New York to make it big. Yes, plenty of other employees were there for the money, and the money alone. Women (like your mom once was) who were working their way through school. Not just a cliché. Women who were doing whatever they could to keep their kids fed. Even so, there remained a non-negligible portion of employees for whom the chance to display some of their more mainstream gifts appealed greatly. They ran with it.

After I made the announcement about a week before the law took effect, Samantha, a guitarist who played to single-digit crowds in coffeehouses on her off time, asked, "Does it have to be Shakespeare?"

"Well, no, I suppose not," I said, delivering a completely unqualified legal opinion. "So long as it's *artistic*."

"So music?"

"I mean, sure."

This has always been one of my biggest flaws. I'm too permissive. Working exclusively around adults for so many years left me ill equipped to enforce boundaries. I'd rather let people make their own decisions on how to behave—very hands off. How else would you have ended up with that awful haircut in seventh grade? The almost shaved scalp, the pink-tipped devil horns. I let you pick it out, thought, Well, if that's the style... I'm convinced your mom's intimate knowledge of the penalties for manslaughter is the lone reason I wasn't murdered at the doorstep when I brought you home. How was I supposed to know you were going to a wedding the following week? No one told me.

After your mom had gasped and gone pale and sent you upstairs out of earshot, she whisper-shouted at me, threatened to get my visitation revoked. It was the last time Jan made me cry. We'd only been divorced for three years at that point, and we hadn't yet reached our mutual cessation of hostilities. She told me a good lawyer—and she knew plenty of them—could make a compelling argument that that haircut constituted child abuse. Or wanton neglect. Or both.

"So it's a bit extreme," I said. I knew that much when you were getting it cut, and I figured that'd make me the cool parent, because Jan would never go for it. "She loves it. She was petting her head and smiling at herself the entire ride home."

"Are you the adult or not? Because she needs *adult* supervision."

ON OPENING NIGHT—NO, it's wrong to call it *opening night*. The club had been in business since 1993. There was nothing out of the ordinary or extravagant for us to be open. The only difference someone could see from the exterior of the building was an adjustment to the marquee, which typically listed our drink specials. (A different regulation prevented us from advertising "live nude girls" or any variation thereof.) Instead, that evening, the sign stated: GENUINE ARTISTIC PERFORMANCES.

It was a Tuesday, the first of July. The acts that day were mostly standard stripteases prefaced by government-mandated poetry readings, random Elizabethan sonnets spoken in meterless, arrhythmic monologues; some of the girls, standing at the edge of the stage in high-heeled boots and skin-tight shorts, tripping over obscure and obsolete words like *sland'ring* or *tillage* or *usury*. But there were also two performers who staged a reenactment of the final sword fight from *The Count of Monte Cristo* (an act they'd bawdily renamed by omitting a letter from the title). Several girls sang cover songs, some better than the original vocalists in truth. Another woman, dressed in a breakaway pleated skirt, played a clarinet rendition of "Shake Dat Azz" while, as the tune instructs, shaking that ass.

Word spread fast. My competitors in the county (Raquel's, the Squire, the Golden Cantaloupe) followed the intent of the law, not the text, and required their employees to wear nipple pasties and thong bottoms that met regulations. They discontinued lap dances, which we had begun characterizing as audience participation. Attendance at the club surged. For exactly three days.

That's how long it took the county to shut us down. That Friday night—the night before I was to have dinner with you and Jan and Gary, the first time I'd have gotten to see you since wishing you goodbye on your way to college—vice cops threw on the lights and filled the floor of the club.

AT THE COUNTY lockup the following day, your mother posted my bond, and I was disappointed not to have seen you with her. On the drive back to the club to retrieve my car, she explained the charges to me. I was facing fifty or so counts of public indecency for violating the ordinance—the total determined by the number of individual infractions witnessed by a plainclothes officer in the audience on Wednesday, Thursday, and Friday. According to the text of the statute, she told me, the maximum penalty was a fine not to exceed five hundred dollars and imprisonment in the county jail not to exceed thirty days.

I shrugged. "That's not so bad," I said.

"That's per count," Jan clarified. "If they give you the max for each count and run the sentences consecutively, which they would, you're looking at over four years and twenty-five grand."

"Four years!" It wasn't my most levelheaded moment, but having spent a day in jail (getting strip-searched and fingerprinted and using the rest room in front of the other occupants of the holding cell) the thought of spending several years under similar accommodations brought out my temper. "Brilliant goddamn lawyer you are," I said. "You said it was fine. You said it was a loophole. You trying to get me locked up?"

Jan sped through a yellow light. Then she pulled the car over in a convenience store's parking lot. For all her talents—including multitasking—when Jan was mad she was incapable of anything but being mad. Her anger required full concentration. "Number one, fuck you. Number two, just because something isn't against the law, doesn't mean they won't arrest you for it. Trust me. People get improperly arrested all the time. People spend decades in prison for make-believe. Number three, I said classic literature. *Classic literature.* No one's going to argue with Shakespeare. But you've got girls doing topless sword fights and nude karaoke and a dozen other things that ain't Shakespeare. What'd you think was going to happen? Read the affidavits. They aren't charging you for any of the performers who read poetry, because that's not an argument they want to have. They're less likely to win it. And if they did, I'd skin them alive on appeal. They're rewriting the statute right now for that exact reason. But no, you're out there freelancing. Letting them girls do whatever they want. Set boundaries. You never set boundaries. My advice is only as good as it's followed. And number four, seriously, fuck you."

This fight felt ancient, intractable, an echo of a thousand past fights. Letting you get your hair cut, siding with you when you wanted to quit piano lessons, allowing you to stay up past your bedtime and watch R-rated movies. Your mother and me argued about these discrete issues constantly when we were together and beyond, but the core debate was always the same: I thought Jan was too rigid, Jan thought I wasn't rigid enough. We were both right, and our marriage couldn't survive it.

IS THERE ANYTHING I'm forgetting? Anything else you want to know? The court proceedings are public record, but because it may not come across in the transcripts, let me say Jan put on an exquisite defense. She dragged council members onto the stand and questioned them until they looked foolish, mendacious, or both. She cross-examined officers involved with the sting operation and coaxed one into admitting that the law seemed ridiculous to him. Those small triumphs didn't elevate my hopes of winning, though. Jan was laying foundation for the appeal. Our case landed on the docket of an unfortunate judge, who quoted that old legal saw about pornography—*know it when I see it*—and then disallowed all the art professors Jan lined up to testify about the rich tradition of "erotic expression" and its intrinsic merits. Plus, the jury. That was a bad break. Seminole County isn't the most buttoned-up part of Florida, but it's not Miami-Dade, either. Jan had to burn through her peremptory challenges clearing some real nutters, folks who'd have tarred and feathered me given their druthers. By the time twelve of my peers were empaneled, it was obvious what the verdict would be.

Maybe you want to hear about jail. The most important detail is jail is not prison. People use the terms interchangeably, but prisons—that is, penitentiaries—house convicts on long sentences (drug traffickers, armed robbers, murderers), while jail populations mainly consist of lower-level offenders or people who couldn't make bond and are waiting for their trials. I don't know anything about prison. Thank God. If those nightmare documentaries on super-max facilities are even a fraction of accurate, I'm fortunate to not know anything. Jail, however, I've got some first-hand experience. Between my current stay, a handful of genuine DUIs in my youth, and a bogus solicitation charge that your mother got thrown out, yes, I've been. It's not enjoyable, but it's not unbearable. There's the occasional fistfight, the food's terrible (not blaming the kitchen staff in case any of them overhear me, the quality they have to work with is hot garbage), showering in the presence of others is nobody's idea of a good time—or, at any rate, it's not my idea of a good time. Still, never say never, but no one is getting shanked or traded for cigarettes. Besides, since most everyone here are locals, I know half the people inside. Few of the guards and inmates I even employed as bouncers before. It's basically a forced, alcohol-free, years-long high school reunion. As I said, not ideal. I'll live, though.

Perhaps you're curious about my plans when I get out. My release date is in three months. So even if the state supreme court had agreed to hear my appeal, by the time it would've come up and an opinion been given, I'd have served out my sentence anyway. Only thing I really lose is a refund on the fines (chump change) and an opportunity to sue the county for wrongful imprisonment. Maybe I'll file a suit, anyway, to waste their time like they wasted mine. I'm retired, and I've got the money. Sale of the club broke seven figures—a very, *very* good location. County tried to seize the property as fruits of a criminal conspiracy, but Jan shut that down right quick, which is why I'm not even that upset we lost. Because ever since that deal closed, one of my favorite pastimes in here has been to imagine how I'm going to spend it when I get out.

Jail permits lots of time for daydreaming and reflection. I do both, but I prefer daydreaming. What's the difference? Reflection is backward looking. While I, of course, consider steps I should've taken to avoid my conviction, I tend to focus on mistakes earlier in the timeline, thinking about what I should've done to make it work with your mom and be around for you more (given up the club once she got hired by her firm? gotten out of the business once you were born and been a stay-at-home dad? taken firmer stances with you when you were growing up?). I follow the thousands of branching points of my marriage to Jan to their alternate conclusions. None of it will ever happen, none of it can be fixed. It's enough to drive a person mad. You'll forgive me if I don't bother with it too much. However, daydreams are always pleasant, their actualization within reach, residing in possible futures. Running for a position on the council, for instance, which comes with the dual benefit of unseating one of those jerks while being present in the meetings to antagonize the rest of them. I like that daydream a lot. I think about it from time to time. But not as often as this:

After my release, I sell the house in College Park and rent a small apartment in Tampa. Who needs four rooms living alone? I subscribe to the local paper where I see my daughter's name on the front page each morning. She's busy, of course, doing important things, grown-up things, has friends and lovers and colleagues, a full life of her own, and I don't want to intrude on that. I never want to intrude on that. Yet even though she's busy, she calls me every once in a while and tells me about her day. She recommends sandwich shops and coffeehouses, mentions landmarks around the city that are important to her: where she interviewed her first source, where she got lost on the way to a crime scene, where she asked her first question at a press conference. She finds time. She's glad to spend it. And on weekends, she visits.

JOHN SAUL
TAPAS

In the end the sad couple who had said nothing to each other throughout departed, taking their sadness with them, but to make sure none remained the waiter flicked his cloth at the tabletop, so any remnants might at least fall to the floor and not spoil the mood of the next diners here in Granada. Nonetheless any bets that the place would confer happiness looked precarious. At the table in the corner the drama of the black American and his three sons was at full throttle as his lover, as blonde as she was vivacious, blazed another glorious smile at him before throwing another at his youngest son, as if she were distributing bolts of lightning. Her Spanish endearments looked lost on the boys; her quick gestures seemed the sole hope of reaching them. The features of the youngest, his beautiful face, had frozen over.

Receiving the most attention, he was suffering the most. He sat steady, coolly, but jerked away as she reached for his arm, just as he had when she had invited him to touch her exotic leather jacket. Fitting neatly, in a crimson known as brilliant blush, it now lay folded on the chair between them, forming a bulwark of sorts. Suddenly he leapt up altogether when she reached over and tried to hold his cheek, the cheek furthest from her, in a curious embrace which turned into more of a wrestling hold, a clamp to his head, her aim being to plant a kiss on the cheek nearer her. It was doubtful he had ever sat so close to a woman so exuberant, or even so blonde, and going about in such a jacket. To him she was an invader, and she was physical. Her hold to his cheek was too much, too early, yet instead of being embarrassed she had turned already to drizzling more oil on her toast and shaking the salt cellar, holding it upside down so that salt shot into the air without her noticing, causing the two eldest boys to exchange furtive grins.

To save being touched, burned by a perfumed alien hand, the youngest had bolted around the table to his father, who presumably thought it impolitic to return the glorious smiles in front of his children, or even to attempt words in Spanish to this woman at his side. Like his other, mostly silent sons, he held himself in check. There was no sure way of detecting if he sat there tensely after pushing away the paella, or whether he was adept at hiding a tenseness, or really was relaxed. But if he and his sons were coiled springs, her spring had everywhere burst free. Her Spanish yelps of delight at the eldest, who despite everything was enjoying his first baby octopus, clearly reached the far end of the bar, where the young pair with the tiny dog turned to look. The three men perched at the little high table also heard, despite their own big laughs, which at first rose only occasionally above the general swell. To judge by their hooped rugby shirts they were English, as was confirmed when their beer glasses accumulated and they became more and more audible, with talk of football, hired cars, and Hell's Angels. The suspicion of this nationality was affirmed when they turned to emotional matters to do with Yorkshire versus Granada, the merits of various Costa resorts, and England versus Spain.

Perhaps the waiter, the nimbler of the two, should have given the table with the sad couple more than just a flick of his cloth. Introducing an air of suspicion to the bodega, the man of the couple had the long beard of a priest, a man of sanctimony and little lightness. While hovering birdlike over his supper, a plate of croquettes and cabbage salad, he shot dark looks about him, eyes darting from the couple at the counter to the Englishmen and the Hispanic American family in the corner that was not quite a family, to the two women sharing wraps of spinach and tomato over a carafe of sangria which got continually replenished, as if it were coffee in some diner in the United States. His greatest suspicion had fallen on the waiters, the nimble one with the cloth and his less hurried, more genial boss. These flashes of anxiety only drew attention to his holiness, ironically necessitating even greater surveillance on his part, as he checked and rechecked every possible source of terror, down to the tiny dog, covering everyone but his partner, a cast-down woman in a gray cardigan who got up once to stand at the barely stirring gray fish at the bottom of the aquarium, and who otherwise sat silently, drinking water and fingering a heap of the fried cuttlefish known as *chipirones*. Her hands shook, most likely not from nerves but from some ailment. She had followed him out meekly, head bowed as if seeking coins on the ground.

The American may have been just as nervous as the departed priest. A reasonable assumption would be that he was walking the tightrope of not wanting to lose his boys or his lover. While the Spanish woman acted less out of nervousness than from a natural esprit, plunging here and there, commenting, asking, praising, cutting up the air, the American, like his young son, responded coolly, speaking in a mumble, at a low vibration. The boys too remained nervous, fearful. They feared being touched, feared the strange words and the jacket, feared the perfume she said was made by Bulgari, in an exclamation so loud, like an endorsement, that the whole clientele looked up, including even the couple at the counter, where the woman otherwise almost never turned from her companion except to smuggle food down to the dog. Judging by the disgust that had passed over the face of the youngest, the perfume was possibly a variant of chloroform and might prove suddenly suffocating. With the three brothers lying unconscious on the tiled bodega floor and no paramedics yet in sight, she might have unbuttoned them somewhere, or stroked their foreheads, or kissed them. Worst of all, they feared they might turn out to like their father's lover after all and so transgress in a terrible betrayal of their own dear mother.

Having bided their time, sitting through all the tapas such a modest establishment could make available, the two elder sons now turned to ask their father permission for something. They were seeking maybe to build on an earlier success, when the middle child switched on a tablet and the father frowned, only to retract his disapproval at an intercession by his lover. Resorting now to asking permission may have been a clever shift in tactics vis-à-vis the father. Acting from calculation or not, the boys looked at him with an open-faced vulnerability. At a guess this man saw his role as a maker of decisions: yes to the food, a beer for the eldest, no to sangria. On their arrival, as she removed her jacket and for one moment arrested the diners from talking, from breathing, he may have left the choice of table to her, yes, but framed the situation so she would obviously go for the six-seater in the corner.

And so he decided now: the elder two sons had permission to go and explore Granada. They stood with exaggerated slowness as if to point out they could take or leave this minor sortie, just as they might take or leave their father's new partner. Sticking to this slow clock time, they left with decorum, even pausing at the aquarium to check the docility of the fish on the gravelly tank bottom. Out of sight they would almost certainly have run like thieves towards the nearby Plaza Nueva.

The sangria women chatted happily, leaning into each other so closely the necklace of one brushed the table and had to be rescued from trailing in the drizzle of olive oil on their tapa wraps. The partner of the one with the swinging beads took tissues from her Moroccan rucksack and started dabbing. In the orange light at the end of the bar the couple with the dog held hands. Despite the dog regularly tugging on its lead the woman, her black hair particularly prominent given that she seldom turned, looked fixedly at the man. No grenades here, said his T-shirt in Spanish and in English, only Granadines. The man equally was giving her all his attention. Could it be that men in Andalusia, or Granada, or at least along this set of streets on the south side of the Gran Via, are known for paying full attention to women, and women are pleased with their men? The sad couple notwithstanding.

Having drunk no more than a beer apiece, the American and his friend were presented with other alcohol which the boss loudly declared came from the skin of grapes, very fine grapes with very fine skins. The young boy's face unfroze enough to express the thought: Who needed grapeskins? *Orujo*, the waiter wrote on the paper tablecloth. The woman held the American's chin as she made him repeat the word. The boy went to put his hand on his father's mouth, stopping just before they touched. He was told to sit back down.

Slumped in the chair that was too high for him, he stared at whatever was not the woman, or the last of the tapas intended for sharing, or the glasses of thick dark yellow grapeskin, whatever that was exactly. This left him with the surface of the table to look at, or even write on, but it seemed he had no words or drawings ready. Or he could get up, which he did, to look at the fire extinguisher his father had already told him not to fidget with, and next to that a framed photograph that the film star Antonio Banderas dominated. It appeared the boy would have liked to move to the frame to the left of Antonio Banderas, onto the music artiste signing himself Dizzee Rascal, but the photograph of Dizzee Rascal was dangerously close to the crimson jacket on the empty chair. Instead he sat down and working a millimeter at a time so as not to be too obvious, began tearing out the word *orujo* from the table, preparing the paper for its later removal and almost certain destruction. Unexpectedly, momentarily, his fine lips came together in an appearance of contentment. He then took out a plastic toy figure from his pocket, just as the American lifted his partner's hand from under the table and she invited him to look more closely at her nail varnish. He left her hand untouched and shook his head; she stroked his cheek; he smiled faintly.

The sadness and its remnants had been forgotten. In its stead were strong desires, even if the Englishmen wanted nothing, nothing they could put a name to, beer apart. The dog couple were in the fortunate position of wanting each other. They were happy with the now and even happier with what suggested itself would come later when alone and unhampered by the dog and bar stools and plates of baby octopus and clothes and onlookers. They wanted some song repeated. The music played while the football game above the bar, Real versus Atlético, played on without sound. The dog, having for some time found nothing more interesting than crumbs, and been resigned to life on the floor, now wanted to leave no matter what was offered. The young boy likewise yearned for the jacket to be picked up, for Dizzee Rascal to wave them out, and for them to go. Looking ready to be sick, his countenance had resumed its default setting, suggesting he felt trapped by the talk, the ganging up on him. His body was saying the situation was like a fairground ride he wanted to be off, this horrid ride involving perfume, loathsome food, loathsome touchings.

A sudden quiet fell all the way from the kitchens to the doorway to the street, where blossoms lay. This had once opened onto gardens, flower and vegetable plots said to imitate in miniature the fine plantations of the Alhambra. At this lull the American could be heard explaining to his child how the earth turned around the sun. He was describing its orbit with beautiful hands, which his partner reached for ostensibly to refine his explanation, but more plausibly she reached for them simply to touch them. The boy looked more trapped, more sickened than ever, by this lurch into instruction, education, information. Worse, the woman joined the man by pointing a finger at where he had said there would be galaxies, and in approaching the nearest galaxy again went closer to the boy than he cared for. She knocked a hanging light which made a dull bell sound which quickly vanished. The boy blew at the light to try and make it keep swinging. Enough now Elmore, said his father.

At the counter the three Englishmen were getting animated about a footballer who had been filmed at the weekend breathing laughing gas. You should never laugh at the goalkeeper, one said: goalies win games. Win some, lose some, came the reply. Funny that, said the first: winning without scoring. The other promptly spilt drink on the floor. They kept punching one another's shoulders and even flicking wayward food from the others' clothes.

At the end of their song the couple clapped causing the dog to bark. At the corner table the father, leaning in to the boy, told him how the temperature would drop during an eclipse but that the sun had always, or nearly always, been there, certainly long before the earth was there. How did he know? asked the boy. The man smiled for the first time. What do you mean, before the earth was there? the boy asked. A smugness escaped from his father's face into the air, and nearby there was no waiter to disperse it with a flick of his cloth, neither the nimbler waiter or his boss who was distributing drinks everywhere. The son dropped his gaze to talk privately to his plastic toy figure, gripping it tightly in the face of the stupid lesson he would never ever henceforth wish to understand. He squeezed as he might have liked to squeeze the man before him, his father. He looked close to tears. What could he do? Nothing. He looked over at Dizzee Rascal on the wall as if asking himself what Dizzee Rascal would have done. As if Dizzee Rascal would ever have got in such a trap. Do what? He could only ask questions but that led to more talk, more of having adults all over him, an even more united front of the woman and the man.

The Englishmen have returned to discussing the Hell's Angels they encountered a week ago, when apparently a parade of them touring the countryside on Harley-Davidsons drew up and occupied a quiet square by a church. You know, one of the Englishmen remarks, not one flouted the requirement to wear a safety helmet. That's a rebel for you, says a second. Just as, the first continues, the Taliban wouldn't smoke on the London Underground. The third Englishman then says: That waiter is a wag. The other two fail to react, preferring to watch a replay of a foul which had sent a player smashing into boarding advertising Qatar Airways.

After flickers of success in communicating some basics concerning space travel—a matter the youngest seemed to regard as being at last a proper subject—it appears the American has left an explanation of light years to his partner. Close your eyes, she keeps saying to the boy, in an English which has trouble around the vowel sounds. *Los ojos*, she says instead. The boy will not close them. He pulls the head off his figure, looks at it and replaces it. Still the lecture continues. The American has arrived at Jupiter. The boy breathes out explosively. So *what*? he says. Look, the father says, look. This salsa jar is Mars. Look here. Look here. At *what*? the boy says. The words carry past the Englishmen to the couple at the bar. The black hair flicks as she turns so quickly that her face is barely glimpsed. The boss of the bodega triumphantly produces a glass of hot chocolate which he places squarely in front of the boy. *Tres cucharitas*, says the blonde woman. No, no! the waiter replies. What did you say? the American asks her. I don't want it, the boy says. I don't want it.

Larry, if a Hell's Angel came up to you and asked for a beer what would you say? The reply: That depends how many. Angels or beers? says the first. Angels, he replies. The third man: how many how many Angels? OK say there were three? Then then then I would buy them all a beer. OK say there were twenty? I would buy the first one a beer, see how the others were taking it.

As the evening lengthens and more is drunk it becomes more difficult to hear anything above anything, but the Englishmen have clearly mentioned Doncaster several times. The waiters have been dashing around the tables at accelerating speed, the one with the cloth scuttling, the boss more a steady gliding presence. Nothing has been dropped or smashed. A group of young people, several in striped football shirts endorsing UNICEF, has joined tables together before the television screen. Soon there is the jingle of new cutlery being collected, more surges of plates of tapas from the kitchen area, frying smells and *sishing* sounds. In the corner Jupiter, Mars, and Saturn have been regathered into a cluster after their failure to explain the universe.

Having spied the two boys returning, relating their adventures in shrugs, the waiter of the possibly magic cloth checks with the Spanish woman if more food is wanted. Something seems to have snapped or the drink may be to blame or it's the mix of languages, but she twists his words unrecognizably, translating him as having said that the numbers four and seven govern the skies. To his huge satisfaction, unconcealed, the youngest boy notices his father cannot understand this or explain it. Noticing that raising of his father's eyebrows, he traces over them with his fingers until he's told to stop. The couple with the necklace are fastening their Moroccan rucksacks ready to go. The bags are the kind the salesmen claim are real leather by holding the flame of a cigarette lighter against the surface. There is more of another kind of light in the corner, more lightning bolts, more mentions of Harleys at the bar, Doncaster, more touching, more firmly, on the thighs between the young couple at the bar. Sound jumps from the screen for the penalty shoot-out in the football, dividing the restaurant into two, one half showing irritation and the other enthusiasm, as the dog's head sinks flatly between its paws.

The woman rises from the table, the boys uncertain if they should walk out in front of her or not, and settling for going first, thus missing her turning in her jacket to fling in the direction of the kitchen a last fulminating flare, causing the dog to stand and the couple at the bar to turn and rise themselves. To no great cheers Real wins the penalty shoot-out, money goes back and forth on little silver salvers, bills are paid, the cloth snaps at tables, and visible dust hangs and falls. The Englishmen inspect the glasses of grapeskin set before them, conceding there are no close equivalents in Doncaster, nor in Rotherham, nor anywhere known to them in Yorkshire. They debate whether to swallow them in one go or to sip and wonder. With no one apparently looking their way, they settle for sipping quietly and wondering.

SONIA SCHERR
FIRST KILL

Grady woke to sudden light in his eyes and his father's hand on his shoulder. The dream he'd been having slipped away from him like a stone into deep water. To bring it back, he pressed a fist against his chest, hard enough to hurt a little, and buried his face in his pillow. The fabric was nubby against his skin and smelled as sour as his laundry pile. He turned his head until he was breathing fresh air, then pulled the quilt up to his mouth. Next to him, Lila growled softly and eased her body closer to his, so he could feel the in-and-out of her breathing against his belly. Under the covers, where his father couldn't see, he let his bare knee rest on the silk of her tail.

"Grady." His father's hand gripped a little tighter. "Stop playing dead."

Grady pulled the covers down to his neck. He yawned, to look like he was just waking up, and rolled onto his back. Through the open window he saw it was still dark outside. But it was bright, too bright, in his room. The lamp next to his bed hurt his eyes. "Turn it off," he said, his voice croaking. "I want to go back to sleep."

"No you don't," his father said. "We're going hunting."

Grady wondered if his father was joking, which didn't make sense because he rarely joked anymore. Last time they'd practiced shooting, before Grady's mother left, the target was the hard trunk of an oak in their backyard. Grady's father had told him he'd take him hunting in a year, when he turned eleven. Now Grady crawled toward the edge of the bed, accidentally kicking Lila, who gave a half-hearted yelp. "Sorry," he whispered into her gray-brown fur. The light shone in his face, making him squint, but he forced himself to look past it to his father, who was wearing his green camouflage jacket. "When?" he demanded.

"Soon as you eat breakfast." His father reached into the darkness behind him and held up a long slender rifle. Little sparks of light flew off its metal barrel. "I'll let you use the Remington."

Grady sat up. "Can I hold it?"

His father lifted the Remington higher, so the butt tapped the lopsided ceiling fan and sent it into a slow spin. "Not till you get yourself ready, like I asked."

His father turned and walked toward the kitchen, his boots loud on the linoleum. Grady waited a moment longer, then swung his feet onto the wooden floor. The slats were cold enough to make him run on tiptoes to the dresser. He yanked at the knob of the top drawer until it squealed open. Without looking, he grabbed a pair of jeans and pulled them on over his pajama bottoms. Lila watched him, her green eyes calm and unblinking. "Get up," he told her, making his voice stern. "Let's go." He gave her a little slap above her tail to get her moving. Then he tossed the top of his quilt over his pillow.

Lila followed him into the kitchen, where he scooped dog chow into her bowl and refilled her water. She padded over to her food, jerky in her steps because she wouldn't put weight on her left hind leg. The limp had started back in summer, but Grady once again knelt down to inspect it. The leg was spindly, with a couple of patches where the fur was thin enough that he could see right through to her pale pink skin. No different from her other legs.

"It's arthritis," his father said, holding his coffee mug with both hands. "Nothing anyone's going to be able to fix." Softly he hummed the song about the old gray mare not being what she used to be.

"Stop it," Grady said. The song made his stomach clench. He could not remember a time before Lila.

His father hummed the chorus once more. Grady grabbed a plastic bowl from the cabinet, letting it knock against the other bowls in the pile, and tore open a packet of instant oatmeal. A sprinkle of oats fell onto the countertop. With a cupped hand, he flung it sideways, aiming toward the sink. He placed the bowl under the faucet until it was half full of water and then stuck it in the microwave. His father had stopped humming. He was gazing out the window toward the river, taking small sips from his mug. All he had now for breakfast was three mugs of coffee, the instant kind. Grady watched his stubbly face, waiting for some glimmer of expression, but it was secret and still. It made Grady think of the dark surface of the pond by the woodshed where he swam in summer, even though his friend Tony said it had leeches.

The microwave beeped. Grady reached for the bowl bare handed, remembering too late he should have used a towel. It was white hot against his fingertips. Quickly he set it down next to the sink, spilling a little over the side. He added a scoop of brown sugar and a handful of raisins, like his mother always did. Without bothering to mix them in, he shoveled a spoonful into his mouth. It burned his tongue and throat, and he gulped down some orange juice to get rid of the heat. As he ate, he traced the red-and-black squiggles on the countertop. He'd stared at those same squiggles the day after Halloween when his mother had told him she'd be gone for a couple of months to take care of her sister in Newfield. "She's going through a hard stretch," his mother had said, her eyes wandering past Grady to the window ledge where she grew basil and thyme.

Grady nodded like he understood, but he had no idea what she meant. Last time he'd seen his aunt, she'd seemed perfectly fine, arriving with her boyfriend in a red car that had a little window in the roof you could open and stick your head out.

His mother straightened up and looked Grady in the eyes. "I'm sorry. I'll be back before Christmas."

"In time to make our snowman?" Grady asked. It was what they did together every year, right after the first storm. Last winter, they'd propped his father's Red Sox cap on its head, wrapped his mother's green scarf around its neck, and hung Grady's old mittens, the ones with the hole in each thumb, at the ends of its stick arms.

"I hope so," his mother said. Suddenly she hugged him, squeezing tight enough to hurt his ribs. He wriggled backward to loosen her grip. "Take care of yourself," she whispered, her voice low and strange. "Take care of your dad." Her long brown hair grazed his eyelids, then tickled the top of his neck. He pressed his mouth against her shoulder to hold back a laugh, but it escaped from him just the same. Unable to stop himself, he laughed again, louder. His mother let him go, lips twisted together, arms clamped against her chest. She turned away before he could tell her why he was laughing.

Now, Grady shoved aside his half-finished breakfast and ripped open another packet of oatmeal. When the cereal was ready, he placed it in front of his father, who glanced at the bowl without seeming to see it. Grady got out the brown sugar and raisins, but his father waved them away. With his elbows on the counter, his father braided the fingers of each hand together, as if he was in church. Gray light from the window fell on the black hairs below his knuckles, the thick line of dirt under each nail, a slender scab on the fleshy part of his thumb. Then he let his hands fall and rested them on either side of the bowl, palms upward. At the bottom of his fingers were yellow ridges of skin that Grady liked to press when he was little. Lineman's hands, his father called them, because his job was repairing power lines for Silver Falls Electric. But his mother said that wasn't true; his father's hands were rough because he did landscaping work on his days off and refused to wear gloves. Grady found a spoon in the drying rack and dropped it onto the table next to his father's plate.

His father finally took a spoonful of oatmeal. He swallowed it quickly and nodded at Grady. "It's good to have a real breakfast."

"That's for sure," Grady said, even though their breakfast wasn't real, not the way it would have been before. He scratched Lila's ear with his toe and scraped the last bit of oatmeal from his bowl. The cereal was cold and gummy in his mouth. He had to swallow hard to get it down. "Do you think it'll snow this weekend?"

"No," his father said. "It's not supposed to snow."

GRADY WAS HELPING load his father's pickup when he heard tires bite into gravel at the bottom of their driveway. Lila, curled up on the stoop, lifted her head and barked once, then stopped and lowered her chin back into the crook of her paw. A blue Mazda rolled out of the fog and stopped just behind the pickup. Uncle Charles's car. Grady shoved the cooler he was carrying onto the pickup's cramped rear seat. He slammed the door and ran to the driver's side of the Mazda. The engine was still running, and Grady breathed in the smell of exhaust mixed with burning wood and dead leaves. Uncle Charles gripped the steering wheel with one hand and pinched the bottom of his lip with the other. His mother called Uncle Charles, her little brother, the Entertainer. Today he looked different than usual, and Grady realized it was because he wasn't smiling.

Grady knocked on the car window with both hands.

Uncle Charles cut the engine and opened the door. He got up slowly, unfolding his large body from the seat. The bottom of his red beard was hidden in the collar of his puffy down coat, as if it was growing up toward his chin instead of the other way around. He still didn't smile.

"Hey, kiddo," he said, "You're up early today."

"Dad and me are going hunting. Up in the reservoir woods."

"He's going to let you shoot?"

"Yeah. I'm going to use the Remington."

"That's good." Uncle Charles looked thoughtful. "Remember to aim straight through the heart and lungs. You want to kill the deer quickly. It'll hurt less that way."

"I'll do that."

"Maybe you'll get your first kill. Heck, maybe you'll even get a buck."

"Maybe." Grady pictured the deer falling to the ground, heard the crackle of dry leaves as he rushed toward the dying animal, felt his father's arm once again on his shoulder, this time giving it a little squeeze.

Uncle Charles patted Grady's head, the corners of his eyes crinkling. "Aunt Pat will have to make venison stew."

Grady wrapped his arms around himself, suddenly cold now that he'd stopped moving.

"Hey, where's your coat?"

"Inside."

"Is that where your dad is, too?" Uncle Charles had turned serious again.

Grady nodded. "He's getting the guns ready."

Grady heard the screen door open behind him. "They're ready," his father said, looking at Uncle Charles.

Uncle Charles took a step forward, then stopped. "Sorry to bother you so early in the morning. I was on my way into town and figured you'd be up."

"Yes," his father said, "we're up."

Grady kicked a pebble toward the wheel of the pickup. Something was funny. The men were talking as if they barely knew each other, as if they had to be careful about what they said.

"I hear you're taking Grady hunting."

A smile flickered across his father's face. "Thought I'd get him started. Today seemed like a good day for it, with the mild weather they're predicting."

"I'd say so." With the heel of his boot, Uncle Charles drew a wide arc in the dirt, then erased it with his toe. "I won't keep you. Just wanted to let you know that Leslie stopped by last night."

His father nodded. Grady stopped kicking pebbles. Leslie was his mother.

"She had something she wanted me to tell you. I said she should tell you herself, but I'm not sure she will, and I thought you should know."

His father looked at Grady and tilted his head toward the house. Grady pretended not to notice.

"We're bringing the brown tarp, Grady. It's in the mudroom. Fold it."

Grady walked slowly to the door, sliding each foot in the dirt as if he were on skates. The men were silent. He held the screen door so Lila could follow him inside, then let it go. It banged shut behind him. After a moment, the outer door clicked closed, too.

In the mudroom, Grady crouched down below an open window. The men had moved farther from the house; their voices rose and fell but their words drifted away before he could make sense of them. When he peeked above the windowsill, he saw they were standing beside the pickup, facing each other. With one hand his father shaded his eyes, though he was staring into fog. His father's back was straight. Uncle Charles leaned against the passenger's side window, looking at something in the front seat. Suddenly Grady wanted to run outside and drag his father back into the house before Uncle Charles could say anything more. Instead he clutched the windowsill, pressing his chin against the rough wood until it stung.

Uncle Charles briefly jostled his father's arm, then got into his car. After he drove away, his father stood for a long time with his back to the house. Finally he turned and trudged slowly up the driveway, his eyes on the ground. Grady leapt up and grabbed the tarp off the table. He started folding it, but the material was stiff and bulky and he couldn't get the sides to match up evenly. Without saying anything, his father took the tarp from him and folded it crisply in two, then folded it again. "Let's move out," he said. "We're getting a late start."

"Be one sec. I've got to leave Lila some food and water for her lunch."

"Should have thought of that a little sooner."

"I did. Just didn't have a chance to get it."

"Now's your chance then. Hurry."

Grady ran into the kitchen, Lila right behind him, and grabbed the bag of chow from under the sink. As he scooped it into Lila's bowl, Grady felt his father looking at him. He turned around. His father pressed a palm against the side of his forehead and squeezed his eyes closed, like he often did when he was tired. Then he gave his head a little shake and opened his eyes wide. "Take her," he said quietly.

"Who?"

"Lila."

"Will she be able to keep up?"

"She'll do well enough."

"But what if she barks?"

"She's pretty quiet. And if she isn't, she can wait in the truck."

"You sure?"

"It'll be good for her. She could use the exercise."

"All right." Grady found her red collar in the kitchen drawer and gently fastened it around her neck.

LILA RODE BETWEEN them, her ears slightly flattened, her eyes darting to things in the fog Grady couldn't see. Grady scanned stations until his father told him to quit playing with the radio. Grady let his hand fall onto his lap. A twanging guitar bled through static. After a minute, his father slapped the dial and the music cut out. The only noise came from the hum of the wheels against pavement and the whine of the engine. Grady closed his eyes and let himself fall into the cocoon of sound, then jerked awake when his father braked hard at the crosswalk in front of Allen's General Store.

"Stupid woman—just stepped into the street," his father said. "What does she think this is, some kind of nature trail?"

As his father hit the gas, Grady made a little noise of agreement, like he knew he was supposed to. He knelt on the vinyl, facing backward, and saw the woman's blonde curls swing over her shoulder as she turned to glare at them from the sidewalk. She wasn't wearing a coat, and her breath made a little cloud in the chilly air.

"Get your behind in the seat," his father said, and Grady slid back down, twisting his body forward. As he buried his hands in Lila's fur to warm them, he wondered where the woman was going. Probably just to the store, he decided, or else she would have worn a coat.

They followed the road out of town and past the elementary school where Grady went to fifth grade. The empty playground looked smaller than it did during the week. Just inside the wooden fence, strips of mist curled around the bars of its jungle gym. Grady imagined climbing to the top and gripping the damp metal rung, then jumping into the sandpit below. He and Tony had done it just a few days ago, until Mrs. Fielding told them to stop. Suddenly he wanted to ask his father to let him get out here, in a place he knew.

"How far is it to the Reservoir Woods?" he asked.

"Not far," his father said. "Just past the water treatment plant. Close enough to walk from here if we didn't have so much gear."

Grady tapped his toes on the grimy floor mat. He felt like the marionette he'd made in art class, unable to keep still, as if someone else was controlling his arms and legs. He zipped up his windbreaker to his chin and shoved his hands into the pockets.

"Mr. Fidget," his father said, his voice sounding the same as when he commanded Lila to sit.

"I'm cold," Grady said.

His father turned up the heat. "You're lucky, that's what you are. I was thirteen when I first got to go hunting. And it wasn't with my father. He was God-knows-where most weekends. My older brother took me—your Uncle Dan."

"Did you kill anything?"

"I was stupid. Shot at a doe while it was running. It kept going. Left a trail of blood. I thought for sure we'd find it. But we didn't."

"What do you think happened to it?"

"Bled out somewhere." His father touched his palm to the side of his head. "I didn't hit it like I should have."

"In the heart or lungs," Grady said.

"Yes." His father glanced down at him, smiling.

Grady placed a hand on his own neck. It was warm and soft. He could feel his pulse just beneath his skin. He pressed against the spot and the throbbing grew stronger.

"Shouldn't have been so hard on myself, though," his father said. "You make mistakes. Most people don't kill a deer their first time out."

"Uncle Charles said maybe I would." Grady shoved his hands into his pockets. It wasn't what he really wanted to say.

"He did, did he?"

"Yeah. Is Uncle Charles OK?"

"He's OK." His father looked steadily at the road.

"And Mom?" He felt a little breathless.

"Seems like it."

Grady wanted to ask his father another question, but he couldn't quite put it into words.

"She's all right but she's not coming home to live," his father said. "That's what Uncle Charles came to say."

Grady pressed his hands deeper into his pockets. The plastic of his windbreaker suddenly felt sweaty against his palms. He felt like his father had just told him about some disaster that had happened very far away. "Why isn't she coming home?"

"That's something she'll have to tell you herself."

"Is she going to stay with Aunt Cindy?"

His father took a sharp breath. "No."

Grady wanted to know where she'd be staying, but his father's tone made him stop. Instead he asked, "When will I see her?"

"I don't know." His father reached over Lila and squeezed Grady's arm just above the wrist. "I'm sorry."

Grady drew back, surprised. He rubbed the spot where his father's fingers had gripped, half expecting a mark to appear.

His father quickly put his hand back on the steering wheel. "So it'll be just us for a little while. But we'll be fine." His voice sounded funny, more like a recording than his father.

Grady stared out the window. They were passing the cemetery where his grandmother was buried. Perched above the rusty iron gate was a stone angel, one of its wings half broken off so that the stub still attached seemed to point at the ground. Without thinking, Grady took a gulp of air, getting ready to hold his breath like he always did when they passed a graveyard. Then he let it out. He no longer cared what might happen.

"Grady?" His father's jaw twitched. "Did you hear what I said?"

"Yes."

"What did I say?"

"We'll be fine," Grady mumbled.

"Don't forget it," his father said.

"I won't."

"Good."

Outside, the fog had mostly burned off, but clouds were moving in from across the river. They filled up the sky quickly, like someone blowing into a gray balloon. A few flakes swirled in front of the car and landed on the windshield. "It's snowing," Grady said.

"That's not what I call snow." His father flicked on the wipers and the flakes disappeared.

"Our snowman. We were going to build a snowman."

"What snowman?"

"You know." Lila turned her head to look at him, but he didn't lower his voice. He felt like everything depended on making his father understand. "The snowman we always build after the first storm. Mom—"

All at once his father swerved to the side of the road and cut the engine. "Stop talking like that, Grady." His voice was a string pulled tight. "I don't want to hear anymore about it."

They sat without speaking. A car rushed by, its headlights two bright wands that Grady could still see when he closed his eyes.

"Do you understand me?"

"Yes."

His father turned on the engine and pulled back onto the road. Grady leaned down until his mouth touched the tip of Lila's ear. The hairs were soft against his lips. "No," he whispered, low enough so his father wouldn't hear. "I don't understand."

THEY PASSED THE water treatment plant and turned onto a dirt road that went uphill. They had to drive in the middle because of the deep gullies on either side. As they rounded a curve, a red squirrel dashed across the road in front of them, its tail brushing the dirt. Grady followed it with his eyes. He'd read in a book about a boy who could tell what birds were thinking just by gazing up at them, but the squirrel disappeared into the grass before he could get a good look at it. After what seemed like a long time, they drove by a turnoff to the reservoir and the road flattened out.

"Almost there," his father said.

Grady leaned forward in his seat and peered into the thick woods that came up nearly to the edge of the gravel. He'd begun to feel excited again. He opened the window, stuck his hand out, and let the cool air rush through his fingers. A pinecone grazed his palm. Grady tried to grasp its wooden spikes but it slipped away, bobbing on a low-hanging branch.

His father eased the pickup onto the side of the road. Grady jumped out, his feet nearly sliding out from under him in the soft gravel. He caught himself and sprinted to the back of the pickup. His father turned off the engine, then took his time getting out of the truck. Slowly he walked over to Grady and gave him the Remington. Grady gripped it with both hands. He'd only ever fired a shotgun before. This rifle was made for deer hunting. He ran his fingers the length of the smooth, straight barrel. He touched his finger to the trigger. The gun was lighter than he'd expected. He shifted it in his arms, trying to find a comfortable position for carrying it.

"Careful," his father said. "Point it down."

Grady flipped the gun so it was aimed at the ground, then climbed the steep bank to the edge of the trees. He skipped alongside them a little ways until he got to a path leading into the woods, wide enough for only one person and slippery with pine needles.

"Grady." His father's voice came from the far side of the pickup. "Planning on getting Lila?"

"Sure I was," he said, though he had forgotten. Grady leaned his gun against a tree and jogged back down to the road. Lila was standing on the passenger's seat, watching him. He opened the door and put his arms around her neck. Her breath was warm against his cheek. "We weren't going to leave you," he told her.

Behind him, his father made a sound that seemed to disagree.

"I wasn't," Grady said, this time more to his father than to Lila.

"Put her on the leash until we get into the woods," his father said.

Grady clipped the leash to her collar and led her toward the trees. She stopped to sniff a clump of grass, pulling at the leash. Grady tugged back to get her to follow.

In the woods, Grady took off her leash and let her run ahead. The path was even narrower here, as if it wasn't meant for humans at all. Grady kicked the damp leaves and listened to the whispery sound his footsteps made. Soon his shoes were soaked through and the cuffs of his jeans were wet, though he felt warm enough as he tried to keep up with his father.

It became harder the farther they went. The stiff bristles of baby pine trees batted at his shins. Ferns sprouting on either side clung to his ankles, making him trip. He walked through a spiderweb and felt its sticky threads tickle his eyelids. He swiped at them but they only moved to his chin and lips, like ghostly fingers. His father, who plodded from room to room in their small house, glided quickly along the path. It was as if he had turned into some kind of forest animal, Grady thought.

Lila bounded back to him with a leafy branch in her mouth. Grady took it from her and tossed it up the path. She too seemed different. He squinted until her limp almost disappeared. Grady remembered when he was little and she used to knock him over when they played fetch in the yard. He stopped for a moment to catch his breath. His mouth tasted grimy. He let it fill with saliva and then spat into the underbrush, making a popping sound with his lips. He made the sound again, just to hear it, and stretched his arms toward a yellow vine barely above his fingertips. Next to him, a boulder was covered in dried-up leaves that looked like the barnacles he'd seen last summer when the three of them had gone to the ocean. Grady tried to peel one off, but it was stuck to the rock and crumbled in his hand. He used the butt of the Remington to sweep pine needles into a soft nest, then set the gun on the ground and scooped up a fistful of dirt. Ahead, his father stopped and turned around, his mouth partway open like he was about to say something. Instead he cocked his head to the side, which meant Grady needed to hurry up. For a moment Grady wished his father would disappear into the woods so he could stay in this spot forever. But he picked up the gun and ran to catch up.

The path turned into a small stream that ran downhill over tangled roots. Grady stepped from rock to rock as Lila splashed in the shallow pools. The stones were slick and flecked with silver that glittered in the clear water. All at once his father crouched down. Grady, right behind him, had to stop so quickly he skidded and almost fell into the stream.

"Look," his father said. He pointed at a heart-shaped print in the sand next to the streambed.

Grady knelt down, too. He placed his hand inside the heart.

"A doe, probably." His father stood up again. "Too small to be a buck."

"Do you think it's nearby?"

"Maybe not this one. But there could be others." He motioned for Grady to follow him uphill away from the stream. "We'll wait for a little while and see if they come."

His father unfolded the tarp halfway and laid it at the foot of a pine tree. They sat down against its rough trunk. The bark jabbed into his back and Grady shifted from side to side, then sat up straight again. He suddenly felt cold and drew his knees to his chest.

"This is the hardest part," his father said. "We've got to be quiet. And wait."

Lila was still wading in the water and Grady called to her. She ran to them and sat down on the tarp, water dribbling from her tail. With his fingers Grady combed her wet fur. Her sleek, smooth body reminded him of a river otter.

His father glanced at Lila. "She's going to scare away the deer."

Grady kept on combing. He felt his face get hot. He wanted to say, It was you who said we should take her. Instead he shrugged. "I don't think so. She'll be good."

His father looked away, across the stream. "Guess she has been, so far."

Grady watched him. His face had the same faraway expression as this morning. He no longer reminded Grady of a forest animal; instead, he was his father again, but in changing back to what Grady was used to he'd become more of a stranger.

His father took a handful of bullets out of his waist pack. Grady picked one up and held it in his cupped hands. "That's not for playing with," his father said, and Grady let it drop onto the tarp.

"I'll show you how to load the gun, just in case," his father said, his voice gentler. "It's a little different from what you're used to."

He pressed a lever so the shooting end of the gun swung downward, then dropped a bullet into the chute. He told Grady to cock the hammer when he was ready to fire. "That's all," he said, handing it back. "Not a lot to it."

Grady carefully set the gun down beside him. It felt heavier now that it was loaded, though the bullet had been light in his hands. His father sat quietly, his own rifle resting on his knees. Grady stretched his legs toward a spot of sun on the forest floor. He unzipped his jacket and eased his back against the tree, nestling into a smooth strip of bark. His arm rested next to his father's. He could feel its warmth through his jacket.

"I wouldn't get too comfortable," he father said, though he didn't move his arm away. With the hand farther from Grady, he lifted a pair of binoculars from around his neck and peered through them. Slowly he adjusted the knob in the middle and turned his head from one side to the other. "Nothing there yet. Have a look."

Grady brought the binoculars to his own eyes. Two bright circles blended into one hazy tunnel. He fiddled with the knob until a cluster of red smudges turned into little berries hanging from a tree on the other side of the stream. He jerked his head upward so the picture changed abruptly to gray crisscrossed by dark lines—branches against the sky. Then he swung the binoculars toward his own legs. But they no longer seemed to belong to him. These were giant's legs. He started counting the blue-white threads in one frayed knee, stopping at twenty. He inched the binoculars higher—and that's when he saw the speckled patch of tan slide toward him. He turned the binoculars slightly to the left. A white tail flicked against a clump of leaves, bright like a clean rag against the layers of brown. He tilted the binoculars downward and found the narrow head, nose touching the ground. The ears, big enough for Grady to slip his hands inside, never stopped twitching. He leaned back until he could see the entire animal. A deer, feeding just beyond the stream.

He tore the binoculars from his neck and shoved them toward his father. "Look!" he said in a loud whisper. And then pointing: "There."

His father raised the binoculars once again. He seemed to take forever to adjust them.

"Do you see it?" Grady asked. Lila blinked her eyes and thrust her head forward, her black nose wriggling. Grady rested one hand on her back, to keep her calm, and reached for the Remington with the other.

"I see it." His father kept peering into the binoculars, the lines beside his eyes deepening. After a moment, he let the binoculars drop onto his stomach. "It's a doe. Too far away, though. We can't get a good shot."

"Are you sure?" Grady gripped the gun tighter, as if that could make his father change his mind. But even as he slid his sweaty fingers toward the trigger he heard a branch snap on the far side of the stream. Squinting, he thought he saw a dark shadow melt into the trees.

"Maybe we'll have another chance." His father scratched his forehead, hard enough to leave a white line. "If we're patient."

STILL LEANING AGAINST the tree, Grady lifted his legs, one at a time, to warm them. He could feel the cold seeping through the tarp and into his jeans and pajama bottoms. His wet cuffs rubbed against his ankles; when he rolled up the stiff fabric, the skin underneath was red and itchy. It seemed like a long time had passed since they'd seen the deer, though the spot of sunlight just beyond his feet had barely moved.

His father cleared his throat. It sounded louder than usual to Grady, and he turned to look at his father, who was staring into the woods. His hand was pressed against the side of his face so Grady couldn't see his eyes. "There's something else we need to do now," his father said.

Grady wanted to ask him what. Instead he nodded like he knew and picked up the gun again. With his back to Grady, his father scooped up the remaining bullets from the tarp and shoved them into his waist pack. He zipped the pack shut, then opened it again and took out two bullets. He held them out toward Grady, still turned away. Grady took them and waited for his father to say more. Finally he put them in his pocket.

His father got up slowly, leaning against the tree. He stood without moving, his hand still resting on the trunk, long enough that Grady wondered if he was all right. As he was about to ask, his father stepped back and slid the tarp out from under Lila. She sank her claws into it, so that his father had to shake it to get her off. Even with her hind legs on the ground, one of her front paws stayed stuck. His father knelt down and unhooked it. It left tiny pinholes in the plastic.

"What are you doing?" Grady asked. The question flew out before he could stop it. Right away he felt a little sick.

His father said nothing. After a moment, though, he waved his hand for Grady to follow him. Together they spread the tarp on a flat patch of ground a short distance away. When Grady pressed his palm against the plastic, he could feel roots and ferns and stones underneath. He tried to smooth out the lumps.

"Leave it," his father said, still crouched on the other side. "It doesn't matter."

His father stood up, his back to Grady, and walked over to Lila, who was sniffing something in a clump of ferns. He refastened her leash and wrapped it twice around the trunk of the pine, tucking the handle underneath. It was bright against the dark wood, and looked as if it might come off if Grady tugged at it, like a girl's hair ribbon. Then his father knelt down in front of the dog. Standing beside the tarp, Grady watched him take a biscuit from his waist pack and feed it to her. Grady figured it might taste like metal from being mixed up with the bullets. But she ate it quickly, like she always did, so she must have liked it well enough. Grady wished she would quit. His father only fed her treats when he wanted her to do something. He said they wouldn't work if you gave them to her at any old time. Grady would sometimes sneak her a biscuit when his father wasn't around, brushing any crumbs under the covers or onto the floor.

Now, his father fed Lila another treat. Grady sat down again on the bare ground next to the tarp. Something stopped him from joining his father and Lila. He rested his head on his hands and closed his eyes, suddenly tired, then opened them again. His father was calling his name.

Grady got up slowly, shuffling his feet in the dry leaves that covered the path. He imagined more and mores leaves falling, until they covered the tarp and reached the low branches of the trees and then filled the bright spaces where the forest met the sky. He was swimming through the leaves.

"What are you doing?" his father called. "I told you to get over here."

Grady jogged the rest of the way. His father pressed a biscuit into his hand. Grady closed his fingers around it, then pressed tighter, until it began to crumble.

"Feed it to her," his father said.

Grady kept his hand in a fist. He let his arm dangle by his side. Lila crawled closer to him and nuzzled his hand. Her nose was wet against his skin. He opened his fingers and let her eat the broken pieces of biscuit. Then he stuffed his hands in his pockets.

His father scratched the soft fur behind Lila's ears. He touched the folds of skin above her eyes. Finally he turned to Grady. "You know what you need to do, don't you?"

Grady shook his head, more times than he needed to. He kept his eyes on the ground.

"Look at me, Grady." His father's hands were on his shoulders. "She's old. She's sick."

"She's not." It was all he could of think to say. Lila had lain down again. Her curled tail lifted once, brushed the ground, then wrapped itself neatly around her body.

"C'mon, Grady. It's the right thing."

"No." The word flew from him again and again. He stepped backward so the pine was between himself and Lila, then turned around, facing away from her.

His father followed him, sighing loudly. He picked up the gun and held it out. The cold metal touched the skin of Grady's wrist. Grady jerked his hand away. He clenched his stomach and arms and legs. He squeezed his eyes shut. He held his breath. He needed to harden himself, so that nothing from the outside world could ever get in.

His father was still holding the gun. "Take it." His voice was loud enough to make Lila whine. "When I tell you to do something, you need to do it. Do you understand?"

Grady felt himself nod. He took the gun, pointing it down toward the dirt.

"The sooner you do it," his father said, almost softly now, "the sooner it'll be over with."

His voice sounded like it did when he'd told Grady to go inside while he talked to Uncle Charles. Grady never wanted to hear it again. He opened his fingers. The gun fell onto the ground.

"What the hell are you doing?" his father said.

"Nothing." He was no longer afraid. "I'm not doing anything." His words floated high above him, into the trees. He followed them with his eyes.

"That's not how you handle a gun."

A sharp sting against his cheek made him jerk his head to the side. Grady gritted his teeth, waiting for a slap on the other cheek, but it didn't come. Instead, his father crossed both arms against his chest. His head was tilted forward so Grady couldn't see his face. Grady took a step toward him. He heard a funny sound come from his own throat—like a laugh that had gotten stuck. "You can't make me do anything." He stopped. It was true.

"No." His father sounded like he was speaking from far away.

"Why don't you do it? Why don't you kill her?"

His father shook his head.

"Why don't you?" He said it again, jumping up toward a thin tree branch high above his head. He felt like he could touch that branch if he wanted to, could grab a hold of it and swing until his toes touched the sky.

His father stumbled and sat. His shoulders shook.

Grady went quiet. The wild feeling drained from him all at once.

His father was still on the ground, head bent.

"Hey," Grady said. His father didn't move. "Dad?"

His father said something Grady couldn't understand. Grady knelt down in front of him. He was sobbing, his face twisted so he didn't look like his father at all. Grady leapt back. He had never seen his father cry.

Grady bit his lip, breathing as if he had just run very hard. His heart seemed to be beating in the air around him. Pinecones hanging from a tree blurred into a solid curtain of brown. He blinked until they became clear again. His father was still crying. Grady wanted to hit him with the gun and also to hide his own face in the frayed collar of his father's jacket.

Instead he stood up as tall as possible. He took a deep breath and pretended he was looking down at himself from the tops of the trees. Then he walked around to the other side of the pine. Quickly he picked up the gun from where he'd dropped it on the ground. Lila was stretched out next to the trunk, her back to him, her head upright. Her gaze followed a faint rustling in the woods. Through her fur he could see the bones of her spine, separate yet joined, like the beads of a necklace. He shifted his weight onto one leg and stretched out the other one to touch her. Then he stopped and planted both feet together. He cocked the hammer on the Remington, like his father had taught him, and walked around so he was facing the dog. Without letting himself look at her face, he lifted the gun to his shoulder, aimed at her chest, and squeezed the trigger. The shot exploded in his ears and forced him into a squat. In front of him, Lila's head was on the ground. Her legs twitched, as if she was trying to run away. Blood darkened the leaves behind her front paws. Grady took a bullet from his pocket and reloaded the gun and again pulled the trigger. This time, Lila was still.

Grady put the gun down and clasped his hands together. He was no longer watching himself from above. Instead he was pinned to the ground, his body so heavy it was hard to move. Looking up, he saw only his father, blocking the trees in his big green jacket. He was no longer crying. He touched Grady's shoulder. He said something, but the noise of the last gunshot echoed in Grady's head, burying the sounds before they could become words. Grady needed to get to Lila. As he reached his arms toward her, he felt the recoil once again, though he had not touched the gun. This time, it flung him back, back toward the tarp. He sat down where he'd landed. He placed his hands on the ground to steady himself. He waited for it to stop.

ALLEN FORREST
LONDON NOIR, #3

BEATE SIGRIDDAUGHTER

SNAPSHOTS OF THE WIFE OF THE MAN WHO WOULDN'T DANCE

In the center of her dreams couples dance. Bodies tenderly lean into each other and the sweeping violins caress. Men and women they dance. Hers is not an uncommon story.

Today she will dance in the street. The wind is generously mild. The sun is high. The music already plays with her mind. Let's call her Maria.

Her soul is full of sunlight and approval. At long last he has agreed to go with her. There'll be a free beginner lesson to start off the dance. He'll be delighted to discover how much he already knows from their sporadic living room lessons.

He looks up from his computer screen as she saunters past him on the way to the kitchen. Let's call him Dan.

"Hey there, good-looking! Good morning to you on this glorious day. Do you want to go for a hike in the mountains?"

Her heart skips. Something dull like a cudgel seems to press against it. He has forgotten. She does not want to believe it, not when it is so important to her. The poster has been on the refrigerator door for three weeks and she reminded him yesterday. She does not want to fight with him. She feels a swell of hatred rise inside, a surge of acrid contempt. She prays to powers she doesn't trust. Let him remember. Let him remember. Please.

Their ten-year-old daughter Belinda coughs in her bedroom. She was invited, too, but has a slight fever and opts for computer games instead of bright sun for two hours of mostly adults cavorting around.

"Something the matter?" Dan asks.

"We had a date to go dancing this afternoon." The words scratch Maria's throat. She is angry at herself for using the past tense already.

"Oh, right," he says. Belinda coughs once more. "I think I better stay home, though, and take care of Belinda."

"A moment ago you were inviting me to go hiking."

"Yes," he says. "I wasn't thinking, was I? I wouldn't feel good leaving Belinda by herself when she is sick."

She wants to accuse him. But what would be the use? She remains silent. Only her eyes contract.

At the breakfast table, Belinda tells them in singsong interrupted by coughs that it's perfectly OK for them both to go.

"I wouldn't feel right," he says. "What if you suddenly took a turn for the worse?"

"Don't be ridiculous, Daddy. I can be on my own for a few hours. It's just a cold."

"You never know," he says.

CONTEMPT WASHES OVER Maria, oozing with self-righteousness. She goes hiking with him. She goes swimming with him. She goes to bed with him. So he should go dancing with her. It would only be fair.

Her bones hang heavy. She will go alone. She will not enjoy herself, but she will force her head up high. She will feel sorry for herself.

She is a poor marketer of her most cherished dreams, mostly because she inconveniently believes that others have a right to their own minds and she has no right to manipulate them.

He said he would come and for days she was thrilled with her good luck. Now that it is time to go, he has forgotten. He makes other plans, compelling plans, appealing to her sense of responsibility. The truth is, he would rather go to war than dance in public. Combat would gain him more respect than dance among his fellow men, and he would rather impress his fellow men than her. As a result, he would rather have her stand in public, alone at the edge of the dance floor, embarrassed, unclaimed. Where is the chivalry in that?

She longs for the dizzy joy of being human, strong, sinuous, alive. She knows she must reach for the joy, but it hurts that she must reach for it alone. It feels like reaching up for stars with a dislocated shoulder.

She is too old now to be alone. Because he will not come with her (he is old now, too—another perfect excuse) she will stand on the sidewalk and feel hollow and unwanted as her dreams dissolve like fairy glitter in the dust among the dancers in the middle of the cordoned-off summer street.

True, when she was younger it wasn't that much better. She already stood unwanted on the sidelines then. But then there had still been hope. Like there had been hope for the last few days of looking forward to this thing he had agreed to do.

Embarrassment and loneliness are slimy demons and she cannot battle their moist horror while making nice. It's civil war inside, forced on her soul against her will. She feels betrayed and angry. She also loves him, though the love feels bland and burdensome now.

IN THE DUST of the street, the sun beats down. From time to time, she blows up at the moist bangs clinging to her forehead. She hadn't thought to bring bobby pins. Her anger catches fire like kindling under glass.

When he wants something badly—often it involves sex—she makes it happen. But for her, nada. When she wants something—romance or dance—he'd rather take a nail in the head.

She can't force love like a man can force sex. There's no satisfaction to be had from insisting on love. That's how they're unequal. He can be contemptuous and still have sex. Not so with love. Although perhaps there is contempt when she groups him together with all his fellow men. Each one like every other one: each one afraid that just the appearance of sentiment would make them look bad. Or else afraid they wouldn't shine in the arena of love. Maybe that's what they can't bear. So they stoically shake hands—provided they manage to survive their battles—in a world of violence and greed and competition, things she doesn't want to be part of in the first place. That way they can continue excelling at something that may not be entirely human. But at least they excel. Women offer only limited competition there. After all, why compete in something you don't even want?

Maybe if they were to make a game of brutal competition out of dance, rather than a practice of relationship and charming exuberance, then they'd be willing to participate. But it's been done. Couples beating each other on the dance floor, dancing for first place, dancing to kick ass. It doesn't sound particularly gratifying.

She just wants to dance out here in the street, happily, with no concern for being better or worse than anyone else. Just move these limbs, just flex these muscles, move these hips, these thighs, these arms. Just fly. Spin. Whirl.

HER MIND DRIFTS. She sees them walking in the sand. Waves were lapping with the sun about to set. There was a covered stage, Latin music, festive, happy.

"Look, there's a dancer on stage," he said as though making her a gift.

Or the time he came home waving a small envelope. "Surprise! Tickets," he said, dropping his briefcase. "Indonesian dancers. Karla at work raves about them. I got us tickets to their last show in town."

How her abdomen constricted. She knew he wanted to be praised for pleasing her. She tried to be grateful. He meant well. He wanted her to be happy. He wanted her to be surrounded by dance, to witness it. He gladly spent fifty, sixty dollars a ticket to sit with her in a theater watching lithe young Indonesian women perform, rather than going out to dance a single step for free. That was his kind of gift, much like a young boy brings his mother a snake or a tarantula.

He assumes she would avidly watch other people dance. She wonders whether that is like him wanting to make love and being satisfied with watching pornography instead. Maybe. Enough men seemed to be doing that with gusto.

At the time, she, of course, was too ashamed to 'fess up about the tickets. Making a fuss always led only to battle, and even back then she was already too tired and too weak for war. Besides, if she explained she wanted to dance, not watch others dancing, he might label her a narcissist. Maybe she is one. She wants to participate. She always wants to be at the center of her own stage.

He might have guessed. He didn't.

THE DANCES IN the street will last all summer, ten weeks, a different class each week. She loves them all. Cha-cha. Salsa. Bachata. Swing. Tango. She knows she will not mention this again. The schedule will continue to hang in the center of the refrigerator door, spelling out vague longing for anyone willing to notice. If vagueness ends up rejected, that is not nearly as humiliating as when an outright promise is forgotten despite his often-voiced invitation: All you need to do is ask. The story of every love on earth. And love in hell and in heaven too perhaps.

WHY WOULD ANYONE ever promise what he doesn't want to keep? Because, like everyone else, he too wants to be loved, of course. He wants to be the good guy. Instead, he has become the man of good intentions. A fine black line. Often he collects his reward in advance just for the lovely good intention. A premature reward is good enough when all is said and done. Never mind the empty hole in the universe where a promised action should have gone. Time heals all wounds. Time fills all holes.

He said once, with kindness and some pleading in his eyes, "I know you will always forgive me." He is probably right.

Later he will reiterate a favorite motto of his: that's all in the past now and has to be let go. Water under the bridge. A personal system of remorse and absolution. It is all so familiar.

The truth is too shameful to admit.

The truth is even more shameful to endure.

SHE WATCHES THE throng of active dancers in the street kicking up dust. She watches the bright play of joy on their faces. That's what she longs for. She also senses desperation and frustrated nonchalance around her. She is not alone.

She knows she will keep dancing. Somehow. Or stand outside of the dancing crowd on the sidewalk, moving her hips from side to side, just in case a potential partner might notice her yearning and take pity—she's almost sure that's what it would have to take by now: pity.

In her dreams he dances sinuously, beautifully. Her husband, that is, though anyone at this point would do. In her dreams she wears flowers in her hair.

She shudders to remember how pleased he looks when she lets him off the hook, in dance as in everything else, flapping like a happy fish thrown back into the sea.

She has no words for the sorrow she feels when she fully understands how he really, really doesn't want to do this. He is willing to spend hours massaging her body and do other mechanical things to stimulate her with what, in his book, is pleasure. But this? What she really wants? No.

It is just as mechanical. Muscles move. Pleasure follows. She keeps trying to explain. He cannot understand.

"Just tell me what feels good," he says. "Just ask."

She tells him, she asks, and he'll do anything but that. Go to war. Sit with their daughter. Take out the garbage. Go on vacation. Do nothing. Sit still. Go to church. Visit a botanical garden. But dance? No. Not that.

WHEN SHE GETS home she will no doubt make a conciliatory speech, apologize for guilt tripping everybody by pointing out that he'd rather be hiking than dancing. Or stay home with Belinda.

Belinda will giggle and will call him ridiculous, never mind that he is her dad to whom she owes a measure of respect. What's done is done, the two of them will declare in unison. And that takes care of that as far as they are concerned.

Maria is surprised, too, that Belinda—her own daughter, for crying out loud—isn't more interested in dancing. More her father's daughter than hers, it would seem.

Maria really doesn't want to be here with the cheerful dancers anymore, but she has to stay on principle now.

She wasn't born a masochist, no. But it's become such a habit to endure and habits die hard. His needs, his preferences are so much more important than her own. Nowadays even her daughter's preferences and needs already carry more weight than her own. Who teaches that? Who benefits? Does anyone?

Once, before Belinda was born, he said if she taught him, he'd be delighted to go dance from time to time. There have been countless living room sessions over the years. It is never enough. He quickly forgets. Men are good at forgetting, she has found.

He doesn't forget sex, though. Not once has he forgotten sex. Then again, how would she know if he forgot about sex for a moment? She laughs. She is absurd. Also furious.

A man slams his partner into her and glares at her as though it is her fault for standing still at the edge of the dance space. For a moment he looks as though he expects her to apologize. Like hell she will. His partner smirks, but doesn't make eye contact. There is too much anger in the world.

This isn't fun. She stands here on her pillar of principle and is bound to process the depth of sadness because she has ended up in the maw of unrelenting hatred for Dan's fuddy-duddy self-consequence.

Early training: His mom studied football so she could converse about it to please his dad. Did his mom have any passionate interests? Nobody knows. 'Nuf said.

SHE REMEMBERS STUMBLING down an icy, snow-packed path in spring, Dan charging ahead, then once in a while stopping to let her catch up as she slipped or stomped in the heels of her boots, trying to match his long-legged strut down the mountain.

"That's why you won't dance," she told him. "Because you need to be ahead. Not with. You need to be best. The leader. The expert." She was quite out of breath. "You need for us to beg you. 'Wait for me. Wait up.'"

He didn't respond.

HER ANGER BURNS. Soon enough she will be ash, then dust. Does that mean she is healing at last? Or does it mean she is dying? It is probably good that she isn't in the grip of unadulterated depression. So long as there is anger, there is life.

At times she expects tears and is surprised by a churning coldness instead, brittle disdain. She would welcome clean, elegant sadness, but she is shocked to meet this unexpected numbness instead, as though her heartbeat barely squeaks through the threat of paralysis.

How she misses the enthusiasm she once had for him. She doesn't want to hate him or judge him or condemn him. Hence the steely bands of indifference and numbness she is trying to put in place around her heart.

She wants to climb out of this cold fire. She doesn't see a ladder or a foothold, and the walls of numbness look so high. Her anger itches like skin healing under an unbending cast.

HELL IS LIKE this, something whispers inside her. Somewhere in the distance people are having fun: they dance, they set up parties, or, for that matter, they admire sunrises from on top of hiked mountains. Hell is this, being surrounded by beauty, and being not forbidden, but merely excluded.

She has all the hunger, all the need, and he has no appetite. She is afraid of choking on her own need and the sharp pepper of anger at not getting it met.

She is embarrassed in the throng of people. She no longer makes sense, not even to herself.

SHE WATCHES AS a ninety-year-old woman—the loudspeaker announcing her age—cheerfully gyrates with a young teacher. Maria envies the money that can buy that kind of attention. She watches a girl who doesn't look a day older than eighteen and has only taken the free introductory lesson—"that is my daughter, she's never danced before," an older woman next to Maria proudly proclaims—but dances every dance on wobbly feet. She doesn't have to stand on the curb, not once. Maria envies the girl's peach skin, her loveliness, her future, her beginner's luck.

She watches a young Asian man look around for a partner. His eyes skim over her, skip past, though the two of them danced well together, twice, during the group lesson. She asks a surprised but cheerful Asian woman her own age to dance. They dance briefly. They laugh. That's always important. The happy-look laughter. Nobody wants to witness the cracks on the surface of a breaking heart. Everybody on occasions like this strives to look happier than they really are. It is a look you put on like makeup, like an attractive mask.

She steps back to the dusty curb. The sun beams bright torment. She has forgotten to bring a visor or a hat.

A YOUNG MAN suddenly holds out his hand to her. He is heavyset, not stylish in his faded jeans and orange T-shirt. Long dark blond sweaty hair. Enthusiastic eyes.

A sudden: Who? Me?

He dances like a dream. He leads her into spins. He twists her and himself under loosely crossed arms.

"That was great," he says when the music stops. He smiles with generous brown eyes.

Then he fades back into the crowd. The thank you in her chest kept humming for a while before the dust returns and the hunger.

She feels she has never been where she has always wanted to be, at least not for long, and now she is old. Ache drags at her shoulders.

She wonders where God is. She could use some of His advertised love.

ARE THERE PEOPLE alive who are not outsiders at all? Like the dazzling dance teacher whose whole face is a laughing mouth, whose laughing mouth has no end, whose eyes glitter with genuine joy, like the orange T-shirt dancer who teases into her periphery with a magical brief presence and then melts away again? Surely those two belong in their own lives. Then why doesn't she belong?

SOON ENOUGH IT will be winter and no one will dance in the street. Perhaps she will sit on the edge of a dance floor in some café—outside of the action again, but persistent.

She wants to cry. She has been good. She has paid her dues. She has not been particularly beautiful. She has not been ugly either. Just your average yearning, aching woman trying to find her path, and trying to spend some of her time on that path dancing, not just shuffling along with the unobtrusive steps of duty. The dance should be louder than any fear that she doesn't belong. Her heart beats to the same delicious rhythm as the seductive music everyone else can hear.

THE SUN HAS given her a throbbing headache.

She yearns and yearns and yearns.

A NEW FEAR suddenly. Perhaps one day, many years of fighting and bickering later, he will graciously sigh and offer to go dance with her. She will gently lay her hand on his arm and tell him, "Don't worry about it anymore. I understand. You really don't want to." She will swallow hard at the golden relief on his face when he hears the permanent reprieve.

She is used to the pain. She is tired. Why ruin a familiar feeling? She will burn out with suffering and with desire. She is good at that.

Besides, she would suddenly have a partner, that's true, but it would be a mixed blessing. He would be a novice, clumsy, looking sheepish and apologetic. And with him by her side, no more surprise appearances of young magicians who already feel better in memory than they probably did in reality.

The original hope that her husband would try dancing with her and then he'd like it to his own surprise—that hope is long gone. He doesn't like much. He likes sex, food, and massages. Doesn't necessarily matter in what order or with whom, so long as he gets a good deal.

What have we done? her ragged heart sobs.

She puts her hand over her heart to hold it safely in place. She whispers, "It will be OK, my love. It will be OK." She half believes it.

She leaves before the sting of tears.

ON HER WAY home, the sentiment is dust and hunger. Her face is flushed from the sun.

The bus driver seems angry, too. He makes jarring stops.

She is the wife of the man who will not dance. She has tried to explain how dancing nourishes her body and her soul. She has tried to bribe with sex. She has tried to compel with ultimatums. She has been meek. She has been mousy. She has made demands. She has stomped her feet in unbridled rage. She has been defeated.

Who taught him the things he believes? That it is unmanly to dance. That it is dangerous to please a woman. And why?

This is her life and she wants it. She is grateful and graceful. She smiles. She misses her dreams fiercely.

She will slip on dancing shoes again, first the right, then the left.

She doesn't know when. She doesn't know why.

She feels a bottomless music inside her. A longing to move, to respond to a lead, to engage her body. To bend with her body's joy.

She will dance in the street with her homeless soul, a soul long used to sleeping under bridges.

The humming and rocking of the bus, steadier now—perhaps the driver's anger, too, has dissipated—makes her sleepy. She hopes she won't miss her stop. Though maybe if she missed her stop, then...

CURTIS SMITH
PLAYGROUND

The soldier chased his son across the playground. Cushioned steps, woodchips, and rubber mats. Around them, a fenced perimeter, surveillance cameras. The boy was six, taller and faster than he'd been before the soldier's deployment. The soldier stooped, and his fingers raked the boy's jacket, all part of a charade that the boy was faster than him. The boy laughed as he weaved between the monkey bars. The soldier happy too, the knowledge his son was growing stronger and that one day his father's inability to keep pace would be the truth.

The soldier rested on a bench. His son wrestled himself up a climbing net. The playground's structure like a fort, parapet walkways, corners anchored by roofed turrets. The boy waved then disappeared into a wooden chute. Late October, the sky edging gray, frost mornings and early sundowns. Between the soldier's sneakers, a half-buried glove. He picked it up and wiped off the woodchips. The glove small, a toddler's hands. He placed the glove atop a fence post, an empty wave, the chance to be claimed. A pack of older boys scrambled from the wooden chute. The boys held their hands like guns, their fingers aimed at each other's hearts. "Bang! Bang!" they cried, a running battle. The soldier walked over and peered into the chute's shadowed space. His son sat in the middle. "You OK?"

The boy crawled out. "Just hiding." He ran after the older boys, his hand fashioned into his own gun. He disappeared, this landscape of alcoves and nooks, but his voice carried. "Bang! Bang!"

The soldier reclaimed his bench. The breeze stirred the leaves along the fence's base. His son could climb the rope net; he could kick higher on the swings. This place the same, but his boy had changed. The soldier changed, too. His gunner's horizon-searching focus. The desert's sear still in his lungs.

He guessed the boy was ten or eleven. Skinny, the way most village kids were. Bare feet, soles the tan of the dust that swirled in the wake of tanks and trucks. The boy's eyes closed, an expression of sleep. His middle ripped open, and beneath, a mingling of blood and sand. The soldier's shadow fell over the boy, the soldier's limbs stone until his sergeant pulled him away. The boy buried half a world away, yet last night, as the soldier tucked his son into bed, he saw the boy curled on the floor. The boy's pose unchanged, and in the soldier, the knowing that the boy's size and age waited for his son, a future as certain as a glove he'd grow into and be forced to wear. The soldier on the bed's edge, paralyzed by his son's sleeping breath and the empty space on the toy-littered carpet.

"Daddy!"

The soldier surveyed the playground. A mother pushed her bundled daughter on the swing. The older boys stormed a turret, their fingers pointing, the sound of gunfire. "Daddy!" the soldier's son called, but the boy was hiding, an invitation for his father to find him. The soldier looked, the wooden chute, a turret. Adrenaline curled his hands into a rifle's grip. He tried to call his son's name, but he couldn't. He took a breath and swallowed, his throat a well choked with heat and dust. His voice barely a whisper. "Talk to me, buddy."

DONNA D. VITUCCI
SHELTER

I.

The open door to violins and screaming won't still the deaf coming to our door, palms out and open, their alms cry tugging the safety pins in our necks. There is pain and it's painful. It's embarrassing how we flinch when we could just as easily thread the needle and walk, disappear sewn in either way. How babies curdle within their mothers' milk shocks even the newscasters. Pick your lottery numbers, honey, because the swim is far above your stroke. Before the engorged world turns sour, rock me, mama, roll me off and away. Once skies clear over Beijing and the waters of Indira ebb, then please peel the foil covering off the densest chocolate so I may stand near to breathe the corners of what you have and suck it deep into my lungs like coal dust.

II.

Freeze tag and swinging statues passed to you the value of stillness. Thrown into a crouch, you remained motionless even when buyers stepped so near you could chew their breath. Hiding gave a way in.

Make yourself small, crawl into a minute and hindered space, disappear right up into your arm, sleeve left dangling so they want to explore what's empty. No matter the obscene or the ludicrous. Invite them in.

Lot and his woman stand guard at the crossroads. You don't even see their lesson when you sit at their feet with your lunch. History mocks the atmosphere, and you can be the smoke that dissipates, too, if you must. Examine each eyelid and nostril, nothing ruffled, her dress forever lifted above the ankle. They are statues crying hard salt tears, one struck by God and the second froze by grief.

Lacking will and ignorant of rules, we inhabit the same frame of sky. Our thin soles read the color of broke pavement; crack the whip and fling me out across it. I'm stuck where attachment ain't allowed, you say. Suffer my mitten then on your glove as the headwinds plot their wars. The soup we split is weak in vegetables; note the gripe of gruel on your winter-sliced cheek.

Your beard chaps my whole lower face and I suffer this to kiss. Inside your mouth the grease of French fry, the potato's starch breaking down your poor molars. Hello hunger. Peck peck and peck. Winter marries us, bludgeons us. In the back lot of the shelter we are the frieze on a February night, bleating through our softened teeth: *open the doors.*

III.

You'd like to think it was the freeze that beat down Billy, and the wind scouring west to east around the Legal Aid building shaved the points of his shoulders, but he was born a low life. He had clavicles, elbows, wing bones, a rib staircase up to his throat; a matching framework hung down his spine like a dress, the hair on his neck hiding the hook. None of his bones could be verified. Billy wore a gray bubble coat in the parking lot where he spun Allie around by her grimy sleeve. They had been moving in the same direction, then stutter-stopped, stuttered again; she rooted and he began a rush-off while still pinching her arm or her hand or her sleeve or the cuff of her sleeve. Let him drag her or leave her; she was a board marker in his game.

"Sure ain't no place for children," Billy said.

Allie hunched deeper into the puff of knit tube thing she wore around her neck. The church basement had so many items for free she couldn't name but grabbed up. A fat-faced volunteer told her it was a cow. More stupid information swallowed and misinterpreted.

Allie shrank as Billy blustered, "I won't let you railroad me." He said he used to work at Lord's Gym, was a prize in training, all hands bet on his bulldozing. He was sculpted, he said. That was before.

Allie said, "I don't run you." Her arms were tender sausages she failed to lift. "If you want, go." She could never anyway heft or redirect his weight. His squat build gave him a low center of gravity, where she revolved, his fire making her cold surface gleam. In his absence she might slip right by you unseen, swear to God, maybe filch your wallet, too. "I can take care of myself," she said.

She dipped her chin to hide the fear he might see in her face. Once he knew his upper hand meant anything to her she was lost. So *Scram*, she thought, and tasted her own funky breath shuddering inside the cow, the puny firewood of her heart aching to burn down Billy and her and the shelter they'd been run out of for rutting in the janitor closet.

"Pale as dead, cold as winter…" He described her out loud as he whittled her, his fine prick stabbing and that meant she lived, toast on the end of a fork over the corner drum fire. How was fucking Billy different from baring her chest for the Hopscotch Man in the library bathroom? Hand over the prize piece by piece and she decided when and who, get a bit of bread she longed to cup in her palm, then pass over to Hopscotch for the Baggie, the ripe little grape-sized pillow. What Billy didn't know Billy wouldn't know. He pulled her now by her scarf in the parking lot, opaque shine from the streetlight ruining both their faces. Allie did not wish to lie down and die with him, and that's what he wanted. He roped her to him with her scarf, an expiring man rising out of the drink, she his papoose and he the mother tongue. He cuddled her and puffed his newest desire into the worried skin of her face, her teary-tired eyes and eyelashes wet with prism.

Billy whispered, "Come with me to Helentown."

Did one more ledge really matter?

They waddled the sidewalk in their piles of rummaged winter, pinging off each other with an asymmetric hip-bump, Allie's cow swaddling her neck, and Billy's arm grasping hold of the cow. Once they set to pacing, the world cranked up. Hopscotch leaned on the Helentown trestle, the lesion behind his ear accepting vibrations of the oncoming train, the pulsing stars, Allie, and the guy who used her all advancing. Them and this roughened picky-pocket stroking the smooth of his knife handle.

STAN LEE WERLIN

VIETNAM VORTEX SUTRA

Vortex, *noun: a mass of fluid with a whirling or circular motion that tends to form a cavity or vacuum in the center and to draw toward this cavity or vacuum bodies subject to its action. See also:* **Wichita vortex—** *concept originated by Allen Ginsberg in his anti-war poem "Wichita Vortex Sutra." The poet believed "a vortex of hatred that defoliated the Mekong Delta" was spawned from the prohibitionist actions of Women's Christian Temperance Union leader Carrie Nation on December 27, 1900, in Wichita, Kansas, the first location in which she used an ax to escalate the violence of her attacks on saloons when she led a small group of women in a raid to destroy a hotel bar. The poem can be seen as a lengthy mantra or sutra recited to foster peace.*

Eddie sits with his back wedged against the concrete light standard at the street-side entrance to the dorm, cradling his roommate Johnny's head in his lap. They are shirtless in the midevening twenty-degree cold and seemingly quite drunk when Joey Kaye, another junior who lives in the dorm suite next to theirs, returns from a late day shift at his off-campus job. He enters the spacious courtyard and sees them splayed out there together on the frigid gray pavement. Even in the cold, the air reeks of Jack Daniels. They must have had a long head start. They've clearly been drinking for hours.

Joey starts to ask "What the—" when Eddie sees him and yells out "Fuck, Joey, I'm number ten. Number-fucking-ten." For some reason he's hyperventilating, sucking air in and out quickly, each breath a sharp white arrow of fog flying out and away from his mouth to punctuate the darkness. "December 6, man, I'm screwed. I'm fucked. I'm screwed." Johnny can't hold up his head, much less get to his feet, but he manages to slur out his own death sentence, heavy and thick in his mouth: "Number thirty-three. March 17. Better get yourself to that Vortex thing in the Yard, or get upstairs and tune it in, they're moving right along. Hup-two-three-four!" And that's when Joey suddenly remembers what's going on. How could he have forgotten! He takes off for the dorm entrance and leaps the stairs to his third floor triple two and three at a time, the adrenaline surging through his body as he jams his key into the lock and bursts through the heavy metal door.

TONITE
HARVARD YARD—HARVARD SQUARE
DOPERS, GROPERS, PROTESTERS, ANTI-TESTERS, DRINKERS, THINKERS,
AND ESPECIALLY ALL YOU SELECTIVE SERVICE DRAFT-ELIGIBLE UNDERGRADS!!
COME TO THE

VIETNAM DRAFT VORTEX!

FEATURING:
- LIVE BROADCAST OF THE VIETNAM DRAFT LOTTERY FROM SELECTIVE
  SERVICE HEADQUARTERS IN WASHINGTON D.C.
  - VOODOO DOLLS OF LBJ AND TRICKY DICK
- WHILE SUPPLIES LAST! THE UNDERGROUND BESTSELLER "THE RISK OF
  BLACK BEAR MAULINGS AT 101 UNPATROLLED CROSSING POINTS ON THE
  MAINE-CANADA BORDER: A CONFIDENTIAL GUIDE"
- CITY MAPS OF MONTREAL, TORONTO, QUEBEC, OTTAWA, WINNIPEG,
  AND POINTS WEST

In Joey's room there's just an eerie silence. Vijay and Mickey aren't there. They're probably up in the Yard, listening in to the litany of dates and numbers, getting stoned, already grieving or celebrating or just waiting to hear the only date that matters to anyone on this night. Down the hall he can hear what sounds like a crowd of fifteen or twenty sophomores and juniors jammed in together listening to the radio, screaming at the radio, ready to hammer the radio into a thousand tiny pieces as numbers and dates are called out and they see their lives forever altered, their careful plans dismembered, their bodies falling away into the impossibly hot, humid, treacherous snake-infested jungles and rice paddies half a world away in Southeast Asia.

He follows the noise and enters a quad where the sweet scent of dope is overpowering. "Vijay? Mick? You guys here?" No answer. He knows most of the faces in the room, and the tension is palpable despite the giddiness from the weed. "How far along are they?" he asks, and then, pleadingly, desperately, "Anyone hear May 31st yet? Please tell me no, just tell me no!" He gets an answer from a junior lying flat on his back, red-eyed and giggly. "Just reached number fifty, man. I think I heard a 31st already. Maybe two 31sts. Can't remember the months though." Joey calls out one last time, "May 31? Come on, anyone?" Someone he doesn't recognize forms a gun with his thumb and forefinger. He pulls the imaginary trigger and laughs loudly. "You're toast, man," he grins. He points and pulls the trigger again. No one else says a word. Now Joey's panicky.

In his room, he grabs his heavy coat and a pair of gloves. The thin yellowing pages of Eric's last letter rest on top of a clutter of socks and underwear and sweatshirts along with the envelope it had arrived in two years earlier. As always, his eyes are drawn to the unique Army & Air Force APO postmark. Twice that morning he had read each page, the first thing he had done to prepare for the wretched night that is now upon them. Its quiet observations and single searing question are an endless torment etched deeply in Joey's mind as he races out of the dorm.

JOIN THE HOOTENANNY AT
VIETNAM DRAFT VORTEX!
YOUNG GIRLS
ARE YOU MARCHIN'?
HUSBANDS
ARE YOU FIGHTIN'?
SOLDIERS
ARE YOU FALLIN'?
GRAVEYARDS
ARE YOU DYIN'?

December 1, 1969. The first Vietnam draft lottery. The night when future conscriptees find their date of birth carefully sealed in one of 366 short blue plastic cylinders poured into a large glass bowl at Selective Service Headquarters in Washington, D.C., and then drawn out one at a time to become the official "1970 Random Selection Sequence, By Month and Day." The results will determine who encounters Viet Cong soldiers lurking in the heated darkness clad only in black pajamas and their incongruous conical bamboo hats, who invades the grid of clandestine stealth tunnels in Cu Chi, who risks finding his cock shredded and his abdomen eviscerated by a Bouncing Betty anti-personnel mine buried in the thick jungle undergrowth that explodes at the slightest pressure from a heavy American combat boot. Newscasts have reported that it's likely anyone with a number up to 195 will be drafted. Above 195 looks safe. This is the way the lucky will be separated forever from the unlucky, the future lawyers from the future soldiers killed in action. For some, the night will offer salvation. For others, it will be the beginning of a nightmare. Joey hasn't prayed at a religious service for several years, but he's praying tonight. All his classmates are.

The Draft Vortex organizers are hoping for a turnout of ten thousand. Something to really make a statement about student solidarity and opposition to the war. For a month a slew of signs have been posted in dorms, dining halls, classrooms, anyplace that caters to students. A few have even found their way into the overhead ad spaces on the Green and Red Line subway cars and in the T stations that see steady traffic every day from the Boston area college crowd they're meant to attract. They provoke nervous laughter, blending macabre gallows humor with the lyrics of political protest songs and a sprinkling of angry counterculture poetry.

Still, no amount of false levity and strained bravado can mask the atmosphere of deep moral apprehension that pervades this night.

Joey barely glances at Eddie and Johnny as he passes them still collapsed on the pavement. He races through the slush and snow, navigating the icy streets and uneven brick sidewalks trying not to slip. Five minutes to get from the river to the Yard. All the while, his feet churning and his arms windmilling for balance when he unexpectedly slides on a slick spot, he thinks about Eric.

Eric. His childhood idol, his older cousin. Assigned to the Army's 173rd Airborne Brigade, so proud of that, so eager to serve and go to Vietnam. His letters mostly innocuous chitchat about military discipline, the drudgery of breaking down and cleaning his assault rifle day after day after day, the cultural diversity of the guys in his platoon from Alabama and Oregon and Rhode Island and a dozen other states. Passages about the endless heat and the air thick and fetid and dripping with humidity and his uniform always sticking wetly to his body and a thousand other things to take his mind off the combat ops he chose never to describe. Not once a mention of the VC, no derogatory references to the gooks or the dinks or the slants or even Charlie. It was almost as if he simply could not bring himself to acknowledge the humanity of the soldiers he was supposed to maim and slaughter in any way he could. He named the enemy a single time. PAVN. The People's Army of Viet Nam. He took the time to carefully write it out in Vietnamese: *Quân Đi Nhân Dân Vit Nam.* It seemed to Joey an utterly unknowable language when he saw the words printed in Eric's childlike hand. He tried to imagine what the markings on the vowels and letters meant, how one might pronounce the words, where the accents and inflections might be. An alien corner of the world. Each time he received a letter, Joey could only think, *What are you doing there, Eric?*

And then November 3, 1967. Dak To. Nineteen brutal days of fighting. Eric's brigade ambushed on Hill 875. Killed in action in the American victory: 87. Eric's final letter to Joey delivered only after the family had already learned of his death. It's like every other letter, chatty, philosophical, occasionally brooding, devoid of important details about where they are, who's been wounded or killed, who's survived. Until out of the blue, on the last page, the single terrifying question and all that it implies. *Are you capable of depravity, Joey Kaye?*

WOMEN OF WELLESLEY! WOMEN OF SIMMONS!
UNCLE SAM NEEDS YOU! EASE THE TENSION!
SCREW YOUR FUTURE SOLDIER BOY SILLY
THEN COME TO THE
VIETNAM DRAFT VORTEX!

Joey dashes across Mass Ave, the headlights of oncoming traffic dimmed and opaque from the icy gray slush that sprays up from the road. He sidesteps a raucous crowd milling on the sidewalk and reaches the Yard: twenty-odd acres of freshmen dorms, classrooms, administrative offices, libraries, the imposing Memorial Church, and several large open grassy areas crisscrossed by numerous walking paths.

It's a miracle the University Police haven't closed the Draft Vortex down before it even started. But somehow the mood looks peaceful, maybe a bit rowdy and nervous, even oddly, inexplicably festive. Instead they keep a low profile, fanning out just enough to be visible while they leave the students to their doings and look the other way about whatever's being smoked in the open air.

In the corner of the Yard where Joey enters, freshmen have opened their second-floor windows to the cold and are playing Beach Boys music loudly through powerful stereo speakers. "Fun Fun Fun" reverberates as Joey passes by. The celebration of carefree California innocence, fast cars, surfing safaris, and playful sunshine blondes offers a kind of jarring tranquilizer, momentary anesthesia to help escape thoughts of what's happening. "Good luck," one of the freshmen calls down to Joey and tosses him a beer.

"Are you fellas kidding? The Beach Boys? Lives are at stake here, guy. Whole futures are at stake." Joey is furious.

"Hey, lighten up, man. Lighten up. We're just trying to take your mind off it. Come on up and drink with us. Or smoke. We've got plenty of dope to go around." He holds up a joint as if he needs to prove it and motions Joey toward the side stairwell.

"You're next, you know," Joey calls back. "Think this draft is a one-time deal? They're coming for you too. You're the fish in the barrel next year. Got The Doors? Can the Beach Boys and put on something that matters." The kid in the window stares at him blankly for a moment and then nods. A few seconds later 'Til her daddy takes the T-bird away stops in bouncy midverse and soon there's the eerie minor chord guitar and tambourine intro to Jim Morrison's dark, disquieting dirge: This is the end, my only friend, the end. "Yeah," Joey shouts and waves up, "yeah, that's better, this is the end, that's for sure." He stomps away in the snow toward the large central commons on the west side of the Yard. For the first time, he hears the anonymous voice from Washington boom out over the loudspeakers, tonelessly repeating the month and day without inflection.

November 12. Zero-Six-Six. And a short time later: July 25. Zero-Six-Seven.

There's a loud groan nearby, a streak of profanity from a short beefy student in a dark winter parka who whips his beer bottle into a low snow bank and walks quickly to the nearest gate, stunned into silence by the irrevocable verdict he just heard. He doesn't look up. He doesn't want to catch anyone's eyes, as if to do so would be a humiliation, an attempt to seek pity or sympathy from those still waiting for their own fate to be announced. A girl standing there in tears calls his name out—"Charlie!"—but stops herself from running after him.

When Joey gets his first glimpse of the inner commons, the scene before him is surreal. Ten thousand would be a generous count, but there are easily several thousand participants, mostly male undergrads. In the center of it all, a large banner hangs crookedly on flagpoles rising above two six-foot black stat-icky amplifiers. "WELCOME TO THE VIETNAM DRAFT VORTEX!" Smaller banners abound: "RESIST THE DRAFT," "END THE WAR NOW," "MAKE LOVE NOT WAR." Groups of students—two, three, ten, twenty at once—are gathered everywhere, at the entrances to each building, on the long snowy flight of stairs leading up to the pillared library entrance, in every available open area. Some hold beer bottles or cans; many more are brazenly passing joints and oversized panatellas, their tips so frequently flaring orange and red with every toke that in the darkness it looks like a hellish sprinkle of special-effects fireflies has invaded the Yard.

Joey's eyes are drawn not to the clusters of students but to the many males standing alone, shifting their weight back and forth from one foot to the other as they breathe into their hands for warmth. They hug themselves and sway slightly, bending their knees as if genuflecting in prayer while they wait for the next birth date to be announced. This is proper, he thinks. This is right. We are all solo tonight. Among the draft eligible, nearly a million scattered across the country, camaraderie in these few hours would only be a forced, false pretense. And yet right now he wants to find Vijay or Mickey or almost anyone he knows.

May 19. Zero-Seven-Five.

Someone nearby shouts out: "See you in Da Nang."

November 6. Zero-Seven-Six.

The same voice: "There's your ticket to the Mekong Delta. Don't forget to write."

He races aimlessly across the Yard looking in every direction for a familiar face. At the end of one pathway orange-robed Hari Krishnas tirelessly clap their finger cymbals together, swirling in tight circles, calling to their Lord as they chant their sacred mantra again and again. *Hari krishna, hari krishna, krishna krishna, hari hari, hari rama, hari rama, rama rama, hari hari.* In the background, the amplifiers drone on.

December 25. Zero-Eight-Four.

Joey stops and breaks into laughter. *Jesus himself has just been drafted.* "Sleep in heavenly pea-eace," he sings out. "Slee-ep in heav-en-ly peace." Several nearby students laugh at the irony with him. He passes a tent where members of the violent Weathermen faction of the Students for a Democratic Society are camped out, haranguing loudly for a new American revolution. Their well-known campus leader waves a battered megaphone back and forth wildly, shouting in every direction, "The draft is an act of violence against you! The draft is the true vortex tonight! It will suck you in and kill you! Resist!"

February 15. Zero-Eight-Nine.

"Anyone hear May 31 yet?" he calls to the crowd nearby. Heads shake. No one answers. One of the Weathermen tries to engage him. "Hey, man, screw these numbers. Don't even acknowledge them. Come to our next meeting. None of us will ever see the Ho Chi Minh Trail. We've got big plans!" Joey knows they bombed a public memorial in Chicago two months earlier. He wonders if they'll detonate the statue of John Harvard tonight. Anything is possible. Everything is possible. Nothing is possible. Democracy. Communism. Nihilism. He doesn't picture himself blowing up the Capitol anytime soon.

January 26. Zero-Nine-Two.

July 1. Zero-Nine-Three.

October 28. Zero-Nine-Four.

Ten yards further on he finally sees familiar faces: Vijay, Mickey, a dozen of their friends. They greet him lustily. "Glad you found us, man." His sense of impending disaster dulls momentarily. It's all right to breathe again, to stop holding his breath as if that were the way to somehow halt the spate of numbers steamrolling over them. "What about May 31?" he pleads. "Am I a dead man yet? Am I a dead man? How about you guys?" He searches their faces for a sign of their fate.

"Don't know," Vijay says, crossing his fingers on both hands, shaking them in the air. "We missed the first fifty dates. Someone said Nussie came up number two. Archambeault drew number fifty-two just after he got here with Donna and threw up all over her. Maybe they're keeping a list where the amps are set up. Let's head over there." He hands Joey a joint. "You're really gonna want this, man," he gloats. "Definitely takes the edge off." Joey puffs greedily and surveys the scene nearby. It's louder now, noisier than a few minutes ago, more like a disorganized free-for-all.

"I gotta get a line on this soon, guys," Mickey moans. "Someone told me you have to carry a full-time course load and be in good standing or they'll cancel your student deferment. I heard a story about a guy who dropped a course and bang, his draft board swooped in and took him."

"So what's your point, Mick?" Joey asks. "You're OK, right?"

"No, man, I dropped the Stat course last week and I'm on the edge of failing Organic. I'm gonna be a sitting duck unless I come up lucky tonight. I could be royally in trouble." He looks from Joey to Vijay and shakes his head back and forth slowly to underscore his situation. They don't know what to say. They've heard stories like this, tough draft boards bearing down on shaky students. Suddenly they know Mickey could be one of them, sitting in a C-130 transport juddering to a stop at an airbase somewhere in South Vietnam, coming under withering enemy fire.

There's a pause in the number-calling as they trot briskly across the Yard. An incongruous ROTC recruiting station has been abandoned. Guitar-wielding singers are camped out in the entranceways of several dorms surrounded by students trying to keep one ear on the announcements while listening with the other to the anti-war anthems of the day. One balladeer is cycling through Phil Ochs: "Draft Dodger Rag," "I Ain't Marchin' Anymore," "The War Is Over." His cadences are strident, his fingers slamming away at the chords. Two dorms down, another leads a sing-along of Country Joe McDonald's "I-Feel-Like-I'm-Fixin'-to-Die Rag." Joey joins in loudly, a brief catharsis until they finish the last verse and in the sudden lull the numbers start up again.

November 29. Zero-Nine-Nine booms through the air. A clean-cut Asian kid with a football-player physique stops in his tracks right in front of Joey, a shattering look of fear sudden and deep in his eyes as if, without warning, the world has gone completely dark and silent around him and there is nothing left to feel. The girl clinging to him clutches at his neck. They hold each other in a shivering embrace. He's choking out something about Canada. "No, no, no, no, no," she whispers back.

Near the amps, the sound is harsh and deafening. *June 6. One-One-Zero* nearly blows out Joey's eardrums. The one volunteer there who's keeping the microphone close to the radio so that the feed is broadcast through the speakers isn't helpful. "Nah, there's no one here keeping track. I can barely hear myself think. Can't help you." He sucks hard on the tiny remnant of spliff he's holding in his roach clip.

Mickey lights another joint and it cycles quickly from him to Vijay to Joey and around again until it's gone. "Thanks, Mickey-Dick," Joey says. "Got another one?" He does. Soon they're too stoned to concentrate.

September 2. One-Six-One.

"How'd we miss fifty numbers?" Vijay wonders. He mumbles something incoherent. The crowd noise swells unexpectedly as his birthday is called. *October 15. One-Seven-One.* They don't hear it.

And then: *September 24. One-Nine-Five.* The magic number. Safety. Someone grabs the microphone and exhorts the crowd to celebrate. "If you're still here and haven't heard your date yet, the Vietnam Draft Vortex just turned into a party! We'll keep broadcasting until the lottery is over. But—congratulations!" There are still close to two thousand students in the Yard, and they offer up a loud prolonged cheer. Now each new date and number is greeted by gleeful shouting and clapping, the tension easing, the grim private nightmare of the first hours gradually giving way to relief and joy.

At about *October 10. Two-Two-Zero,* genuine realization takes hold: the gun has been pulled away from the temple, the scalpel withdrawn from the delicate skin at the throat. The risk has passed. Except, of course, if you missed out on hearing the first fifty or sixty or seventy numbers as Joey and Mickey and Vijay have. For them, each passing number means fewer and fewer are left and if they're not in the dwindling group of dates steadily being announced then they're on the wrong side of that lawyer-soldier equation and it's one-two-three what are we fightin' for.

Forty dates go by. Cheers and individual shouts of ecstasy are scattered across the Yard. Then forty more. Joey, Mickey, and Vijay have come up empty. They've allowed themselves to drift apart and are now standing alone, each one mustering up whatever reserve of private courage he can. The hazy fog of the marijuana high has given way to real fear and even in the chilly cold their clothing is soaked with the sweat of crushing anxiety.

January 7. Three-Zero-Six.

April 8. Three-One-Two.

May 31. Three-One-Three.

Joey falls to his knees in the snow when he hears his birthday called. He can't believe it. "They just called May 31!" he shouts to the nameless students nearby, to anyone who will listen. "Did I hear that right? Did they just call May 31?"

"Yes, yes, May 31," several people shout at the same time. "*May 31. Three-One-Three.*"

Joey's heart beats wildly. A girl he doesn't know leans over him and confirms it again: "May 31. You're free!" He grabs her gloved hands and pulls her down on top of him and he's hugging her, he's kissing her bright red lips, he's laughing so hard he can't begin to catch his breath. "Oh God, oh sweet God whatever you are, thank you, thank you, thank you!" If he tries to stand up he knows he'll pass out or fall down again from sheer emotional exhaustion so he just sits there and tries to be still. The girl he kissed has already disappeared into the crowd.

When he's able to stand he finds he has shut out everything around him. He wonders if this is how it feels to be resurrected. His senses seem temporarily suspended. Faces are a blur, the cacophony of sound that's everywhere—the music, a hundred conversations, the periodic loudspeaker announcements—are somehow muted and indistinct. It's as if he's been placed in a cocoon, insulated from reality, neither fully present nor fully absent in the world.

He knows about reality, though. He knows all about reality now. Reality is Three-One-Three. Nothing else matters but that. As if some other entity has taken over his body, he finds himself walking toward an exit gate. He knows he should go back and celebrate with everyone else still in the Yard. The Vietnam Draft Vortex has turned from grotesque death watch to spirited carnival. We're the lucky ones, he thinks. We're the lucky ones.

He looks around for Vijay and Mickey. Somehow they've drifted out of sight, out of mind. He's drawn instead to thinking about the students he saw just a couple of hours ago who threw their books down or got that glassy-eyed zombie look or who just laughed and tried to put on a brave face when their numbers were called. Will they become irrationally angry for the happenstance of their birth: the day, the hour, even the exact minute? 11:59 p.m., you'll never hold that AK-44. 12:01 a.m., today we'll train you on how to clean the breach. *April 3. Zero-Eight-Three.* If only it had been April 2. *October 6. Zero-Eight-Seven.* If only a day later. *March 11. One-Three-Six.* One day either way. He thinks about the guy who took off his coat, and then his gloves, and then his boots and the rest of his clothing and walked naked out of the Yard and stepped into traffic shouting, "Hey Hey LBJ how many kids did you kill today?," until the Cambridge police gathered him in and quickly whisked him away.

Breathless, exhilarated, numb from the bracing cold, Joey eventually makes his way back to the dorm alone. With his mind still churning and his body charged with adrenaline, sleep is impossible. When Vijay and Mickey straggle in together near dawn, exhausted, they wordlessly stumble to bed.

Four days later, the Rolling Stones will release "Gimme Shelter" and the fun-fun-fun freshmen will open their windows at midnight and blare its powerful driving refrain out into the silent Yard: *War, children, it's just a shot away, it's just a shot away.* A small crowd will gather and grow, and soon half the freshman class will be standing there listening as they play it again and again.

At the start of second semester, Mickey (*August 16. Zero-Four-Four.*) will soundlessly slip out of the dorm one morning and disappear. There will be no contact with family, friends, the university. Two years will pass before he tracks Joey down and calls him from a location in western Canada he refuses to divulge.

In April, protesters will riot and trash the Square. Tear gas canisters will fly in the streets of Cambridge. Plumes of toxic smoke will reach as far as the student dorms along the Charles River until phalanxes of city and state police and the National Guard are called in to restore order.

Through all of this, the haunting question Eric wrote from a censored place of deployment on the march to his terrible destiny will never be far from Joey's thoughts. He has run the gauntlet of the lottery, but as much as he wants to he can neither dismiss nor ignore the challenge Eric put to him. Harsh and uncompromising, it unmoors him profoundly. He hears that question in Eric's voice, nasal and twangy and guttering as his mouth fills up with blood and the life spills out of him at Dak To. He imagines it repeated in his mother's quiet lilt and in the low angry timber of his father multiplied by too many Scotches in too short a time. *If your life were on the line, would you be capable of the grenade, the bayonet, the knife grasped tightly in your hand and aimed at the gut or the throat or the genitals, the knife grasped tightly in your hand and thrust to wherever it is that the other life will be erased? Are you capable of depravity, Joey Kaye?*

The answer, buried deep in his throat like something poisonous and unfathomable, rises up inside his mouth against his will, relentless as birth. It batters itself at the back of his teeth, a seething and dangerous entity striving to be freed into the light and air, whirling in the maelstrom of psychological chaos accelerated by the moral ambiguity of this futile undeclared war. So many thoughts still circle together in Joey's mind: the way the irrational calculus of luck can fracture lives, cleave friendships, scour souls, rend families. He tightens his lips, struggling to swallow back that single terrible word, praying to be granted the grace of uncertainty even while he knows that it will always be out of reach.

KELLY WOLFE
BEAUTIFUL BICUSPID

Every Saturday I walked the circle of white tents at the local farmers' market, thought it important, responsible, to buy fresh fruits and vegetables from nearby farmers, once spent seven dollars for a softball-sized cantaloupe, robbery, I thought, until I tasted its flesh, which, to this day, remains the fruit of my life. Adorable, flavorless, purple plums the size of cherry tomatoes were six dollars for a pint. A brick-sized everything bagel with two inches of cream cheese was five dollars; each purchase dropped into a canvas tote, gray with age.

A year prior I had moved to a small New England town where I knew no one and had no friends to take a job teaching at a nearby university. I'd discovered too late the chair of our department was translucent, evil, and worse, tenured. My unhappiness was the color of sooty snow, and I was cheered by the vendors, whose livelihoods required affability.

One Saturday I saw a luminous young woman standing before a display of round tins. I moved toward her; I wanted to be luminous too. She turned, open a lid, and told me to sniff.

Lavender-scented essential oil cakes, handmade in her kitchen, would soften my hardened skin, make me shine again. The price was ten dollars, well worth it. I bought that and a small brown vial labeled *Replenishing Oil* for my face, twenty dollars, and waved away the offered plastic bag.

Before bed, I smoothed the lavender cake over my limbs and rubbed the Replenishing Oil into the tic-tac-toe board between my eyes. The woman I'd wake up to be was beautiful, beaming light, soft and replenished. Sleep came in the whisper of affirmations, after a double dose of valerian root, a natural herb.

New England's milky, muted morning light crawled between my vertical blinds, woke me, and I floated to the bathroom mirror to admire my new face. There was no difference, except for a raised blackhead, as large as a Sharpie tip, above my left eyebrow. It was painful, so I touched it, felt something hard poke from my skin. I squeezed until I expelled a human tooth, a pearlescent bicuspid, more perfect than the teeth in my mouth, stained with forty years of coffee and red wine. It left behind a large, bloody crater, traumatic and gooey. This was no improvement at all.

The label on the vial included the young woman's email address, so I wrote her to say I'd used the Replenishing Oil, and now my forehead had given birth to a bicuspid. The vial contained neem oil, I wrote, which is supposed to force impurities from the skin. I asked her if she thought the neem oil was responsible for the bicuspid. She wrote back to say she was so sorry this had occurred, but that no one else had ever had a similar reaction. She said neem oil does drive impurities from the skin, but a bicuspid isn't exactly an impurity, especially a beautiful bicuspid.

I went back to the bathroom mirror and studied the bloody hole in my face. This, I thought, was just more fucking bullshit. I wondered, at that moment, when the affirmations would kick in and things would start to look up. But I also read it is important not to form attachments to results only, because it is the process, the journey, we must appreciate. I keep a box of old jewelry from ex-boyfriends hidden in my underwear drawer, and it was in there I placed the beautiful bicuspid. I shook the box, rattled together all the trinkets, listened as the tooth joined other memories, weird and ugly, survivable.

The following Saturday I went to the farmers' market and avoided the luminous young woman with her stack of tins. Instead, I struck up a conversation with a nice woman selling shrink-wrapped soaps she made from goats' milk. She showed me a photo of herself with the goats. They were cute, brown and white, black and white, adorable, you know, goats. They lived in her backyard. She milked them herself. That's how she got the ingredients she needed for the soap. I was charmed, bought several soaps, lavender scented, the color of a bruise, and she threw in one for free. That night, I bathed with the soap, emerged from the shower fragrant and soft, no bloody skin craters, teeth only in my mouth.

Eventually, I found another job and moved a thousand miles away to a tropical, sunny yellow beachside town, palm trees dancing overhead, bikini-clad shoppers in the grocery store. But I still order the goat milk soap from the woman I met at the farmers' market. She always includes a note, thanking me. I know I could buy goat milk soap at the Whole Foods a short drive away, but I've read it's important to celebrate the good things that come your way. Plus, you know, goats.

TARA ISABEL ZAMBRANO
NO MAN'S LAND

The room is full with refugees dressed in black, even children. All the women are wearing a hijab, patting their half-asleep babies. The men look like a mixed bunch, some with scrawny beards and twisted teeth, others holding a rosary, facing west and whispering prayers. The head of every family holds onto a number. When his turn comes, he speaks his name and profession to Rahim, a middle-aged coordinator. Some men say it with pride. Some are confused, their mouths half open when asked to sign/thumbprint on a declaration and leave their phones behind. They walk with their backs erect knowing others are staring at them. Not everyone is so blessed.

Rahim leads the chosen ones out into a dark alley where two matadors are waiting. People left in the room resist but are held back. At daybreak, they'll be sent back to their villages and asked to apply again.

The matadors drop the selected refugees at a village near the border. Rahim collects the money, instructs them to hike in groups of two or three at most. On the back side of an old receipt, he draws the border, and a crooked line over No Man's Land. He hands it to the group supposed to go first. Then he says a prayer and leaves. Men and women stay silent; they know better than asking questions or raising concerns at this time. They form groups and clutch tightly onto their children, water, and wrapped pickled bread. With every step, the desert overwhelms: treeless, desolate space under a star-poked sky, a land with no pretense.

The refugees keep walking, their wind-blown faces glancing at the horizon, hoping to reach a safe place before dawn. Their shoes are filled with sand. They look back occasionally and something wedges in their dry throats. To overcome their exhaustion, they think of their future and freedom. The boredom extra money might bring. Then the moment of panic arrives when everything they've known has vanished: the smell, the sight, their past, their home. The familiar heartache. The desert is nothing like they've imagined. The swollen feet, the cramps, the burning eyes, the wailing kids longing for a bed. Then the shrieking whistles, warnings, and searchlights. Already they want to return. But they keep walking forward. And before the bullets hit, they try to catch a final glimpse of each other, scattered in different directions, body parts like seeds in air, still clasped onto their belongings.

MARILYN STABLEIN
ZEBRA COLLAGE

KELLI ALLEN served as Managing Editor of *Natural Bridge*, is the Poetry Editor for *Lindenwood Review*, and directs *River Styx*'s Hungry Young Poets Series. She is a professor of humanities/creative writing at Lindenwood University. Her chapbook *Some Animals* won the 2016 Etchings Press Prize, and *How We Disappear* won the 2016 Damfino Press chapbook award. Her poetry collection, *Otherwise, Soft White Ash* (John Gosslee Books, 2012), was nominated for the Pulitzer Prize. www.kelli-allen.com

DAVID ALPAUGH has published ninety-three "Double-Title" poems in journals that include *American Journal of Poetry, California Quarterly, The Hypertexts, Lighten Up Online, Mudlark, Spillway, X-Peri*, and in the 40th anniversary issue of *Gargoyle*. His controversial essays on Po-Biz have appeared in *Chronicle of Higher Education, Poets and Writers, Mudlark, Rattle, Scene4*, and *Stride*. He teaches for the Osher Lifelong Learning Institute (OLLI) in Concord and Berkeley, California.

ISAAC JAMES BAKER has worked as a freelance writer, editor, newspaper reporter, and communication specialist. His first novel, *Broken Bones*, based on his time in a psychiatric hospital, was published in 2014. When he's not writing, he can be found chasing surf wherever he can find it.

TOM BALL has published eight books of short stories with *PBW* magazine and *Down in the Dirt* magazine as well as *Magazine Conceit*. He has traveled widely and has also created a number of board games. He currently lives in Canada.

JOCKO BENOIT is the author of two collections of poetry, *An Anarchist Dream* and *Standoff Terrain* (Frontenac House, 2010). His poetry has most recently appeared in *The Fiddlehead, New Ohio Review, Poet Lore, Southern Poetry Review*, and *Spillway*.

ROY BENTLEY is the recipient of a Creative Writing Fellowship in Poetry from the National Endowment for the Arts, and fellowships from the Florida Division of Cultural Affairs and the Ohio Arts Council. His fifth book of poems, *Walking with Eve in the Loved City*, is a finalist for the 2018 Miller Williams Prize and available from the University of Arkansas Press.

SHINJINI BHATTACHARJEE's work has been published in *Cimarron Review, DecomP, Indianola Review, Tinderbox Poetry Journal*, and elsewhere. Her chapbook *There Is No Way to Alter the Gravity for a Doll* is forthcoming from dancing girl press. A Pushcart Prize and Best of the Net nominee, she is also the founding editor of *Hermeneutic Chaos Literary Journal* and Hermeneutic Chaos Press.

LUCY BIEDERMAN is the author of *The Walmart Book of the Dead*, Grand Finalist of Vine Leaves Press's 2017 Vine Leaves Vignette Award. Her recent stories, poems, and essays have appeared in *wigleaf, Zocalo, Public Square*, and *AGNI*. She is a lecturer in English at Case Western Reserve University.

STAR BLACK is a poet, photographer, and artist. She has authored six collections of poetry and teaches in the MFA program at Stony Brook Southampton. Her poems have been anthologized in *The Penguin Book of the Sonnet*, *110 Stories: New York Writers After September 11*, and *The Best American Erotic Poems: From 1880 to The Present*. Her collages have been published in *One of a Kind: Unique Artist's Books* by Pierre Menard Gallery.

LINDA BLASKEY is poetry editor for *Broadkill Review* and coordinator for the Dogfish Head Poetry Prize. Her work has been selected for *Best New Poets 2014* and for the Raleigh, North Carolina, Poetry on the Bus Project. She has twice been a recipient of fellowship grants from Delaware Division of Arts. Her short story, "The Haircut," was chosen by InterAct Theatre's Writing Aloud! program for dramatic presentation at the Adrienne Theater in Philadelphia.

PAULA BONNELL's April 2017 chapbook *tales retold* follows *Before the Alphabet* (2013); *Airs & Voices*, selected by Mark Jarman for the Ciardi Prize (2008); and *Message* (1999). Poems online in *The Poetry Porch*, *The Fictional Café*, *Rattle* (with audio), and elsewhere. In print: *APR*, *Gargoyles* past, *Hopkins Review*, *Hudson Review*, *Spillway*, etc. paulabonnell.net

ANN BRACKEN has authored two poetry collections, *No Barking in the Hallways: Poems from the Classroom* and *The Altar of Innocence*, and serves as a contributing editor for *Little Patuxent Review*. Her poetry, essays, and interviews have appeared in anthologies and journals, including *Bared: Contemporary Poetry & Art on Bras & Breasts*, *Fledgling Rag*, and *Texture*, among others. Ann's poetry has garnered two Pushcart Prize nominations. She offers writing workshops in prisons and community education centers.

SHIRLEY J. BREWER (Baltimore, Maryland) graduated from careers in palm reading, bartending, and speech therapy. She serves as poet-in-residence at Carver Center for the Arts and Technology in Baltimore. Recent poems garnish *Barrow Street*, *Poetry East*, *Gargoyle*, *Comstock Review*, *Slant*, and other journals. Poetry books include *A Little Breast Music*, *After Words*, and, new in 2017, *Bistro in Another Realm*. www.apoeticlicense.com

CHRIS BULLARD lives in Collingswood, New Jersey. He received his BA in English from the University of Pennsylvania and his MFA from Wilkes University. Finishing Line Press published his poetry chapbook, *Leviathan*, in 2016 and Kattywompus Press published *High Pulp*, a collection of his flash fiction, in 2017. His work has appeared in publications such as *32 Poems*, *Green Mountains Review*, *Rattle*, *Pleiades*, *River Styx*, and *Nimrod*.

NANCY NAOMI CARLSON has received grants from the NEA, the Maryland State Arts Council, and the Arts & Humanities Council of Montgomery County. She has authored seven titles, including four books of translations. *Hammer with No Master* (poems by René Char) was a 2017 CLMP Firecracker Poetry Award finalist. Her work has appeared in such journals as *APR*, *Georgia Review*, *Poetry*, and *Prairie Schooner*. www.nancynaomicarlson.com

DORITT CARROLL is a native of Washington, D.C. Her poems have appeared in *Coal City Review*, *Poet Lore*, *Nimrod*, and *Slipstream*, among others. Her collection *GLTTL STP* was published by BrickHouse Books in 2013, and her chapbook *Sorry You Are Not An Instant Winner* was published in 2017 by Kattywompus. She has served as poet in residence at the Shakespeare Theatre Company and runs the Zed's reading series.

ANNE CHAMPION is the author of *Reluctant Mistress* (Gold Wake Press, 2013), *The Dark Length Home* (Noctuary Press, 2017), and *The Good Girl Is Always a Ghost* (Black Lawrence Press, 2018). She was a 2009 Academy of American Poets Prize recipient, a 2016 Best of the Net winner, and a Barbara Deming Memorial Grant recipient. She currently teaches writing and literature in Boston, Massachusetts.

ALAN CHAZARO is a public high school teacher pursuing his MFA in writing at the University of San Francisco. He is the current Lawrence Ferlinghetti Fellow and a graduate of June Jordan's Poetry for the People program. As a first-generation Chicano, his work often examines the social and cultural complexities of being American. His poetry is forthcoming in *Iron Horse Review*, *Huizache*, *BorderSenses*, and *Bateau Press*, among others.

CHARLES CICCORETTI lives in Arlington, Virginia, near his high school. He started writing incidentally after he dropped out of a photography class. Now, a prolific writer, he's written one complete screenplay, five incomplete screenplays, and a constellation of unfinished short stories. His life goal is finalizing one.

GRANT CLAUSER lives in Pennsylvania and has published four books: *Reckless Constellations*, *The Magician's Handbook*, *Necessary Myths*, and *The Trouble with Rivers*. Poems have appeared in *American Poetry Review*, *Painted Bride Quarterly*, *Tar River Poetry*, and others. He also writes about electronics, teaches poetry at random places, and chases trout with a stick. His blog is www.uniambic.com.

KATHARINE COLES's memoir, *Look Both Ways*, will be published by Turtle Point Press in 2018; her seventh collection of poems, *Wayward*, is due from Red Hen Press in 2019. She is a poet-in-residence at the Natural History Museum of Utah and the Salt Lake City Public Library, for the Poets House program Field Work. Distinguished Professor of English at the University of Utah, she has received grants from the NEA and NEH and a 2012 Guggenheim Fellowship.

ROBERT COOPERMAN is the author of seventeen poetry collections, most recently *Draft Board Blues* (FutureCycle Press) and *City Hat Frame Factory* (Aldrich Press). He won the Colorado Book Award for Poetry with *In the Colorado Gold Fever Mountains* (Western Reflections Books). Other recent collections include *My Shtetl* (Logan House Books) and *The Words We Used* (Main Street Rag). Cooperman is also the author of six chapbooks, including the forthcoming *Saved by the Dead* (Liquid Light Press).

KATHLEEN CORCORAN grew up in Logan, West Virginia, and later taught English in Nigeria for four years. She and her husband settled in Owings Mills where they continued teaching. A Pushcart Prize nominee, she has published a chapbook, *Bloodroot*, and her poems have recently appeared in *Naugatuck River Review, Persimmon Tree, Paterson Literary Review, Tar River Review,* and *Comstock Review.*

KELLY CRESSIO-MOELLER's poetry is forthcoming in *Menacing Hedge* and *North American Review.* Read her previously published work at *Boxcar Poetry, Crab Orchard Review, Gargoyle, Poet Lore, Radar Poetry, THRUSH, Tinderbox Poetry Journal, Valparaiso Poetry Review,* and *ZYZZYVA* among others. Her poems have been nominated for the Pushcart Prize, Best New Poets, and Best of the Net. She is an associate editor at Glass Lyre Press. Visit her website at www.kellycressiomoeller.com.

BARBARA CROOKER is the author of eight books of poetry; *Les Fauves* (C&R Press, 2017) is the most recent. Her work has appeared in many anthologies, including *The Poetry of Presence* and *Nasty Women: An Unapologetic Anthology of Subversive Verse.* She has received a number of awards, including the WB Yeats Society of New York Award, the Thomas Merton Poetry of the Sacred Award, and three Pennsylvania Council on the Arts Creative Writing Fellowships.

GREGORY CROSBY is the author of the collection *Walking Away From Explosions in Slow Motion,* forthcoming from The Operating System in the fall of 2018. He teaches creative writing at Lehman College, City University of New York.

DANA CURTIS's third full-length collection of poetry, *Wave Particle Duality,* was just published by blazeVOX Books. Her second collection, *Camera Stellata,* was published by CW Books. Her first book, *The Body's Response to Famine,* won the Pavement Saw Press Transcontinental Poetry Prize. She has received grants from the Minnesota State Arts Board and the McKnight Foundation. She is the editor-in-chief of Elixir Press and lives in Denver, Colorado.

JIM DANIELS is the author of numerous poetry books, including the recent *Rowing Inland* (Wayne State University Press), *Street Calligraphy* (Steel Toe Books), and the forthcoming *The Middle Ages* (Red Mountain Press). A native of Detroit, Daniels teaches at Carnegie Mellon University in Pittsburgh.

Four hundred publications in, **MARK DECARTERET** has appeared next to Charles Bukowski in a lo-fi foldout, Pope John Paul II in a high-test collection of Catholic poetry, Billy Collins in an Italian fashion coffee table book, Mary Oliver in a 3,785-page pirated anthology, and a bunch of fine, fine writers in *Gargoyle.*

BARBARA DECESARE is talking to you with a naturalness that he guessed, with simplicity and sense of humor that makes, when the poem requires effort, you do so with gratitude and enthusiasm. Confess, with sharp humor, Elvis, driving, dinners and parties, animals and some unusual characters, legends Italian, puns and jokes of three ways, laughing at everything it can be, and ask questions about anything interesting, tender, painful, cruel.

After leaving Indiana for a rather extended and varied second childhood in New Orleans, **MATT DENNISON** has published work in *Rattle*, *Bayou Magazine*, *Redivider*, *Natural Bridge*, *Spoon River Poetry Review*, and *Cider Press Review*, among others. He has also made videos with poetry videographers Michael Dickes, Swoon, and Marie Craven.

DON DUSSAULT lives in the San Francisco Bay Area. His history includes a master's in English literature, a brief spell as an expatriate, and a jumble of jobs. He's published seven other literary pieces and is wrapping up a multivoiced trilogy ranging across three continents and four generations of a dysfunctional family.

DEBORAH ELLIOTT DEUTSCHMAN has had poems and stories in a number of places, including *North Dakota Quarterly*, *New Criterion*, and the *New Yorker*; a novel, *Signals*, published by Seaview Books/Simon & Schuster and PEI paperbacks. She has also done screenplays and film adaptations. Her work has been translated into French, recently in *Sarrazine Rue Saint Ambroise* (issue on American writers, www.revueruesaintambroise.com). And she has just finished a novel and a collection of poems.

LIZ DOLAN's poetry manuscript, *A Secret of Long Life*, nominated for a Pushcart, has been published by Cave Moon Press. Her first poetry collection, *They Abide*, nominated for Ashland University's McGovern Prize, was published by March Street. An eight-time Pushcart nominee and winner of Best of the Web, she was a finalist for Best of the Net 2014.

M. SCOTT DOUGLASS is the founder, publisher, and managing editor of Main Street Rag Publishing Company. He is a Pushcart Prize nominee and a North Carolina Arts & Science Council grant recipient. His cover designs have won two PICA Awards and several Indie Press nominations. His work has appeared in *Asheville Poetry Review*, *Midwest Review*, *Gargoyle*, *North American Review*, *San Pedro River Review*, and *Slipstream* (among others).

GEORGE DREW is the author of seven poetry collections, most recently *Pastoral Habits: New & Selected Poems*, *Down & Dirty*, and *The View from Jackass Hill*, winner of the 2010 X.J. Kennedy Poetry Prize, all from Texas Review Press. His eighth, *Fancy's Orphan*, appeared in 2017 from Tiger Bark Press. Recently, Drew won the Knightville Poetry Contest, the New Guard, his poem appearing in the 2017 edition.

Generally, we function inside genres. The formation is set inside the memory of genre itself. **CM DUPRÉ**, au contraire, erases boundaries between art, its histories, theory, and criticism. Distinctions in her painting as in her writing reformulate; there's infinite play with concepts. Bridges extend from tender glance to biting mockery. Reality, carefully reexamined, amends allegiances, reenters her process through latticing coming from divergent studies: World Literature, Art, Philosophy; extensive travel; developed intrigue for language and mystery.

JAMES DYE lives in Worcester, Massachusetts, where he writes and makes art. He has a respectable vertical leap and enjoys fish tacos. His artwork can be found at jamesdye.org.

DAVID EBENBACH is the author of a poetry collection, *We Were the People Who Moved* (Patricia Bibby Prize); a nonfiction guide to the creative process; and three short story collections and a novel (Drue Heinz Prize, Juniper Prize, Orison Fiction Prize, and the Washington Writers' Publishing House Prize). His PhD in psychology is from the University of Wisconsin–Madison and his MFA in writing is from Vermont College. He teaches creative writing at Georgetown University.

KARI ANN EBERT has poems in *Broadkill Review, cahoodaloodaling*, and the online journal *Leaves of Ink*. She was nominated in 2016 for the Pushcart Prize for her poem "Heartbeat."

MEG EDEN's work is published or forthcoming in magazines including *Prairie Schooner, Poetry Northwest, Crab Orchard Review, Rhino*, and *CV2*. She teaches creative writing at Anne Arundel Community College. She has five poetry chapbooks, and her novel *Post-High School Reality Quest* is published with California Coldblood, an imprint of Rare Bird Books. Find her online at www.megedenbooks.com or on Twitter at @ConfusedNarwhal.

JULIE EILL's prose has appeared in *Room, Hypertext*, and *Carve Magazine*, as well as the anthology *Gravity Dancers* (Paycock Press, 2009). Her story is an excerpt of a novel-in-progress.

CATHRYN ESSINGER is the author of three prize-winning books of poetry—*A Desk in the Elephant House*, from Texas Tech University Press, *My Dog Does Not Read Plato*, and *What I Know About Innocence*, both from Main Street Rag. Her poems have appeared in *Poetry, Southern Review, New England Review, Valparaiso Poetry Review, Antioch Review*, and *Alaska Quarterly*, among others.

DAVE ESSINGER's debut novel *Running Out* was released by Main Street Rag Publishing Company in 2017. He received his MFA from the School of the Art Institute of Chicago, and is a fiction reader for *Slice* magazine and General Editor of the AWP Intro Journals Project. He currently teaches creative writing and edits the literary magazine *Slippery Elm* at the University of Findlay, in Ohio. Find him online at www.dave-essinger.com.

Born in 1929, **JEAN ESTEVE** came to poetry early and late. She was hard at it in second through sixth grades for the Manhasset, New York, school magazine. She began again some fifty years later, four children grown, quill evolved into word processor, and the Tillamook County Library's few shelves providing material for studying what poets had been up to all those years.

ALISON FAIRBROTHER is a native New Yorker, ex-journalist, and upright bass enthusiast. She received her MFA from Stony Brook University, where she was a graduate council fellow and taught creative writing and literature to undergraduates. Her short fiction, essays, and nonfiction can be found in *Abundant Grace*, *Southampton Review*, *Guernica*, *Washington Monthly*, *Alternet*, and *Salon*. Alison works in editorial at Riverhead Books.

LANE FALCON's poems are published or forthcoming in *Fifth Wednesday Journal*, *Chattahoochee Review*, *Rhino*, *Qu*, and more. She lives in Alexandria, Virginia, with her two kids.

IRENE FICK's first collection of poetry, *The Stories We Tell* (Broadkill Press) received first place awards from the National Federation of Press Women and the Delaware Press Association. Fick's poetry has been published in *Poet Lore*, *Mojave River Review*, the *Broadkill Review*, *Philadelphia Stories*, *Adanna*, *Pittsburgh Poetry Review*, *Pudding Magazine*, and *Delaware Beach Life*, as well as in four anthologies. She lives in Lewes, Delaware, and is active in the Rehoboth Beach Writers' Guild and Coastal Writers.

GARY FINCKE's latest collection is *Bringing Back the Bones: New and Selected Poems* (Stephen F. Austin, 2016). His collection of personal essays, *The Darkness Call*, won the Robert C. Jones Prize for Short Prose (Pleiades Press, 2018). "The Infinity Room," his newest manuscript of poems, won the Wheelbarrow Books/Michigan State University Prize for Established Poets and will be published in 2019.

SETH FISCHER's writing has appeared in *Guernica*, *Joyland*, *PANK*, *Best Sex Writing*, and elsewhere. Seth is also the nonfiction editor at *The Nervous Breakdown* and was a contributing editor at *The Rumpus*. He teaches for Antioch University Los Angeles, UCLA-Extension, and Writing Workshops Los Angeles. He has received fellowships from Ucross, Jentel, Lambda Literary, and elsewhere.

ALLEN FORREST is a writer and graphic artist for covers and illustrations in literary publications and books, the winner of the Leslie Jacoby Honor for Art at San Jose State University's *Reed Magazine* for 2015, and whose Bel Red landscape paintings are part of the Bellevue College Foundation's permanent art collection in Bellevue, Washington. He lives in Vancouver, British Columbia.

JARED FRANK lives in New York, where he works in the field of public health. He formerly served as coeditor-in-chief of *Fortnight Literary Press*, a student-run literary magazine at the University of Michigan. He has previously published work in *Entropy Magazine*.

VISHWAS R. GAITONDE spent his formative years in India, has lived in Britain and the United States, and has been published in those countries as well as elsewhere. His work has appeared in *Mid-American Review*, *Bellevue Literary Review*, *Iowa Review*, *Santa Monica Review*, *The Mantle*, *Fifth Wednesday Journal*, and other publications. His distinctions include a residency at the Anderson Center, Minnesota, and a Hawthornden International Fellowship, Scotland. He can be found on Twitter at @weareji.

CHRISTIEN GHOLSON has two books of poetry, *All the Beautiful Dead* (Bitter Oleander Press, 2016) and *On the Side of the Crow* (Hanging Loose Press, 2006); along with a novel, *A Fish Trapped Inside the Wind* (Parthian Books, 2011). A long eco-poem, "Tidal Flats," can be viewed online at *Mudlark* (entire Issue 63). He lives in New Mexico.

SID GOLD is the author of three full-length collections of poetry and a two-time recipient of a Maryland State Arts Council Individual Artist Award for Poetry. His work has appeared in *Southern Poetry Review, Poet Lore, Flock, Free State Review*, and *Tar River Poetry*, among others, and is forthcoming in *Backbone Mountain Review*. A fourth book, *Crooked Speech* (Pond Road Press), will appear in 2018. A native New Yorker, he lives in Hyattsville, Maryland.

ANDREW GRETES is the author of the novel *How to Dispose of Dead Elephants* (Sandstone Press 2014). His fiction has appeared in such publications as *Witness* and *The Pinch*. He is currently a doctoral student at the University of Southern Mississippi. His website is andrewgretes.com/.

ERIC GREINKE's new books for 2018 are *Masterplan: Collaborative Poems with Alison Stone* (Presa Press) and *Shorelines* (Adastra Press). New work also appears in *Big Scream, Cape Rock Poetry, Forge, Freshwater Literary Journal, Ibbetson Street, Iconoclast, Lake Effect, Lilipoh, Over the Transom, Paterson Literary Review, Pinyon, Plainsongs, Schuylkill Valley Journal, Switchback, Trajectory*, and *Wild Goose Poetry Review*. This is his second appearance in *Gargoyle*. He is a contributing writer for *Schuylkill Valley Journal*. www.ericgreinke.com

JIM GROSS, James Bernard Gross, has appeared in presses such as *Exquisite Corpse, Intrepid, Greenfield Review, Gargoyle, Poetry Ireland Review, Still: journal haiku*, and *Antigonish Review*. His new book, *Fingerings for words* (Chester Creek Press, introduction by George Economou; Richard Ede III and Robert Walp, illustrators), has been catalogued in special collections at Princeton University, Stanford, Notre Dame, Newberry Library, University New Mexico, University of California–Berkeley, University of Connecticut, University at Buffalo, and the College of William and Mary.

MICHAEL GUSHUE is cofounder of the nanopress *Poetry Mutual*. He co-curates the occasional reading series Poetry at the Watergate. His latest book—in collaboration with CL Bledsoe—is *I Never Promised You A Sea Monkey*. He lives in the Brookland neighborhood of Washington, D.C.

HEDY HABRA has authored two poetry collections, *Under Brushstrokes* and *Tea in Heliopolis*, winner of the USA Best Book Award. Her story collection, *Flying Carpets*, won the Arab American National Book Award's Honorable Mention. A recipient of the Nazim Hikmet Award, she was an eight-time nominee for a Pushcart and Best of the Net. Her work appears in *Cimarron Review, Bitter Oleander, Drunken Boat, Nimrod, Poet Lore, World Literature Today*, and *Verse Daily*. Her website is hedyhabra.com.

ALAN HARAWITZ has been living in a small town on the southern coast of Maine for more than seven years now, where there is lots of snow, lots of cold weather, sweet birdsong every morning, and very little traffic—all of it contributing to the writing life. His poems have been published in more than a hundred magazines including *Poet Lore, Hanging Loose, Rattle, Common Ground Review*, and *Blueline*.

JOHNNY HARTNER is a graduate of Carnegie Mellon and Duquesne Universities with degrees in English and a full-time professor at the Community College of Allegheny County. He has had publications in *Earthwise, Poetry Motel, Illya's Honey, Taproot, The Brentwood Anthology*, and *The Great American Smart Ass Anthology*. He is eternally living in Bon Air with his Boston terriers Lulubelle and Ozzie.

CYNDY HENDERSHOT is Assistant Professor of English at Arkansas State University. She is the author of *I Was a Cold War Monster: Horror Films, Eroticism, and the Cold War Imagination; Anti-Communism and Popular Culture in Mid-Century America; The Animal Within: Masculinity and the Gothic*; and *Paranoia, the Bomb and 1950s Science-Fiction Films*.

ROBERT HINDERLITER's fiction has appeared or is forthcoming in *Columbia Journal, Sycamore Review, Fugue, Phoebe, Fourteen Hills*, and other places. He grew up in Kansas, went to graduate school in Oregon, and now lives in Gwangju, South Korea.

TIMOTHY HOUGHTON's *The Internal Distance (Selected Poems 1989–2012)* appeared in a bilingual (Italian/English) edition from the Italian press Hebenon/Mimesis Edizioni in late 2015. The book was presented in Florence at the Museo Casa di Dante. Recent publications include *Stand, Cyphers, Oxford Poetry*, and *Agenda*. He has worked at Yaddo, MacDowell, and Hawthornden Castle. He conducts bird surveys for Audubon.

J. HOWARD coordinates A Splendid Wake. Her poems have appeared in *MiPOesias, On Barcelona*, and *Winners: A Retrospective of The Washington Prize*. She was a 2016 winner of the Moveable Words contest in Arlington and teaches writing at Montgomery College.

NANCY IANNUCCI is a historian who teaches history and lives poetry in Troy, New York. Her work has been published or is forthcoming in numerous publications including *Bop Dead City, Typehouse Literary Magazine, Three Drops from a Cauldron* and *Autumn Sky Daily Poetry*. Her debut chapbook, *Temptation of Wood*, is due out in May 2018, published by Nixes Mate Review.

DONALD ILLICH has published work in *Iowa Review, Nimrod, Passages North*, and other journals. He lives in Maryland.

BRUCE A. JACOBS writes poems, plays drums in jazz groups, and writes books about racism. He admires poets Yusef Komunyakaa and Nickole Brown and drummer Chris Daves. He lives in Washington, D.C. His blog is aliasbruce. typepad.com.

BRAD JOHNSON's first full-length poetry collection, *The Happiness Theory* (Main Street, 2013), is available at bit.ly/BradJohnsonBooks. Work of his has also been accepted by *Hayden's Ferry Review, J Journal, New Madrid, Meridian, Poet Lore, Salamander, Southern Indiana Review, Tar River Poetry*, and others.

JEFFREY N. JOHNSON's poetry has been published in *Carolina Quarterly, Birmingham Poetry Review, Red Rock Review, South Carolina Review*, and *Gargoyle*. He was awarded the Andrew Lytle Fiction Prize from *Sewanee Review*, and his novel, *The Hunger Artist*, was a finalist for the Library of Virginia's People's Choice Award. His first story collection, *Other Fine Gifts*, was recently released.

RICHARD JONES's new book, *Stranger on Earth*, is forthcoming from Copper Canyon Press in June 2018. Editor of *Poetry East* and its many anthologies—such as *Paris, The Last Believer in Words, and Bliss*—Jones also edits the free worldwide poetry app, "The Poet's Almanac." His website is www. RichardJonesPoetry.com.

GEORGE KALAMARAS, former Poet Laureate of Indiana (2014–16), is the author of fifteen books of poetry, eight of which are full length, including *Kingdom of Throat-Stuck Luck*, winner of the Elixir Press Poetry Prize (2011) and *The Mining Camps of the Mouth* (2012), winner of the New Michigan Press Prize. He is Professor of English at Indiana University-Purdue University Fort Wayne, where he has taught since 1990.

STEPHEN KESSLER's new book of poems, *Garage Elegies*, is due this spring from Black Widow Press. www.stephenkessler.com

ROSE KNAPP is a poet, producer, and multimedia artist. She has publications in *Lotus-Eater, Bombay Gin, BlazeVOX, Hotel Amerika*, and others. She has a chapbook with Hesterglock Press and a collection forthcoming with Dostoevsky Wannabe. She has EPs & LPs released on D.M.T. Records, Hylé Tapes, Always Human Tapes, Far East Sound, and others. She currently lives and works in Los Angeles. roseknapp.net

LUISA KOLKER is a shamanic-psychotherapist and writer based in Santa Fe, New Mexico.

LAURIE KOLP's poems have recently appeared in *Stirring, Whale Road Review, Rust + Moth*, and more. Her poetry books include the full-length *Upon the Blue Couch* and the chapbook *Hello, It's Your Mother*. Laurie lives in Southeast Texas with her husband, three children, and two dogs.

BETH KONKOSKI is a writer and high school English teacher living in Northern Virginia. She has published work in literary journals for many years, including past issues of *Gargoyle*, *Baltimore Review*, and *Mid-American Review*. Her chapbook of poems, *Noticing the Splash*, was published in 2010 by Bone-World Press.

LA LANTZ. "Strive to be the person upon whom nothing is lost." —Henry James.

Before moving to Washington, D.C., **RAIMA LARTER** was a college professor in Indiana who secretly wrote fiction and tucked it away in drawers. Her work has appeared in *Gargoyle*, *Writers Journal*, *Mulberry Fork Review*, and others. Her first novel, *Belle o' the Waters*, is due out from Mascot Books in 2018. Her second novel, *Fearless*, will be published by New Meridian Arts in 2019. Read more about Raima and her work at her website, raimalarter.com.

LAUDANUM AT 33 is a writer, video/sound artist, and media archivist who has previously published in *Gargoyle* as well as *Killing the Buddha*, *Echo*, and *SMITH Magazine*. She has also shown her work at Minneapolis Institute of Art, the Soap Factory, and the Peck School of Arts. You can find her musings on cinema and pop culture on her site, The Holy Shrine, as well as various projects online. She currently lives in southern Minnesota.

LYN LIFSHIN has written over 125 books and edited 4 anthologies of women writers. Her poems are in virtually every major anthology of recent writing by women. She has given more than seven hundred readings and has been poet in residence at the University of Rochester, Antioch, and Colorado Mountain College. Winner of numerous awards, including the Jack Kerouac Award for her book *Kiss The Skin Off*, Lyn is the subject of the documentary *Lyn Lifshin: Not Made of Glass*.

EDWIN MADRID has published several collections of poetry, including *La búsqueda incesante* (Mexico, 2006), *Latitud cero°* (Colombia, 2005), and *Mordiendo el frío* (Colección Visor de Poesía, Spain, 2004). He has received a number of awards, such as the Casa de América de Poesía Americana award (Spain, 2004) and the national poetry award Escritores Ecuatorianos de los 90 (Quito, 1992).

When she isn't writing, **CHRISTINE MA-KELLAMS** teaches psychology at the University of La Verne. Her recent fiction has appeared in *ZYZZYVA* and *Kenyon Review*, among others.

SAUNDRA ROSE MALEY has had poems in *Dryad*, *Beltway Poetry Quarterly*, *Full Moon on K Street: Poems about Washington D.C.*, and *D.C. Perspectives*. Her first book of poems, *Disappearing Act*, was published in 2015 by Dryad Press. She coedited *A Wild Perfection: The Selected Letters of James Wright* with Anne Wright, and they are currently working on a book about Wright and translation, tentatively titled "Where the Treasure Lies."

STEPHEN MALIN's journal publications include *Antioch Review, Beloit Poetry Journal, Green Mountains Review, Sewanee Review,* and many more. Appearing on *Verse Daily* and other electronic outlets, his poems have also been anthologized in *Poetry Southeast,* and in the *Southwest Review*'s half-century collection; while more of his work, translated into Russian, was reprinted abroad in *Amerika Illustrated.* His collection, *Underlight,* came out in 2014.

AOIFE MANNIX is a poet and writer. She has published four collections of poetry and a novel, and has also been a poet in residence for the Royal Shakespeare Company and BBC Radio 4's *Saturday Live.* She has toured internationally with the British Council, including most recently in Mexico, Vietnam, and Nigeria. She has a PhD in creative writing from Goldsmiths, University of London.

MICHAEL MARK is a hospice volunteer. His poetry has appeared or is forthcoming in *Alaska Quarterly Review, Bellevue Literary Review, Cimarron Review, Columbia Poetry Review, Gargoyle, Pleiades, Poet Lore, Potomac Review, Prelude Magazine, Rattle, River Styx, Spillway, Sugar House Review, The Sun, Verse Daily,* and Ted Kooser's *American Life in Poetry.* His poetry has been nominated for three Pushcart Prizes and the Best of the Net. michaeljmark.com

RICHARD MARTIN's most recent work is *Goosebumps of Antimatter* (Spuyten Duyvil, 2018). He is the author of six books of poetry and two short story collections—*Altercations in the Quiet Car* and *Buffoons in the Gene Pool.* Martin is a past recipient of a National Endowment for the Arts Literature Fellowship for Poetry. He lives in Boston with his family.

SUSAN H. MAURER's poetry collections include *Josephine Butler: A Collection of Poetry, By the Blue Light of the Morning Glory,* and *Raptor Rhapsody.* She has been published in fifteen countries, and appeared in the *Help Yourself, Autonomedia,* and Soft Skull's *Off the Cuffs* anthologies. Magazine credits include *Virginia Quarterly Review, Confrontation, Gargoyle,* and *Volt.*

MARK MAXWELL's first novel, *nixoncarver,* was published by St. Martin's Press. His second novel, *Kings of the World,* is forthcoming from EM Press. Maxwell's short stories have appeared in *Gargoyle, Santa Monica Review, Numero Cinq,* and *The Brooklyn Rail.* "Thin Places" is an excerpt from Maxwell's unpublished novel "The Sweetwater Stranger," which chronicles the lives of the citizens of Sweetwater, Wyoming, and the final days of David Foster Wallace.

JEN MICHALSKI's second novel, *The Summer She Was Under Water,* was just released by Queens Ferry Press. She is the editor of the journal *JMWW* and host of *Starts Here!*

MILES DAVID MOORE is founder and host of the IOTA Poetry Reading Series in Arlington, Virginia, and the author of three books of poetry. In April 2016, he received an award from the Arlington Arts Council for his services to poetry.

CHELSEA MORNINGSTAR is an artist based in Delaware. She likes cats a great deal, but often wonders why writers include cats in their bios. She has four children, at least three of whom are very likely not cats. She thinks.

DANIEL MUELLER is the author of two collections of short fiction, *How Animals Mate* (Overlook Press, 1999), winner of the Sewanee Fiction Prize, and *Nights I Dreamed of Hubert Humphrey* (Outpost 19 Books, 2013). He directs the creative writing program at University of New Mexico and teaches on the creative writing faculty of the Low-Residency MFA Program at Queens University of Charlotte.

ELISABETH MURAWSKI is author of *Zorba's Daughter*, winner of the May Swenson Poetry Award; *Moon and Mercury*; and two chapbooks. *Heiress* will be published by Texas Review Press in the fall of 2018. Publications include *Yale Review*, *Field*, et al. A native of Chicago, she currently lives in Virginia, in another Alexandria.

TERESA BURNS MURPHY is the author of a novel, *The Secret to Flying* (TigerEye Publications, 2011). Her work has been published in *Amazing Graces* (Paycock Press, 2012), *Dreamstreets*, *Penmen Review*, *r.kv.r.y*, *Southern Women's Review*, *Stirring: A Literary Collection*, *THEMA*, *Tower Journal*, and *Westview*. www.teresaburnsmurphy.com

SHERYL L. NELMS is from the Flint Hills of Kansas. She graduated from South Dakota State University. She's had over five thousand articles, stories, and poems published, including fifteen individual collections of her poems. She's the fiction/nonfiction editor of *Pen Woman Magazine*, was a contributing editor for *Time of Singing, A Magazine of Christian Poetry*, and is a four-time Pushcart Prize nominee.

AMANDA NEWELL's recent work has appeared or is forthcoming in *North American Review*, *Rhino*, *storySouth*, and *Scoundrel Time*. A graduate of Warren Wilson College's MFA program, she teaches English on the Eastern Shore of Maryland and likes to box in her spare time.

ERIC ANDREW NEWMAN lives in Los Angeles and is from the Chicago area. He works as an archivist for a nonprofit foundation by day and as a writer of flash fiction by night. He has previously been named as a finalist for the Robert J. DeMott Short Prose Contest and Howard Frank Mosher Short Fiction Prize. His writing has appeared in *Cleaver*, *Exposition Review*, *Heavy Feather Review*, *Necessary Fiction*, *New Madrid*, and *Quarter After Eight*.

JANET OLSONBAKER's fiction has been published in *Slush Pile Magazine*. She lives in Seattle and is at work on a novella, and two collections of linked stories.

ANNETTE OXINDINE's poems appear in *Southern Indiana Review, Willow Springs, Gulf Coast, National Poetry Review, Radar Poetry,* and elsewhere. Originally from Maryland, she lives in Ohio, where she teaches literature.

JANUARY PEARSON lives in Southern California with her husband and two daughters. She teaches in the English department at Kaplan University. Her work has appeared or is forthcoming in places such as *Notre Dame Review, Atlanta Review, Third Wednesday, Pittsburgh Poetry Review, American Journal of Poetry, Chiron,* and *Summerset Review.*

KATE PEPER loves painting with watercolor, reading children's poetry, and designing book covers. When not doing any of the above, she's hiking in Marin County, California, with her husband Bruce and Samusky, Hannah.

MEREDITH POND is a poet, fiction writer, and storyteller. A resident of Takoma Park, Maryland, for twenty years, she currently serves on the selection committee for the community's popular Third Thursday Poetry Series. Contact her at pondmeredith@gmail.com.

MICHAEL PONTACOLONI's poems have recently appeared or are forthcoming in *Copper Nickel, Greensboro Review, Mississippi Review, Colorado Review, Pleiades,* and elsewhere. He lives in Hartford, Connecticut, where he runs a small clothing business.

Before turning to writing full time, **BARBARA ANN PORTE** was a storyteller and a librarian, serving as Chief of the Children's Services Division in the Nassau Library System in New York for twelve years. She now lives in northern Virginia, and is currently working on a collection of modern Ise tales.

ANA PRUNDARU is the author of the forthcoming chapbook *Unstable Tales,* by Dancing Girl Press. Her work appears in *Ghost City Review, Ofi Press, Kyoto Journal, Hermeneutic Chaos,* and others.

KATHLEEN M. QUINLAN's full-length collection, *Moorings* (2016), and pamphlet, *From We to I* (2015), were published by Cinnamon Press. Her poetry has appeared on both sides of the Atlantic, including in *Acumen, Envoi, Comstock Review, Gargoyle,* and *Poetry Salzburg Review.* She edited the book, *How Higher Education Feels: Commentaries on Poems that Illuminate the Experiences of Teaching and Learning* (Sense Publishers, 2016) and is a faculty member at the University of Kent. Find her at www.kathleenmquinlan.net.

CHARLES RAMMELKAMP's latest book is *Mata Hari: Eye of the Day* (Apple bite House, Loyola University). Another manuscript, "American Zeitgeist," has been accepted by Apprentice House. Rammelkamp edits the *Potomac,* an online literary journal, and is prose editor for BrickHouse Books in Baltimore, where he lives.

MICHAEL RATCLIFFE lives and writes between Baltimore and Washington. His poems have appeared in a variety of print and online journals, most recently, *Fredericksburg Literary and Art Review, Fourth & Sycamore, TEXTure,* and *The Wild Word.* His chapbook, *Shards of Blue,* was published by Finishing Line Press in December 2015.

ALAN C. REESE is the author of the chapbook *Reports from Shadowland.* His work has appeared or is forthcoming in *Smartish Pace, Gargoyle,* the *Baltimore Sun, Maryland Poetry Review, Potomac Review, Delaware Review, Welter, Grub Street, Attic, Bicycle Review, Danse Macabre,* and *Loch Raven Review.* He teaches writing at Towson University.

VIRGINIA SMITH RICE is the author of *Whose House, Whose Playroom* (Dancing Girl Press, 2017) and *When I Wake It Will Be Forever* (Sundress Publications, 2014). Her poems appear in *Antioch Review, Baltimore Review, Cincinnati Review, CutBank, Denver Quarterly,* and *Massachusetts Review,* among other journals. She is poetry editor at *Kettle Blue Review* and associate editor at Canopic Publishing.

WILLIAM RIVERA is the author of four collections of poems: *Café Select* (Poet's Choice Publisher, 2016), *Noise* (Broadkill River Press, 2015), *The Living Clock* (Finishing Line Press, 2013), and *Buried in the Mind's Backyard* (BrickHouse Books, 2011). Born in New Orleans, he has traveled widely (in more than twenty countries). Currently retired, he taught agricultural extension and development at the University of Maryland from 1981 to 2009. His poems have been published in various poetry journals.

KIM ROBERTS is the author of *A Literary Guide to Washington, DC: Walking in the Footsteps of American Writers from Francis Scott Key to Zora Neale Hurston* (University of Virginia Press, 2018) and five books of poems, most recently *The Scientific Method* (WordTech Editions, 2017). She is coeditor of *Beltway Poetry Quarterly.* www.kimroberts.org

STEPHEN R. ROBERTS has had poems published in *Rain City Review, Sulphur River Review, Blackwater, Black River Review, Talking River, WaterStone, Riverrun, Connecticut River Review,* and, to get away from all the moisture, *Dry Creek Review.* His full-length work, *Almost Music From Between Places,* was published by Chatterhouse Press.

NICKALUS RUPERT spent most of his life near the Gulf Coast of Florida. In 2015, he completed an MFA fellowship at the University of Central Florida. Currently, he is a PhD student at the University of Southern Mississippi, where he also works as an associate editor for *Mississippi Review.* His fiction is forthcoming or appears in *Harpur Palate, Slice, Pleiades, Literary Review,* and other journals.

JENNY SADRE-ORAFAI is the author of *Paper, Cotton, Leather* and *Malak*. Her poetry has appeared in *Cream City Review, Ninth Letter, Cortland Review, Hotel Amerika, The Pinch,* and other journals. Her prose has appeared in *Los Angeles Review, The Rumpus, South Loop Review, Fourteen Hills, The Collagist,* and other journals. She is cofounding editor of *Josephine Quarterly* and a professor of English at Kennesaw State University.

CURT SALTZMAN was born and raised in Los Angeles. His work has appeared or is forthcoming in *Saint Ann's Review, Sou'wester, Bitter Oleander, Into The Void, Epiphany,* and elsewhere. He lives in France.

NICK SANSONE holds an MFA from Emerson College, where he served as managing editor for *Redivider*. His stories have appeared in *Saw Palm, Minnesota Review, Los Angeles Review,* and elsewhere. He lives in Massachusetts with his significant other and several pets, and he is at work on a collection of short fiction. You can reach him on Twitter @npsansone.

JOHN SAUL is making the contribution from England to Dalkey Archive's *Best European Fiction 2018* and had work in *Best British Short Stories 2016* (Salt Publishing, UK). His short fiction has appeared in several anthologies and in four collections in the UK; details at www.johnsaul.co.uk. His story "Anniversary of a Village" was in *Gargoyle* 66. A member of the European Literature Network, he lives in London.

SONIA SCHERR's fiction has appeared in *Jabberwock Review, Blue Earth Review,* and *poemmemoirstory*. She has held residencies at Blue Mountain Center and Kimmel Harding Nelson Center for the Arts. She has an MFA from the University of New Hampshire, where she won the Dick Shea Memorial Award for excellence in fiction. Sonia is currently in Morocco on a Fulbright Grant, researching a novel set in Casablanca during the 1940s.

With her English degree, subsequent studies, and stubbornness, **CATHRYN SHEA** has earned a living from writing most of her life. Her latest chapbook, *It's Raining Lullabies*, is from dancing girl press, 2017. Find her recent poetry in *Permafrost, Rust + Moth, Tinderbox,* and elsewhere. Cathryn lives in Fairfax, California, and served as editor for the *Marin Poetry Center Anthology*. See www.cathrynshea.com and @cathy_shea on Twitter.

GREGORY SHERL is the author of *The Future for Curious People*.

BEATE SIGRIDDAUGHTER, www.sigriddaughter.com, is poet laureate of Silver City, New Mexico (Land of Enchantment), USA. Her work has received several Pushcart Prize nominations and poetry awards. In 2018, Future-Cycle Press published her poetry collection *Xanthippe and Her Friends*. Červená Barva Press will publish her chapbook *Dancing in Santa Fe and Other Poems* in 2019. She publishes other women's writing in her blog *Writing In A Woman's Voice*.

CURTIS SMITH's stories and essays have appeared in over one hundred literary journals (including *Gargoyle* twice!) and have been cited by *The Best American Short Stories*, *The Best American Mystery Stories*, *The Best American Spiritual Writing*, and *The Best Small Fictions*. He's published five collections of fiction, three novels, and two essay collections. His latest book, a personal take on *Slaughterhouse-Five*, was recently put out by Ig.

MARILYN STABLEIN's collages, assemblages and artist books are exhibited and collected internationally. A recent monograph, *Bind, Alter, Fold: Artist Books*, exhibits thirty-eight of her works. Other books include *Splitting Hard Ground: Poems* (New Mexico Book Award), *Sleeping in Caves: A Sixties Himalayan Memoir*, *Climate of Extremes: Landscape and Imagination*, and *Phantom Circus*. She teaches memoir, poetry, and artist books. marilynstablein.com

GARY STEIN recently won the Brick Road Poetry Press annual contest for *Touring the Shadow Factory* (forthcoming next year). His chapbook, *Between Worlds* (Finishing Line Press 2014), was a contest finalist. He's published consistently in many other fine journals like *Poetry*, *Prairie Schooner*, *Poet Lore*, and *Folio*; holds an MFA from the Iowa Writers' Workshop; and has taught creative writing in high schools and colleges.

KURT STEINWAND has been published in *Cincinnati Review*, *Poet Lore*, *New Millennium Writings*, and *Arroyo Literary Review*. He holds an MFA in creative writing from the University of Tampa, and is a teacher of students with special needs at a middle school in Brandon, Florida, where he lives.

In 1990 *Gargoyle* published the first, and was the first to publish any, of **D.E. STEWARD**'s chain of 360 months, most of which are out in literary magazines. All are now appearing in a complete edition of five volumes of *Chroma* (Archae Editions, Brooklyn, 2018). "Off the Beach" is one of them.

HOLLY STONE's "The Onion Revolution and the Sauerkraut Press" uses a new literary device, vocabulary weaving, which juxtaposes words and idioms of different categories (in this work, food and communication). Vocabulary weaving may be used with any of the poetic forms. "The Little Snow Globe Place in Our Society" is excerpted from this satirical epic.

ADRIENNE SU is poet-in-residence at Dickinson College in Pennsylvania. Recipient of an NEA fellowship, she is the author of four books of poems, most recently *Living Quarters* (Manic D Press, 2015). Poems from her current manuscript appear in *32 Poems*, the *New Yorker*, *Poetry*, *Prairie Schooner*, and *Best American Poetry 2016* and *2018*.

MARC SWAN is a retired vocational rehabilitation counselor. His poems have recently been published or are forthcoming in *Mojave River Review*, *Scrivener Creative Review*, *Broadkill Review*, and *Chiron Review*, among others. His fourth collection, *today can take your breath away*, was published in 2018 by Sheila-na-gig Editions. He lives with his wife Dd in Portland, Maine.

JASON TANDON is the author of three collections of poetry, including *Quality of Life* (2013) and *Give over the Heckler and Everyone Gets Hurt* (2009), winner of the St. Lawrence Book Award.

ADAM TAVEL won the 2017 Richard Wilbur Book Award for his third poetry collection, *Catafalque* (University of Evansville Press, 2018). His work previously appeared in *Gargoyle* 59. You can find him online at adamtavel.com.

SALLY TONER is a high school English teacher who has lived in the Washington, D.C., area for over twenty years. Her work has appeared in *Delmarva Review* and *Clementine Poetry Journal*, and is forthcoming in *Postcard Poems and Prose*.

DEBBIE URBANSKI's stories/essays have been published in the *Sun, Nature*, and *Orion*. Find her at debbieurbanski.com or on twitter @DebbieUrbanski.

JULIA VELASCO is a graduate from the MFA program at the University of South Carolina. She has translated the works of Spanish-speaking poets such as Armando Romero, Eduardo Espina, and Mario Bojorquez. Her own fiction has appeared in *Delmarva Review* and a few other translations from this collection have been accepted for online publication by *Circumference*.

ERICK VERRAN is an MFA candidate at the University of Florida. His poetry appears in *Little Star, New England Review of Books*, and *City of Notions: An Anthology of Contemporary Boston Poems*. A full-length manuscript is forthcoming with punctum books.

DONNA D. VITUCCI is development director of Covington Ladies Home in Northern Kentucky. Her stories have appeared in print and online since 1990. Her third novel, *In Euphoria*, is scheduled for publication in 2018. Her first two, *Salt of Patriots* and *At Bobby Trivette's Grave*, are 5-star-reviewed novels. She posts snippets of creative nonfiction via Facebook because she's addicted to the immediacy of response, even if replies are just heart and flower emojis.

MICHAEL WATERS's books include *The Dean of Discipline* (University of Pittsburgh Press, 2018), *Celestial Joyride* (2016), *Gospel Night* (2011), *Darling Vulgarity* (2006—finalist for the *LA Times* Book Prize), and *Parthenopi: New and Selected Poems* (2000). He has coedited *Reel Verse* (Knopf, 2018). A 2017 Guggenheim Fellow and recipient of five Pushcart Prizes and fellowships from the NEA, Fulbright Foundation, and New Jersey State Council on the Arts, Waters teaches at Monmouth University.

STAN LEE WERLIN's short stories and poetry have appeared in *Southern Humanities Review, Los Angeles Review, Sheepshead Review, Prime Number, Glassworks, Soundings East, Saranac Review, Five on the Fifth, Futures Trading, Bacopa Literary Review, Zone 3*, and *Roanoke Review*. His humorous children's poetry has been published in numerous children's magazines and anthologies. Stan is a Harvard graduate and holds an MBA from UPenn (Wharton). Reach him on Twitter @natsnilrew.

ANNE PIERSON WIESE's first collection, *Floating City* (Louisiana State University Press) was chosen by Kay Ryan to receive the Academy of American Poets Walt Whitman Award. She's been the recipient of a fellowship in poetry from the New York Foundation for the Arts, as well as a Discovery/*The Nation* poetry prize. Her poems have appeared in *New England Review, Raritan, Ploughshares, Hudson Review, Southern Review, Antioch Review, Virginia Quarterly Review,* and *Southwest Review.*

PAMELA MURRAY WINTERS's first full-length collection of poems, *The Unbeckonable Bird*, will be published by FutureCycle Press in summer 2018. Her work has appeared in *Gargoyle, Opossum, Beltway Poetry Quarterly, Gettysburg Review,* and numerous other publications. Pam is one of the organizers of the Evil Grin Poetry Series in Annapolis, Maryland. An MFA stint at Vermont College of Fine Arts taught her much about the miracle powers of poetry and ice cleats.

ROB WINTERS is a computer engineer at NASA who writes enough poetry to have something to read at local poetry events. His poems were accepted for *21: Blackjack Poetry Journal* and published in *District Lines.* He lives eight feet above the high tide line on the Chesapeake Bay with his wife and two birds that do not flock together.

VALERIE WOHLFELD's most recent book of poetry is *Woman with Wing Removed* (Truman State University Press, 2010). Her first collection, *Thinking the World Visible*, won the Yale Younger Poets Prize (Yale University Press, 1994). She holds an MFA from Vermont College of Fine Arts.

EMMA SKY WOLF has had poetry and visual art appear in publications such as *Orion, Gargoyle, Leaf Garden, Poetic Hours, Dark Lady Poetry,* and others. The poet welcomed her first child in the summer of 2017. She lives and works as a resident mental health counselor in Arlington, Virginia. She can be found at skywolf-studio.weebly.com.

MICHELE WOLF is the author of *Immersion; Conversations During Sleep*, winner of the Anhinga Prize for Poetry; and the chapbook *The Keeper of Light.* Her poems have appeared in *Poetry, Gargoyle, Southern Review, Hudson Review,* and many other literary journals and anthologies, as well as on *Poetry Daily, Verse Daily,* and Poets.org. She is a contributing editor for *Poet Lore* and teaches at The Writer's Center in Bethesda, Maryland. michelewolf.com

KELLY WOLFE is an assistant professor of English at Johnson & Wales University in North Miami, where she teaches writing, literature, and communication. Before that, she worked as a journalist for ten years at the *Philadelphia Inquirer* and *Palm Beach Post.* Her essay, "Early Mourning Flight," was named first runner up in the Norton Girault Literary Prize for Nonfiction in 2014 and was subsequently published in *Barely South Review.*

ANDREA WYATT was born in Brooklyn, New York, and now lives in Silver Spring, Maryland. She works for the National Park Service and is coeditor of *The Brooklyn Reader* (Random House/Harmony).

ED ZAHNISER was a founding editor of Some Of Us Press in Washington, D.C., in the 1970s. He has been a poetry editor for *Wilderness, Artz and Kulchur, Antietam Review,* and the *Good News Paper* in Shepherdstown, West Virginia, where he lives. His books of poetry include *Mall-Hopping with the Great I Am* and *At the End of the Self-help Rope*.

TARA ISABEL ZAMBRANO lives in Texas. Her work has appeared or is forthcoming in *Tin House Online, Slice, Yemassee, Moon City Review,* and others. She is an electrical engineer by profession.

May 18 - 20, 2018

Greensboro BOUND
Literary Festival

greensborobound.com

Bird
in
hand

11 E. 33rd Street
Baltimore, MD 21218
birdinhandcharlesville.com

'SCUP?

Scuppernong Books

336.763.1919
scuppernongbooks.com
scuppernongbooks@gmail.com

---

304 South Elm Street
Greensboro, NC 27401

Mon, Tues, Wed, Thurs:
10am – 9pm
Fri, Sat: 10am – 10pm
Sun: Noon – 6pm

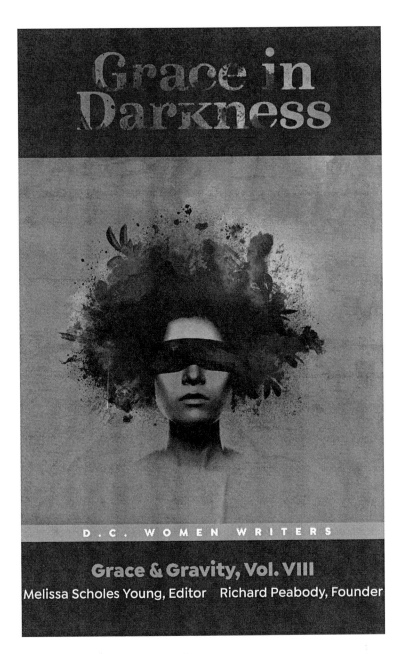

Grace in Darkness

D.C. WOMEN WRITERS

Grace & Gravity, Vol. VIII

Melissa Scholes Young, Editor   Richard Peabody, Founder

Coming May 7, 2018

Available at Politics and Prose, www.politics-prose.com

AMERICAN UNIVERSITY
WASHINGTON, DC

LAST WORDS

"All art is unstable. Its meaning is not necessarily that implied by the author. There is no authoritative active voice. There are only multiple readings." —David Bowie

"Poetry is the shortest distance between two humans." —Lawrence Ferlinghetti

"Time's passage through the memory is like molten glass that can be opaque or crystallize at any given moment at will: a thousand days are melted into one conversation, one glance, one hurt, and one hurt can be shattered and sprinkled over a thousand days." —Gloria Naylor

"And that's why books are never going to die. It's impossible. It's the only time we really go into the mind of a stranger, and we find our common humanity doing this. So the book doesn't only belong to the writer, it belongs to the reader as well, and then together you make it what it is." —Paul Auster

"Books don't offer real escape, but they can stop a mind scratching itself raw." —David Mitchell

"Storytellers are a threat. They threaten all champions of control, they frighten usurpers of the right-to-freedom of the human spirit—in state, in church or mosque, in party congress, in the university or wherever." —Chinua Achebe

"Books have led some to learning and others to madness." —Petrarch

"I want to write about people I love, and put them into a fictional world spun out of my own mind, not the world we actually have, because the world we actually have does not meet my standards." —Phillip K. Dick

"You never know what worse luck your bad luck has saved you from." —Cormac McCarthy

"All art holds the knowledge that we're both living and dying at the same time. It can hold it. And thank God it can, because nothing out in the capitalistic corporate world is going to shine that back to us. But art holds it." —Marie Howe

"A writer always exists in opposition to power." —Don Delillo